Essential Reviews in Experimental Biology
Volume 1

Osmoregulation and Ion Transport:
Integrating Physiological, Molecular and
Environmental Aspects

Essential Reviews in Experimental Biology
Volume 1

Osmoregulation and Ion Transport: Integrating Physiological, Molecular and Environmental Aspects

Edited by

Richard D. Handy
School of Biological Sciences, University of Plymouth, Drake Circus, Plymouth
PL4 8AA, UK

Nicolas R. Bury
Nutritional Sciences Research Division, King's College London, Franklin Wilkins
Buiding, 150 Stamford Street, London SE1 9NH, UK

Gert Flik
Department of Animal Physiology, Institute for Water and Wetland Research,
Faculty of Science, Radboud University Nijmegen, Heyendaalseweg 135, 6525
AJ Nijmegen, The Netherlands

SEB
Society for Experimental Biology

The Society for Experimental Biology
Charles Darwin House, 12 Roger Street, London, WC1N 2JU, UK

Published by the Society for Experimental Biology
www.sebiology.org

First Edition 2009
Copyright © 2009 Society for Experimental Biology
Printed and bound in the UK by Bell & Bain Ltd., Glasgow

A catalogue record for this publication is available from the British Library

ISBN: 978-1-907491-00-9 (Paperback)
ISBN: 978-1-907491-01-6 (Electronic)
ISSN: 2042-3381 (Print)
ISSN: 2042-339X (Online)

Contents

Information about the Society for Experimental Biology (SEB)

The Society for Experimental Biology (SEB) is Europe's leading, not-for-profit organisation embracing all disciplines of experimental biology. Through its large membership and passion for science the society supports and promotes experimental biology, from molecular to ecological, to benefit both the scientific community and the general public. The society was founded in 1923 at Birkbeck College and is now well established with a current worldwide membership of over 1,400 biological researchers, teachers and students. The SEB is somewhat unusual in catering for both plant and animal biologists.

The SEB publishes three main research journals, *The Plant Journal*, *The Plant Biotechnology Journal* and *The Journal of Experimental Botany*. This new review series, unlike the present research journals, will encompass all the areas of science that the society represents. It will provide timely updates of all areas of experimental biology.

Each volume will provide a detailed review of current understanding within a sub-topic of the volume title. In some volumes the chapters will be organized according to the level at which the research is focused (e.g. molecular, biochemical, physiological, behavioural, ecological); in others the chapters may be organized on a more taxonomic basis. Each chapter is written by leading authorities in science that have been invited, based on their international reputation, to provide their perspective on the current status and recent developments within the field. All chapters are peer-reviewed by at least two independent referees prior to acceptance for publication.

The series thus aims to provide an excellent, up-to-date resource for a global research audience within each of the volume topics.

Series Editor: Mike Burrell

Information about the Society for Experimental Biology (SEB)

Preface

This volume was partly derived from a session on 'Drinking, Salt and Osmoregulation' held at the Society for Experimental Biology annual meeting in Glasgow, Scotland, on the 31st March to 4th April 2007. The aim of the session was to bring international experts in the field together to discuss the current status of the topic, but also to look forward and examine the exciting challenges ahead in this field. It was also an opportunity to recognise the long standing contributions of Professor Brian Eddy (University of Dundee) to the field of osmoregulation. Professor Eddy was a founding member of the Osmoregulation Group for the Society for Experimental Biology, and more than 30 years ago he recognised the importance and utility of the comparative approach in the study of ionic regulation. Professor Eddy has made many important contributions to osmoregulation over the years; including fundamental studies on the electric properties of gills and how epithelial potential influences ion transport (Eddy, 1975), some of the most detailed studies on salt and water balance during seawater transfer of salmonids (Bath and Eddy, 1979; Eddy and Bath, 1979), and effects of pollutants on ionic regulation (e.g. nitrite) (Eddy et al., 1983; Williams and Eddy, 1986). He was one of the first to recognise the importance of metal salts in the diet on osmoregulation (e.g. NaCl) (Salman and Eddy, 1988). More recently, his work recognises the subtle relationship between the control of osmoregulation and vasoactive substances such as lipopolysaccharides and nitric oxide (e.g. Eddy, 2005; 2007). Professor Eddy has contributed to the training of numerous scientists in the field, and two of the editors to this volume were fortunate to study in his laboratory. His approach is to let the evidence from the data, rather than current dogma or popularity of a particular technique, drive the scientific thinking and design of the next experiment. He has also been generous in sharing his ideas and unpublished data with colleagues, and many have benefited from this approach.

In this volume we bring together a collection of works on key topics in osmoregulation. This volume includes chapters on the different aspects of osmoregulation, the molecular basis of ion transport and the effects environmental stress on ionic regulation. In each of the chapters the authors have tried to identify the current state of knowledge, but also where the topic is going and the challenges ahead. The volume recognises the importance of molecular methods in the field of osmoregulation, but also that the study of whole organism biology and the comparative approach remain vital aspects of modern experimental biology.

References

Bath, R. N. and Eddy, F. B. (1979). Ionic and respiratory regulation in rainbow trout during rapid transfer to seawater. J Comp Physiol 134: 351–357.

Eddy, F. B. (2007). Drinking in juvenile Atlantic salmon (*Salmo salar* L.) in response to feeding and activation of the endogenous renin-angiotensin system. Comp Biochem Physiol A 148: 23–28.

Eddy, F. B. (2005). Role of nitric oxide in larval and juvenile fish. Comp Biochem Physiol A 142: 221–230.

Eddy, F. B. (1975). Effect of calcium on gill potentials and on sodium and chloride fluxes in goldfish, *Carassius auratus*. J Comp Physiol 96: 131–142.

Eddy, F. B. and Bath, R. N. (1979). Ionic regulation in rainbow trout (*Salmo gairdneri*) adapted to fresh water and dilute sea water. J Exp Biol 83: 181–192.

Eddy, F. B., Kunzlik, P. A. and Bath, R. N. (1983). Uptake and loss of nitrite from the blood of rainbow trout, *Salmo gairdneri* Richardson, and Atlantic salmon, *Salmo salar* L. in Fresh water and in dilute sea water. J Fish Biol 23: 105–116.

Salman, N. A. and Eddy, F. B. (1988). Effect of dietary sodium chloride on growth, food intake and conversion efficiency in rainbow trout (*Salmo gairdneri* Richardson). Aquaculture 70: 131–144.

Williams, E. M. and Eddy, F. B. (1986). Chloride uptake in fresh water teleosts and its relationship to nitrite uptake and toxicity. J Comp Physiol B 156: 867–872.

List of Contributors

Christopher P. Cutler, Department of Biology, Georgia Southern University, P. O. Box 8042, Statesboro, GA 30460, USA

F. Brian Eddy, Environmental and Applied Biology, Faculty of Life Sciences, University of Dundee, Dundee DD1 4HN, UK

Gert Flik, Department of Animal Physiology, Institute for Water and Wetland Research, Faculty of Science, Radboud University Nijmegen, Heyendaalseweg 135, 6525 AJ Nijmegen, The Netherlands

Gideon S. Bevelander, Department of Animal Physiology, Institute for Water and Wetland Research, Faculty of Science, Radboud University Nijmegen, Heyendaalseweg 135, 6525 AJ Nijmegen, The Netherlands

Gordon Cramb, School of Biology, Bute Building, University of St Andrews, St Andrews, Fife, KY16 9TS, UK

James C. McGeer, Dept of Biology, Wilfrid Laurier University, 75 University Ave. W. Waterloo ON, L8S 3C5, Canada

Jonathan P. Good, School of Biomedical Sciences, University of Queensland, St Lucia, QLD 4072, Australia

Nadir A. Salman, Department of Fisheries and Marine Resources, College of Agriculture, University of Basrah, Garmat Ali, Basrah, Iraq

Neil Hazon, School of Biology, Gatty Marine Laboratory, University of St. Andrews, St. Andrews, Fife KY16 8LB, UK

Nicolas R. Bury, Nutritional Sciences Research Division, King's College London, Franklin Wilkins Buiding, 150 Stamford Street, London SE1 9NH, UK

Peter H. M. Klaren, Department of Animal Physiology, Institute for Water and Wetland Research, Faculty of Science, Radboud University Nijmegen, Heyendaalseweg 135, 6525 AJ Nijmegen, The Netherlands

Richard D. Handy, School of Biological Sciences, University of Plymouth, Drake Circus, Plymouth PL4 8AA, UK

Richard J. Maunder, School of Biological Sciences, University of Plymouth, Drake Circus, Plymouth PL4 8AA, UK

Robert Sterling, School of Biology, Bute Building, University of St Andrews, St Andrews, Fife, KY16 9TS, UK

Songul Bekir, School of Biology, Bute Building, University of St Andrews, St Andrews, Fife, KY16 9TS, UK

Stephan Brezillion, School of Biology, Bute Building, University of St Andrews, St Andrews, Fife, KY16 9TS, UK

Chapter 1

Regulation of sodium in the body fluids of teleost fish in response to challenges to the osmoregulatory system

F. Brian Eddy

Keywords: Osmoregulatory challenge, plasma Na$^+$ concentration, fish gills, freshwater fish, drinking

Abstract

This paper reviews physiological processes contributing to regulation of the osmotic concentration of the body fluids of freshwater fish and explores some possible responses to osmotic challenges. The available data suggest that the osmotic concentration of the blood plasma and extracellular fluid (ECF) of unstressed fish is maintained relatively constant though there may be variation about a set point. Plasma Na$^+$ concentration may be increased through ion capture at the gills, and when an upper threshold concentration for Na$^+$ is reached, mechanisms are activated to release Na$^+$ via the gills and decrease the rate of Na$^+$ uptake. Loss of Na$^+$ continues until a lower threshold concentration, then release of Na$^+$ is decreased and active uptake of Na$^+$ increased. The level of adherence to the set point concentration for Na$^+$ (and the concentration of plasma and body fluids) is likely to be determined by the accuracy and sensitivity of osmoreceptors (central or peripheral) and the control of branchial ionic transport systems. In fresh waters of rich or moderate ionic content, the rate of ionic absorption by the gills is depends on the ionic concentration of the bulk water and delivery of ions to the apical uptake site (in the case of Na$^+$ an apical channel) and the degree of electronegativity within the cell. However in ion poor waters the very large electrochemical gradient between bulk water and the cell interior offers little opportunity for Na$^+$ capture. In these conditions, opportunities for ion capture could be increased if there was a mechanism for concentrating ions close to the uptake site. Challenge of the osmoregulatory system of fish with increased internal ionic content (e.g. ingestion of a high salt diet) results in compensatory ionic loss possibly via regulated paracellular pathways in the gills. At the same time ionic absorption by the gills is decreased by yet unknown mechanisms. Depletion of the ionic content of fish results in increased absorption of Na$^+$, possibly enhanced by the recruitment of additional ionic uptake sites on the gills. A principal contributor to osmoregulation in freshwater fish is removal of osmotically gained water by production of dilute urine by the kidney. Unexpectedly, drinking the medium does occur in freshwater fish mainly in conjunction with processing food even though absorption of water in the gut places is an additional osmotic burden. In some conditions excess drinking occurs and this is of interest since it gives an insight into the control of the drinking process in fish. Elevated drinking rates in freshwater fish, sometimes at the high rates seen in marine fish, occur when increased levels of the potent endogenous dipsogen AII (angiotensin II), are present. Excess drinking occurs in freshwater fish exposed to lipopolysaccharide, often associated with gram negative bacteria present in polluted waters. Lipopolysaccharides are thought to stimulate the cytokine system resulting in production of increased synthesis of NO (nitric oxide) and oxygen free radicals. The vasodilatory effects are NO elicits a vasoconstrictor response through the production of increased levels of AII, resulting in stimulation of drinking to inappropriately high levels.

1.1 Introduction

The foundations of understanding salt and water balance in fish were laid down more than half a century ago. The idea that ionic regulation in freshwater fish involved uptake of ions from the surrounding water was demonstrated by Krogh (1937) while in marine fish Keys and Willmer (1932) suggested that excess ions gained from the seawater were excreted from 'chloride cells' in the gills. Over the years, knowledge of the mechanisms of these processes has advanced but understanding of their integration into the processes controlling osmoregulatory homeostasis in fish remains relatively undeveloped.

Fresh waters may range in concentration from almost deionised water to about 20 mOsm while the blood plasma of freshwater fish is approximately 200 mOsm. Since freshwater fish inhabit a hypoosmotic environment they constantly lose ions and gain water across the body surface. Water balance in freshwater fish is dependent on removal of osmotically gained water via the kidney and production of dilute urine with an ionic concentration slightly above than that of the medium. This is achieved by absorption of ions from the filtrate as it passes through the tubules, collecting duct and bladder. Ionic losses from the fish are compensated via the diet and by capture of ions from the water passing over the gills or in some cases the body surface. These events have been explored and reviewed on many occasions (Evans et al., 2005; Eddy, 2006) but the explanation for some processes remain relatively unresolved, and in this review selected topics are explored in subsequent sections. The concentration of seawater is about 1000mOsm and the blood plasma of marine teleosts is approximately 250 mOsm (see also section 5). Marine fish inhabit a hyperosmotic environment and experience continual dehydration. Water loss is compensated by imbibing the medium and absorption of the seawater in the gut. Excess salt (Na^+ and Cl^-) is excreted via the 'chloride' cells or mitochondrion rich cells in the gills, whilst calcium is excreted as a calcium carbonate precipitate via the gut (Evans et al., 2005; Marshall and Grosell, 2006) and selected aspects will be discussed in a later section.

Over the years our understanding of osmoregulation in fish has greatly expanded yet certain critical aspects remain unresolved. These include how the stability of Na^+ concentration (and other ions) in the blood plasma and body fluids is maintained and an understanding of the interactions of the contributing mechanisms. Such mechanisms include the control of the rate of ionic absorption and loss by the gills, the control of drinking rates and rates of ionic absorption and secretion by the gut, control of kidney function and the role of osmoreceptors. This paper advances ideas on regulation salt and water balance, focussing principally on freshwater fish, with the aim that discussion of these issues may lead to new avenues of investigation.

1.2 Freshwater fish – some unresolved issues

1.2.1 Constancy of the ionic concentration of the blood plasma and body fluids

For simplicity and convenience in this and subsequent sections the focus will be on Na^+ although the role of other ions equally important in osmoregulation is recognised. The concentrations of Na^+ and other ions in blood plasma and ECF (extracellular fluid) have been measured on many occasions and the reported values are assumed to represent values characteristic of particular populations. These may differ from the actual value for a particular individual at any moment. Plasma Na^+ concentration for an individual is likely to vary with activities such as feeding, swimming, stress etc as well as with diurnal and seasonal effects. At any instant the concentration of blood plasma Na^+ for an individual fish will depend on the resultant of the rates of Na^+ uptake and Na^+ loss and the control of the rates of branchial Na^+ influx and Na^+ efflux will be a major influence in determination of the concentration of plasma Na^+. This raises questions about how the processes of Na^+ uptake and Na^+ loss by the gills are regulated to achieve homeostasis of Na^+ concentration in the body fluids. Are Na^+ fluxes finely controlled so that blood plasma Na^+ concentration is held close to a set level or is the control less precise such that plasma Na^+ concentration varies noticeably over time about some set point?

How closely is plasma Na^+ concentration controlled in a normally active and unstressed fish over the period of an hour, a day or a season? These ideas are explored in Table 1 and Figure 1 which show that there are general similarities in the mean values for Na^+ concentration in blood plasma from rainbow trout obtained from different studies. The standard errors are in the range $+2–3$ suggesting the range of Na^+ concentrations in these populations may be about 130–150 mmol l^{-1} Na^+. The main contributors to variation are likely to be the temporal variation of the Na^+ concentration in each fish, i.e. has the fish been sampled at a low point or a high point in its cycle (Figure 1). Plasma osmotic pressure and Na^+ levels may also be a function of changes in blood pressure, i.e. an increase capillary pressure will tend to drive fluid into the tissues (Prior et al., 1995). Differences in set point for Na^+ concentration between the fish may also contribute to variability. Resolution of these points awaits data from sequential samples for individual fish. However the idea can also be explored through the study of the mechanisms for branchial Na^+ influx and efflux and through challenging the control of Na^+ homeostasis as discussed in subsequent sections.

1.2.2 Osmosensors in fish

Regulation of blood plasma Na^+ concentration or indeed the concentration of other inorganic and organic ions is but one aspect of an overall process of osmoregulation in fish. Homeostasis of salt and water balance is dependent on osmosensors whose function is to detect deviations from the set point in osmotic pressure and then activate appropriate compensatory mechanisms so that the set point is regained. This aspect has received considerable attention in mammals and a relatively constant osmolarity of the ECF is maintained despite significant variation in salt and water intake. Disturbances in either Na^+ or water balance may produce rapid changes in osmolarity of the ECF, detected by osmoreceptors in the central nervous system. These contribute to the regulation of Na^+ and water balance that maintains the osmotic pressure of the ECF near the set point. The hypothalamus contains an important group of cells referred to as magnocellular neurosecretory cells, which respond to changes in osmotic pressure of the extracellular fluid. Located in these cells are stretch activated cationic channels, their conductance favouring K^+ over Na^+ with a ratio of about 5:1, which transduce osmotically evoked changes in cell volume into functionally relevant changes in membrane potential, with subsequent release of effector peptides such as vasopressin (Bourque and Oliet, 1997; Bourque et al., 2002). There has been little or no work on this aspect of osmoregulation in fish.

Osmoregulation in fish is probably controlled by at least two types of osmoreceptors. One type may respond to changes in internal osmotic pressure and may be located in the hypothalamus, as in mammals. Since many fish species frequently experience changes in the aquatic environment, the second type of osmosensor may respond to changes in external osmotic pressure e.g. changes in salinity. Studies using opercular skin of the euryhaline killifish showed that hypotonic shock resulted in cell swelling and inhibition Cl^- secretion while hypertonic shock had the opposite effect. Responses to hypotonic and hypertonic shock may be mediated via the cytoskeleton in stretch-activated or -inactivated membrane elements (Marshall, 2003), suggesting the possibility presence of peripheral osmoreceptors. Tilapia responded to increased external salinity with a rapid (30 mins) co-induction of two tilapia transcription factors in gill cells and within 4 h mRNA from about 20 stress related genes (Fiol et al., 2006a,b), suggesting that fish have short term as well as longer term mechanisms to respond to osmotic stress. This little investigated area deserves further study at the physiological and molecular levels.

1.2.3 Capture and concentration of Na^+ at the gill surface

Ionic uptake by the gills of freshwater fish has been extensively studied and for reviews see Wright (1991); Lin and Randall (1995). The gill epithelium may

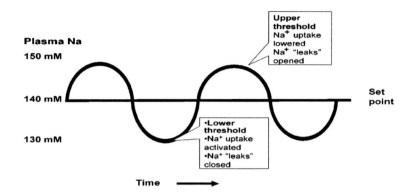

Figure 1. *Variations in blood plasma Na⁺ concentrations of a freshwater fish (e.g. rainbow trout) over time*

In this example it is assumed that a normally active and unstressed fish attempts to maintain blood plasma Na⁺ concentration a set point of 140 mmol l⁻¹ but the achieved Na⁺ concentration varies approximately plus or minus 2 standard errors (see Table 1). Note that the time scale of these events is unknown and there are no units for the x axis. The gills absorb Na⁺ from the medium until an upper threshold of about 150 mmol l⁻¹ is reached and this triggers a decrease in the rate of Na⁺ absorption and an increase the rate of Na⁺ loss via 'leak' pathways in the gills causing plasma Na⁺ concentration to fall. After some time plasma Na⁺ concentration falls below the set point and reaches a lower threshold value of about130 mmol l⁻¹ when Na⁺ uptake mechanisms in the gills are triggered and plasma Na⁺ is increased. At the same time the rate of Na⁺ loss via 'leak' pathways is decreased. The nature of the 'leak' pathways in the gill epithelium (as mentioned on the Figure) is unknown but they could be regulated paracellular or possibly transcellular pathways (see text for details).

contain two morphologically similar but functionally distinct epithelial cells chloride. At the apical surface PNA^+ MR cells pump H^+ outwards by a V-ATPase so creating an electrochemical gradient of sufficient magnitude to attract Na^+ from the water into the cell via a Na^+ channels. At the basolateral membrane Na^+-K^+-ATPase asymmetrically exchanges intracellular Na^+ for extracellular K^+ also creating electronegativity within the cell. Mechanisms for chloride uptake are less well defined but there is evidence that at the apical membrane of PNA-MR cells, chloride ions are absorbed in exchange for intracellular bicarbonate, driven indirectly by a basolaterally located V-typeATPase. However there are species differences and the nature of the anion exchanger remains undefined (Goss *et al.*, 1998; Perry, 1997; Marshall and Grosell, 2006).

Effective Na^+ uptake from water with a Na^+ concentration of about 1 mmol l⁻¹ would require the cell interior to be about -50 mV. However many freshwater fish inhabit waters with a Na^+ concentration of 50 mmol l⁻¹ or lower and in such conditions uptake of Na^+ could only be achieved if the intracellular potential was in excess of -100 mV (Kirschner, 2004). It is unlikely that such large electrochemical gradients could be generated in gill cells and alternative mechanisms for the capture and uptake

Table 1. *Variability of the concentration of Na⁺ in the blood plasma of rainbow trout in fresh water*

Species	Blood plasma Na⁺ (mmol l⁻¹)*	n	Calculated range	Reference
Oncorhynchus mykiss, rainbow trout	139 ± 3	9	133 – 144	Morgan and Iwama (1998)
Oncorhynchus mykiss, rainbow trout	132 ± 3	10	126 – 138	Postlethwaite and McDonald (1995)
Oncorhynchus mykiss, rainbow trout	154	45	143 –165	Manera and Britti (2006)
Oncorhynchus mykiss, steelhead trout	153 ± 2	8	149 – 157	Liebert and Schreck (2006)
Salmo salar, Atlantic salmon (sea water fish)	183 ± 3	6	180 – 186	Potts *et al.* (1989)

For comparison, values for Atlantic salmon in sea water are shown in the last row. *Values are means $\pm$ standard error (S.E.) for n observations, which were used to calculate the range (mean $\pm$ 1.96 of the standard errror) which would contain approximately 95% of the population. For a more detailed statistical analysis see Manera and Britti (2006).

of Na⁺ have been suggested. In media of low conductivity the gills could capture Na⁺ from the water of the respiratory current and concentrate it at the gill surface in areas close to sites for Na⁺ uptake (Figure 2). It would need to be demonstrated (Handy and Eddy, 1990; Playle *et al.*, 1993) that Na⁺ is more concentrated at the gill surface, compared to the medium and that once attracted to the gill surface there is a mechanism to release the Na⁺ for entry to the Na⁺ channel. Whilst such a mechanism may be plausible for Na⁺ uptake it is less fitting for Cl⁻ uptake since the capture zone is likely to exclude anions through mucus or donnan type effects. This leads to the possibility of separates sites or indeed separate types of cell for Na⁺ and Cl⁻ uptake as suggested by Goss *et al.* (2001); Parks *et al.* (2006) and in this context it could be that the Cl⁻/H⁺ exchanger of PNA-MR cells possess a high affinity for Cl⁻.

1.2.4 Challenges to Na⁺ homeostasis

So far Na⁺ balance in an inactive and unstressed fish have been considered. However fish engage in, or are subjected to, a variety of situations with potential to challenge and even disrupt homeostatic processes including ionic balance. Challenges could include relatively stressful activities such as swimming to avoid predators or social stresses. Feeding to satiation or periods without feeding can also be viewed as challenges. Two challenges are considered, first when the internal Na^+ concentration of the fish is increased significantly above normal levels e.g. by consumption of salty food, followed by observation of the regulatory responses by the fish. The second is where the internal Na^+ concentrations of the fish are lowered significantly below normal levels and the responses of the fish are followed. In the design of such experiments care should be taken to minimise stress since this also affects Na^+ balance and could confound the experimental results.

Feeding salt enriched diets to fish is a natural and stress free method of rapidly increasing their Na^+ body load and their responses can be compared to fish not receiving food. Na^+ fluxes of juvenile rainbow trout were determined prior to feeding salty food and then at the earliest possible point after feeding, in practice about 30 minutes, and then at hourly intervals (Figure 3; Smith et al., 1995). Compared to the unfed group, the fish receiving the 'high salt diet' (12% NaCl) showed a significant net loss of Na^+ achieved through decreasing Na^+ influx and increasing Na^+ efflux. The changes in Na^+ fluxes began shortly after feeding, had reached a maximal level by 30 min, and continued at this level for at least 8 hours. At this point the blood plasma Na^+ values for the 'high salt' group were significantly higher than the values for the unfed group and presumably Na^+ efflux remained elevated until blood plasma concentrations had resumed normal levels.

These results point to important aspects of control of sodium balance in fish. First is the response of internal osmoreceptors to increased concentration of the extracellular fluid and activation of pathways to promote lowering of the body Na^+ concentration in the fish. Second is the activation of a pathway promoting an increased rate of Na^+ efflux from the gills. Third is the partial inhibition of the mechanism controlling the rate of Na^+ influx into the gills. The result is an increased rate of Na^+ loss from the fish. As mentioned in a previous section very little is known of internal osmoreceptors in fish and the control of gill Na^+ fluxes.

Although the mechanism of branchial Na^+ influx fluxes in fish have been studied on many occasions there is little information on how the rate is controlled. One possibility is that the activities of the basolateral Na^+-K^+-ATPase and apical V-ATPase in the gill cell are lowered so decreasing the intracellular electronegativity of the cell and attracting less Na^+ through the apical Na^+ channel (see Figure 2). Another possibility is that the number of Na^+ channels can be reduced by their removed from the apical membrane. These could remain as vesicles within the cell for reinsertion in the membrane when required (Nielsen et al., 2002).

Previous work suggested that Na^+ efflux from the gill could occur though paracellular pathways in the epithelium and was entirely by passive diffusion. If this was true then variations in blood plasma Na^+ should be closely coupled to corresponding changes in the rate of Na^+ efflux. A more realistic possibility is that Na^+ efflux is via regulated paracellular pathways as suggested by Postlethwaite and Mcdonald (1995) although the possibility of transcellular pathways remains. Anderson (2001) indicates that paracellular transport is passive, results from diffusion, electrodiffusion, or osmosis down the gradients

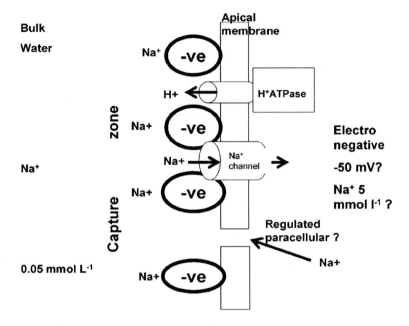

Figure 2. *Capture of Na⁺ at the gill surface*
Effective Na⁺ uptake from water with a Na⁺ concentration of about 1 mmol l⁻¹ would require the cell interior to be about -50 mV. However in ion poor waters the Na⁺ concentration may be 0.05 mmol l-1 or less yet fish are able to absorb Na⁺ against the concentration gradient into the cell where the Na⁺ activity may be about 5 mmol l⁻¹. This would require an unusually large and probably unphysiological electrochemical gradient of well over 100 mV between the cell interior and the medium and the possibility of alternative mechanisms should be considered. One possibility is that parts of the gill surface are populated with electro-negative residues which attract positive ions from the bulk water and concentrate them in the 'capture zone' close to the apical the Na⁺ channel. See text and Kirschner (2004). The electonegativity of the capture zone tends to exclude Cl⁻ ions and possibilities for Cl⁻ absorption may involve a high affinity Cl⁻/HCO₃ exchanger on the apical surface of PNA-MR cells (Marshall and Grosell, 2006).

created by transcellular mechanisms. It does not show directional discrimination and varies enormously among epithelia in terms of electrical resistance. Further analysis of ionic fluxes across fish gills is required to resolve such issues. However the results from (Smith *et al.*, 1995) shown in Figure 3 indicate that elevated internal Na⁺ is an appropriate stimulus to activate the mechanisms for increasing Na⁺ efflux from in the gill but details of the mechanisms which control Na⁺ efflux are little known and await further investigation.

It is difficult to find examples of relatively stress free experiments specifically designed to lower body levels of Na⁺ and then to observe the ionoregularory recovery responses of the fish. Experiments designed to study ionic regulatory responses of trout to swimming or to stress resulted in significantly lowered body Na⁺ concentration and thus the results of the recovery responses provide useful information about these processes. After swimming for a prolonged period (1.8 body lengths s⁻¹ for up to 96 h) plasma and body Na⁺ levels of rainbow trout were little altered but the fish responded with increased Na⁺ influx and reduced

(a)

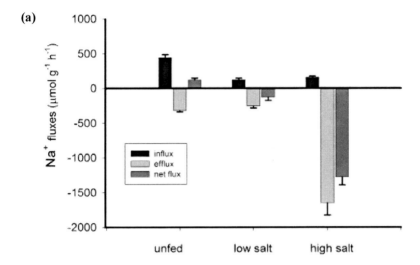

(b)

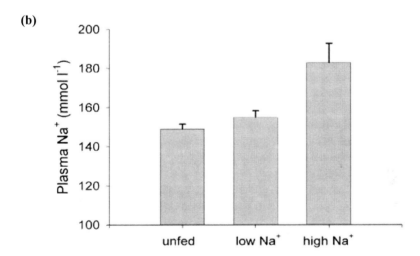

Figure 3.

    (a) *Sodium fluxes (μmol g⁻¹ h⁻¹) for three groups of rainbow trout (50 – 100 g) measured 30 mins after feeding either a low salt or a high salt diet. The third group was unfed. Na⁺ fluxes were measured at hourly intervals and the values remained little changed for 8 h when the experiment was terminated. Mean values and standard errors are for six fish in each group. For details see Smith et al. 1995.*

    (b) *Blood plasma Na⁺ values (mmol l⁻¹) for rainbow trout (50 – 100 g) measured 8 hours after feeding either a low salt or a high salt diet. A third group was unfed. Mean and standard error are shown for six fish. The mean for the high salt diet group is significantly different from the low salt and non fed means. For further details see Figure 3 and Smith et al. (1995).*

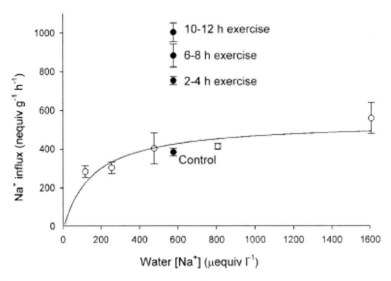

Figure 4.

Na⁺   uptake   in relation to external [Na⁺] (open circles) prior to control and during exercise at approximately 2 body lengths s⁻¹ (closed circles) in water containing 571 µequiv l⁻¹ Na⁺. Values are means ± S.E.M., n = 8–10 per time point for exercise, n = 4 per time point for uptake kinetics. Curves were fitted to kinetic data by nonlinear regression using the Michaelis– Menten equation. Na⁺ max influx = 560 ± 55 nequiv g⁻¹ hr⁻¹, K_m = 138 ± 56 µequiv l⁻¹.   From Postlethwaite and Mcdonald (1995). Reproduced with permission of the Company of Biologists.

in Na^+ efflux. Similar results were seen following 8 h confinement stress though in this case body Na^+ levels were significantly reduced. In both groups of fish, the maximal rate of Na^+ uptake was increased to a value significantly above the rate of control fish (Figure 4). A possible explanation, as mentioned in the previous section might be the activation of latent Na^+ uptake sites (Postlethwaite and Mcdonald, 1995; Nielsen *et al.*, 2002) but this is an area for further investigation.

1.2.5 Drinking and control of water balance

Fresh water teleosts owe much of their evolutionary success to their ability to hyperosmoregulate in an environment that is very dilute compared to their body fluids. It is achieved by their capacity to excrete osmotically gained water via the kidney as dilute urine. On this basis the expectation would be no requirement for freshwater fish to drink and any water absorped by the gut would constitute a costly osmotic burden. It is surprising that drinking does occur in freshwater fish (up to about 0.5 ml.kg⁻¹ h⁻¹), though at lower rates than for marine fish (about 4–7 ml kg⁻¹ h⁻¹), see Table 2. It is interesting to explore the reasons why freshwater fish and why under certain conditions excess drinking occurs (Fuentes and Eddy, 1997; Eddy, 2006).

The physiological basis of drinking in vertebrates has been extensively studied and the rennin-angiotensin system (RAS) is an important element in activation of the dipsogenic response (Fitzsimons, 1976). In marine and freshwater fish as well as in mammals, drinking is imitated by increased circulating levels of angiotensin II (AII), and also by a variety of pharmacological agents when applied to the hypothalamus (Mosimann *et al.*, 1996; Kozaka *et al.*, 2003). In fish decreased drinking occurred following a reduction of endogenous concentrations of AII through inhibition of angiotensin converting enzyme (ACE). A similar response occurs when AII receptors are blocked or when antagonists such as ANP (atrial natriuretic peptide) are administered (Fuentes and Eddy, 1996; Takei and Hirose, 2002). It is of interest that drinking in freshwater fish was not completely abolished by these procedures and that it continued at a basal level.

Increased drinking is associated with feeding in freshwater fish (Tytler *et al.*, 1990; Eddy, 2006) and it has been suggested imbibed water may be needed to moisten the food and to replace water that has been absorbed from the gut during the digestive processes. Increased drinking has also been seen in fish exposed to sewage contaminated freshwaters where the fish are in contact with lipopolysaccharides present on the surface of gram-negative bacteria. Eutrophic waters may support blooms of cyanobacteria and these too produce significant amounts of lipopolysaccharide (Best *et al.*, 2003). While understanding is incomplete, there is some evidence suggesting that lipopolysaccharide enters the gill, and one response may be stimulation of elements of the cytokine signalling system resulting in increased expression of inducible nitric oxide synthase (iNOS) (Best *et al.*, 2003: Eddy, 2005). Increased production of nitric oxide (NO) is primarily aimed at killing bacteria through generation of reactive oxygen species (Campos-Perez *et al.*, 2000). Since NO is a vasodilator, relaxation of vascular smooth muscle occurs in response to the increased circulating levels of NO and normal tone is restored by production of AII, itself a potent vasoconstrictor, as well as acting a potent dipsogen in vertebrates. Fish respond to increased circulating levels of AII with increased drinking, see Table 1, and the assembled data suggest that conditions promoting increased levels of NO are likely to result in stimulation of drinking, sometimes to inappropriate levels (Table 2). This might occur through prolonged stimulation of the 'drinking centre' or inhibition of the processes which limit drinking rate. Resolution of these issues awaits further research.

1.3 Marine fish

This section is not intended to be a full account of osmoregulatory processes in marine fish since these can be found elsewhere in recent reviews (Marshall and Grosell, 2006). Following on from the ideas advanced on control osmoregulation in freshwater fish the aim of this brief section is to identify key points of control in the osmoregulatory processes in marine fish. The evolutionary success of marine teleosts is linked to their ability to hypo-osmoregulate in a dehydrating environment. Withdrawal of body water by osmosis is balanced by an appropriate level of drinking, absorption of the imbibed seawater in the gut and excretion of

Table 2. Drinking in freshwater fish

Treatment	Species	Drinking rate (ml kg^{-1} h^{-1})	Comments	Reference
Unstressed fish	Salmo salar smolts, (30–40 g)	0.4–0.6		Fuentes et al. (1996)
Unfed and fed	Salmo salar juveniles (1–3 g)	0.3 (unfed) 0.7 (fed)		Eddy (2006)
Exposure to SNP (sodium nitroprusside) a NO re-leasing agent	Salmo salar fry (1–3g)	1.5	SNP in the medium at 0.8 mmol l^{-1}	Fuentes et al. (1996)
Administration of losartan, antagonist of AII receptors	Rainbow trout Oncorhynchus mykiss	Excess drinking and distended gut	30–50% of the fish affected. Injected dose 50 mg kg^{-1} (approx)	Fuentes, personal communication
Exposure to cyanobacteria and LPS	Rainbow trout Oncorhynchus mykiss (1–2 g)	1.2 and distended gut	Fish exposed to whole or broken Microcystis PCC 7813 cells.	Best et al. (2003)
Exposure to dietary bio-amines?	Salmo salar adult	Distended gut, 'bloat'	Seen in both marine and fresh-water fish in pens. Presence of algae may be significant	Lumsden et al. (2002) Rørvik et al. (2000) Anderson (2006)
Acute temperature change, 12–17°C	Scophthalmus maximus turbot, (45–200 g)	0.8–1.1		Carroll et al. (1994)
Acute temperature change, 12–17°C	Pleuronectes flesus flounder, (45–200 g)	1–1.6		Carroll et al. (1994)

Comparison of drinking rates are for unstressed fish, fed fish, unfed fish and fish treated to stimulate drinking. Values for marine fish are included for comparison. See text for details.

excess salt via mitochondrion rich cells the gills. In considering the physiological control of these events it could be hypothesised that central osmoreceptors (see section 2) respond to increased osmotic pressure in the ECF by stimulating at least three key processes. The first is the initiation of drinking to an appropriate level, second the enablement of the gut to absorb an appropriate quantity of sea water and third, activation of the branchial mitochondrion rich cells to excrete an appropriate amount of Na^+ and Cl^-. Since the calcium in the imbibed sea water is removed as precipitated calcium carbonate, the gut requires a signal to secrete an appropriate amount of bicarbonate (Grosell *et al.*, 2005). Once the fish has achieved a sufficient degree of hydration the activity of these systems would be reduced until the fish began to again experience dehydration, and the concentration of the ECF increased sufficiently to activate the osmoreceptors. As with freshwater fish (see earlier sections) it is possible that the concentration of the blood plasma varies about a set point, dependent on the sensitivity and response time of the osmosensors, and the capacity and response time of the physiological regulatory effectors. Resolution of these points awaits further information on homeostasis of blood plasma concentrations and responses of the regulatory mechanisms to osmotic challenges.

1.4 Conclusions

Over the years our understanding of osmoregulation in fish has greatly expanded yet certain critical aspects remain unresolved. How closely is the concentration of the blood plasma and the ECF controlled about a set point and what are the main contributors to variability? The set point for osmotic pressure in fish may be controlled by at least two types of osmoreceptors. One may respond to changes in internal osmotic pressure and may be located in the hypothalamus, as in mammals. Since many fish species frequently experience changes in the ionic concentration of the aquatic environment, the second type of osmosensor may respond to changes in external osmotic pressure e.g. changes in salinity.

Absorption of Na^+ from freshwaters with relatively high Na^+ concentration e.g. about 1 mmol l^{-1} would require the interior of epithelial cells to be about -50 mV to provide sufficient electrochemical gradient. However many freshwater fish inhabit waters with a Na^+ concentration of 50 mmol l^{-1} or lower, and in such conditions uptake of Na^+ could only be achieved if the intracellularpotential was in excess of -100 mV (Kirschner, 2004). It is unlikely that such large electrochemical gradients could be generated in gill cells and alternative mechanisms for the capture and uptake of Na^+ have been suggested. In media of low conductivity, the gills could capture Na^+ from the water of the respiratory current and concentrate it at the gill surface close to Na^+ uptake sites. Further work is required to investigate the electrochemical properties of surface of the fish gill, especially those areas close to the ion channels and transporters. Since the gill surface appears to be predominantly negatively charged, mechanisms for anion uptake are problematic and require more investigation.

Fish engage in or are subjected to a variety of situations with potential to challenge or even disrupt homeostatic processes including ionic balance. Two challenges are considered, first where the internal Na^+ concentration of the fish is increased and then the regulatory responses by the fish are observed. Compared to the responses of an unfed group, the fish receiving 'high salt diet' (12% NaCl) showed a significant net loss of Na^+ achieved through decreasing Na^+ influx and increasing Na^+ efflux. These results point to important aspects of control of sodium balance in fish. First is the response of internal osmoreceptors to increased concentration of the extracellular fluid and activation of mechanisms to lower of the body Na^+ concentration in the fish. Second is the activation of a pathway promoting an increased rate of Na^+ efflux from the gills. Third is the partial inhibition of the mechanism controlling the rate of Na^+ influx into the gills. The result is an increased rate of Na^+ loss from the fish.

The second challenge considered is when the internal Na^+ concentration of the fish is lowered and the responses of the fish are observed. Fish subjected to prolonged exercise or fish subjected to moderate stress, showed significantly lowered body Na^+ concentrations, and after about a day responded with maximal rates of Na^+ uptake significantly above the maximal rates of control fish. A possible explanation, might be the activation of latent Na^+ uptake sites in the gill. This is an important area for future research.

Conditions which promote increased levels of nitric oxide (NO) through stimulation of nitric oxide synthase e.g. stimulation of cytokine pathways by lipopolysaccharide, are likely to result in vasodilation triggering production of increased levels of vasoconstrictors e.g. angiotensinII (AII), a potent dipsogen, resulting in stimulation of increased drinking to inappropriate levels. The mechanism could be through continual stimulation of the 'drinking centre' or inhibition of the processes which limit the drinking rate, but these topics await further research.

Osmoregulation and control of blood plasma ionic concentration about a set point in marine fish depends on at least four points of control. The first, in response to dehydration, is initiation of drinking to an appropriate level, second the enablement of the gut to absorb an appropriate quantity of sea water and third, activation of the branchial mitochondrion rich cells to excrete an appropriate amount of Na^+ and Cl^-. Forth, the calcium in the imbibed seawater is removed as precipitated calcium carbonate, the gut requires a signal to secrete an appropriate amount of bicarbonate. There is little known about the control of any of these processes and further research is required.

References

Anderson, C. D. (2006). A review of casual factors and control measures for bloat in farmed salmonids with suggested mechanism for development of the condition. J Fish Dis 29: 445–453.

Anderson, J. M. (2001). Molecular structure of tight junctions and their role in epithelial transport. News Physiol Sci 16: 126–130.

Best, J. H., Eddy F. B. and Codd, G. A. (2003). Effects of Microcystis cells, cell extracts and lipopolysaccharide on drinking and liver function in rainbow trout *Oncorhynchus mykiss* Walbaum. Aquat Toxicol 64: 419–426.

Bourque, C. W. and Oliet, S. (1997). Osmoreceptors in the central nervous system. Annu Rev Physiol 59: 601–619.

Bourque, C. W, Voisin, D. L. and Chakfe, Y. (2002). Vasopressin and oxytocin: from genes to clinical applications. Prog Brain Res 139: 85–94.

Campos-Perez, J. J., Ward, M., Grabowski, P. S., Ellis, A. E. and Secombes, C. J. (2000). The gills are an important site of iNOS expression in rainbow trout *Oncorhynchus mykiss* after challenge with Gram-positive pathogen Renibacterium salmoninarum. Immunology 99: 153–161.

Carroll, S. Kelsall, C. Hazon, N., and Eddy, F. B. (1994). Effect of temperature on the drinking rates of two species of flatfish, flounder and turbot. J Fish Biol 44: 1097–1099.

Eddy, F. B. (2005). Cardiac function in juvenile salmon (*Salmo salar* L) in response to lipopolysaccharide (LPS) and inhibitors of inducible nitric oxide synthase (iNOS). Fish Physiol Biochem 31: 339–346.

Eddy, F. B. (2006). Drinking in juvenile Atlantic salmon (*Salmo salar* L) in response to feeding and activation of the endogenous rennin-angiotensin system. Comp Biochem Physiol A 148: 23–28.

Evans, D. H., Piermarini, P. M. and Choe, K. P. (2005). The multifunctional fish gill: dominant site of gas exchange, osmoregulation, acid-base regulation, and excretion of nitrogenous waste. Physiol Rev 85: 97–177.

Fitzsimons, J. T. (1976). The physiological basis of thirst. Kidney Int 10: 3–11.

Fiol, D. F. Chan, S. Y. and Kultz, D. (2006a). Regulation of osmotic stress transcription factor 1 (Ostf1) in tilapia (*Oreochromis mossambicus*) gill epithelium during salinity stress. J Exp Biol 209: 3257–3265.

Fiol, D. F., Chan, S. Y. and Kultz, D. (2006b). Identification and pathway analysis of immediate hyperosmotic stress responsive molecular mechanisms in tilapia (*Oreochromis mossambicus*) gill. Comp Biochem Physiol D 1: 344–356.

Fuentes, J. and Eddy, F. B. (1996). Drinking in freshwater adapted rainbow trout fry *Oncorhynchus mykiss* (Walbaum) in response to angiotensin I, angiotensin II, angiotensin converting enzyme inhibition and receptor blockade. Physiol Zool 69: 1555–1569.

Fuentes, J. and Eddy, F. B. (1997). Drinking in marine, euryhaline and freshwater teleost fish. In: Hazon, N., Eddy, F. B. and Flik, G. (eds) Ionic Regulation in Animals. Springer, Berlin: 135–149.

Fuentes, J., McGeer, J. C. and Eddy, F. B. (1996). Drinking rate in juvenile Atlantic salmon *Salmo salar* L. try in response to a nitric oxide donor, sodium nitroprusside and an inhibitor of angiotensin converting enzyme, enalapril. Fish Physiol Biochem 15: 65–69.

Goss, G. G., Perry, S. F., Fryer, J. N. and Laurent, P. (1998). Gill morphology and acid-base regulation in freshwater fishes. Comp Biochem Physiol A 119: 107–115.

Goss, G. G., Adamia, S. and Galvez, F. (2001). Peanut lectin binds to a subpopulation of mitochondria-rich cells in the rainbow trout gill epithelium. Am J Physiol 281: R1718–R1725.

Grosell, M., Wood, C. M., Wilson, R. W., Bury, N. R., Hogstrand, C., Rankin, C. and Jensen, F. B. (2005). Bicarbonate secretion plays a role in chloride and water absorption of the European flounder intestine. Am J Physiol 288: R936–R946.

Handy R. D. and Eddy F. B. (1990). The interactions between the surface of rainbow trout, *Oncorhynchus mykiss*, and waterborne metal toxicants. Funct Ecol 4: 385–392.

Keys, A. B. and Willmer, E. N. (1932). "Chloride-secreting cells" in the gills of fishes with special reference to the common eel. J Physiol 76: 368–378.

Kirschner, L. B. (2004). The mechanism of sodium chloride uptake in hyper-regulating aquatic animals. J Exp Biol 207: 1439–1452.

Kozaka, T. Fujii, Y. and Ando, M. (2003). Central effects of various ligands on drinking behavior in eels acclimated to seawater. J Exp Biol 206: 687–692.

Krogh, A. (1937). Osmotic regulation in freshwater fishes by active absorption of chloride ions. Z Vergl Physiol 24: 656–666.

Liebert, A. M. and Schreck, C. B. (2006). Effects of acute stress on osmo-regulation, feed intake, IGF-1, and cortisol in yearling steelhead trout (*Oncorhynchus mykiss*) during seawater adaptation. Gen Comp Endocr 148: 195–202.

Lin, H. and Randall, D. J. (1995). Proton pumps in fish gills. In: Wood, C.M. and Shuttleworth, T.J. (eds) Cellular and Molecular Approaches to Fish Ionic Regulation, Academic Press, San Diego, CA: 229–255.

Lumsden, J. S., Clark, P., Hawthorn, S. Minamikawa, M., Fenwick, S. G., Haycock, M. and Wybourne, B. (2002). Gastric dilation and air sacculitis in farmed chinook salmon, *Oncorhynchus tshawytscha* (Walbaum). J Fish Dis 25: 155–163.

Manera, M. and Britti, D. (2006). Assessment of blood chemistry normal ranges in rainbow trout. J Fish Biol 69: 1427–1434.

Marshall, W. S. (2003). Rapid regulation of NaCl secretion by estuarine teleost fish: coping strategies for short-duration freshwater exposures. Biochim Biophys Acta-biomembranes 1618: 95–105.

Marshall, W. S. and Grosell, M. (2006). Ion transport, osmoregulation and acid-base balance. In: Evans, D.H. and Claiborne, J.B. (eds), The Physiology of

Fishes (3rd Edition) Taylor and Francis, CRC Press, Boca Raton: 177 – 230.

Morgan J. D. and Iwama G. K. (1998). Salinity effects on oxygen consumption, gill Na+, K+-ATPase and ion regulation in juvenile Coho salmon. J Fish Biol 53: 1110–1119.

Mosimann, R., Imboden, H. and Felix, D. (1996). The neuronal role of angiotensin II in thirst, sodium appetite, cognition and memory. Biol Rev Camb Philos Soc. 71: 545–59.

Nielsen, S., Frokiaer, J., Marples, D., Kwon, T. H., Agre, P. and Knepper, M. A. (2002). Aquaporins in the kidney: From molecules to medicine. Physiol Rev 82: 205–244.

Parks, S. K., Tresguerres, M. and Goss, G. G. (2007). Interactions between Na^+ channels and $Na^+HCO_3^-$ cotransporters in the freshwater fish gill MR cell: a model for transepithelial Na^+ uptake. Am J Physiol 292: C935–C944.

Perry, S. F. (1997). The chloride cell: structure and function in the gills of freshwater fishes. Annu Rev Physiol 59: 325–347.

Playle, R. C., Dixon, D. G. and Burnison, K. (1993). Copper and cadmium binding to fish gills: Estimates of metal-gill stability constants and modelling of metal accumulation. Can J Fish Aquat Sci 50: 2678–2687.

Postlethwaite, E. and Mcdonald, D. (1995). Mechanisms of Na^+ and Cl^- regulation in freshwater-adapted rainbow trout (*Oncorhynchus mykiss*) during exercise and stress. J Exp Biol 198: 295–304.

Potts, W. T. W. Talbot, C., Eddy, F. B., Primmett, D. and Williams, M. (1989). Sodium balance in adult Atlantic salmon (*Salmo salar* L.) during migration into neutral and acid fresh water. Comp Biochem Physiol 92A: 247–253.

Prior, F. G. R., Gourlay, T. and Taylor, K. M. (1995). Pulse reverse osmosis: a new theory in the maintenance of fluid balance. Perfusion 10: 159–170.

Rørvik, K-A., Skjervold, P. O., Fjæra, S. O. and Steien, S. H. (2000). Distended, water-filled stomach in seawater farmed rainbow trout, *Oncorhynchus mykiss* (Walbaum), provoked experimentally by osmoregulatory stress. J Fish Dis 23: 15–18.

Smith, N. F., Eddy, F. B. and Talbot, C. (1995). Effect of dietary salt load on transepithelial Na+ exchange in freshwater rainbow trout (*Oncorhynchus mykiss*). J Exp Biol 198: 2359–2364.

Takei, Y. and Hirose, S. (2002). The natriuretic peptide system in eels: a key endocrine system for euryhalinity? Am J Physiol 282: R940–R951.

Tytler, P., Tatner, M. and Findlay, C. (1990). The ontogeny of drinking in the rainbow trout *Oncorhynchus mykiss* (Walbaum). J Fish Biol 36: 867–875.

Wright, S. H. (1991). The interface of animal and aqueous environment: strategies and constraints on the maintenance of solute balance. In: Hochachka, P. W. and Mommsen, T. P. (eds) Biochemistry and Molecular Biology of Fishes, Elsevier Science, Amsterdam: 165–180.

Chapter 2

Osmoregulation in elasmobranchs

Jonathan P. Good and Neil Hazon

Keywords: Elasmobranch, NaCl transport, gill, gut, kidney, rectal gland, osmoregulation

Abstract

Elasmobranch fish typically maintain body fluids slightly hyperosmotic to the surrounding environment. This is achieved by regulating the concentrations of organic and inorganic osmolytes, principally sodium, chloride, urea, and trimethylamine oxide. The concentrations of these osmolytes are altered, independently of each other, in response to changes in environmental salinity. These alterations are necessarily coupled with changes in the direction and magnitude of osmotic water exchange with the environment. This chapter describes the function of major elasmobranch osmolytes, and the roles of the gill, gut, liver, kidney, and rectal gland in osmoregulation at varying salinities.

2.1 Introduction

The majority of extant elasmobranch species inhabit a marine environment and maintain body fluid osmolality slightly hyperosmotic to seawater (SW). This is achieved through retaining a combination of organic and inorganic osmolytes, as well as regulating fluid volume. Sodium (Na^+) and chloride (Cl^-) are two of these major osmolytes, and in SW elasmobranch plasma concentrations are lower than the surrounding environment: typically around 250 mmol l^{-1} (typical values for the water are around 500 mmol l^{-1}) (Smith, 1931b; Hazon and Henderson, 1984; Pillans and Franklin, 2004). Plasma osmolality is rendered to a hyperosmotic level via the retention of nitrogenous compounds in the extracellular fluids, the major constituent in most species being urea with a concentration of around 350 mmol l^{-1} (Ballantyne et al., 1987). A ureosmotic strategy is unusual, but has also been studied in other species; notably holocephalans, coelacanths, lungfish, the killifish (*Rivulus marmoratus*), and the crab-eating frog (Rana cancrivora) (Griffith, 1991; Frick and Wright, 2001; Wright et al., 2004).

Urea is formed by the ornithine urea cycle (OUC), and retention of such a high concentration may ordinarily have toxic effects via protein denaturation (Yancey and Somero, 1978; Yancey and Somero, 1980; Yancey et al., 1982). The role of urea in elasmobranch osmoregulation is discussed in detail below (see liver function). After urea, trimethylamine oxide (TMAO) is the second most important organic solute accumulated in elasmobranch fish at concentrations of 35–180 mM. TMAO plays a significant role as an osmolyte, with levels varying in response to changes in environmental salinity (Forster and Goldstein, 1976; Sulikowski et al., 2003; Pillans et al., 2005). In addition to TMAO, other methylamines including betaine and sarcosine contribute to the non-urea organic osmolyte content (Withers et al., 1994a; Withers et al., 1994b; Steele et al., 2005). Methylamines have also been implicated in counteracting the toxic effects of urea (Yancey, 1994; Yancey, 2005). Some beta amino acids, e.g. taurine and alpha alanine (Yancey, 2001), also make up a component of the non-urea organic osmolytes, although these compounds are regarded as compatible rather than counteracting solutes in terms of protein structure (Yancey, 1994). At least in vitro, an optimal ratio of 2:1 urea to non-urea organic osmolytes appears to be optimal for counteracting the disruptive actions of urea on protein structure and function (Yancey, 1994).

These differences in osmolyte concentrations for marine elasmobranchs result in gradients for the following movements across the semi-permeable surfaces:

- A large efflux of urea
- Influxes of ions, notably Na^+ and Cl^-
- A small influx of water

The relative concentrations of these osmolytes are regulated by the gills, the gut, the rectal gland, and the kidney; the functions of these principle osmoregulatory organs are described later. Through the action of these organs, elasmobranchs are able to selectively alter the relative concentrations of principle osmolytes in the body fluids, in relation to SW (Smith, 1931a; Smith, 1931b; Pillans and Franklin, 2004). In this way, the internal concentrations of individual osmolytes can be maintained at different levels to those in the external environment.

Euryhaline elasmobranchs, such as the bull shark (*Carcharhinus leucas*) and the Atlantic stingray (*Dasyatis sabina*), adopt a similar osmoregulatory strategy in SW (Smith, 1931a; Smith, 1931b; Pillans and Franklin, 2004). Through the action of the organs noted above, elasmobranchs in freshwater (FW) maintain reduced, although still considerable levels of urea, along with a less severe reduction in Na^+ and Cl^- (Table 1) (Thorson *et al.*, 1973; Piermarini and Evans, 1998; Pillans and Franklin, 2004). These concentrations of principle osmolytes in FW lead to the following fluxes:

- A large influx of water
- Effluxes of ions, notably Na^+ and Cl^-
- A large efflux of urea

There are therefore fundamental differences in the osmoregulatory requirements of SW and FW elasmobranchs: FW elasmobranchs experience a far greater influx of water than those in SW, and the gradients for Na^+ and Cl^- are directly opposite in the two environments. Animals in both environments face a continual loss of urea, although this is compounded in FW by the magnitude of the difference between internal and external osmolality. These variations lead to different priorities for osmoregulation in the two environments, such as the retention of Na^+ and Cl^- and a greater pressure on volume regulation in FW. Although classically marine elasmobranch fish were believed to be unable to acclimate to dilute environments, as more species have been investigated, laboratory studies have demonstrated that some species can acclimate to reduced salinities, but not to full FW (Morgan *et al.*, 2003a; Cooper and Morris, 2004; Steele *et al.*, 2005; Good *et al.*, 2008); these species can be regarded therefore as partially euryhaline (Hazon *et al.*, 2003).

There are also a group of stenohaline FW elasmobranchs, all of which belong to the family Potamotrygonidae. These stingrays are widespread throughout the river systems of South America draining into the Atlantic Ocean. Some of the Dasyatidae complete their life cycle in FW (Compagno and Roberts, 1982), but the potamotrygonid stingrays are the only obligate FW species, having lost the ability to survive in waters of salinity greater than 100 mOsm Kg^{-1} (Brooks *et al.*, 1981). Key to this is the inability of the kidneys and gills to retain urea (Thorson, 1970), and the absence of salt secretion from a degenerate rectal gland (Thorson *et al.*, 1978). It has been reported that plasma urea concentrations are as low as 1.2 mmol l^{-1}, and that these elasmobranchs are ammoniotelic as opposed to ureotelic (see Table 1) (Wood *et al.*, 2002).

At the cellular level, free amino acids play a vital role in osmoregulation and regulating cell volume (Forster and Goldstein, 1976). In vertebrates, intracellular osmotic parameters are typically isosmotic with those of the extracellular fluid. Changes in environmental conditions are therefore necessarily coupled with changes in intracellular volume and osmolyte concentrations. Urea freely diffuses across plasma membranes (Fenstermacher *et al.*, 1972); therefore, the intra- and extracellular concentrations are not dissimilar. This is not the case with intra- and extracellular concentrations of TMAO, which can differ markedly (Sulikowski *et al.*, 2003; Pillans *et al.*, 2006), due to variations in Na^+-dependent and independent membrane transport mechanisms (Wilson *et al.*, 1999). This trend is also true of free amino acids, which constitute 1% of extracellular fluid osmolality and 19% of that of intracellular fluid (Perlman and Goldstein, 1988). Acclimation of Batoids to decreased salinity has been proven to affect free amino acid concentrations. In the little skate, *Raja erinacea*, significant decreases in free amino acid concentrations were measured in wing muscle and erythrocytes upon acclimation to 50% SW, although concentrations in the heart were unaffected (Boyd *et al.*, 1977). Similar effects were also observed in the brain of the *D. sabina* acclimated to 50% SW (Boyd *et al.*, 1977). Clearly, free amino acids play an important role in regulating cell volume, particularly during salinity transfer in euryhaline elasmobranchs. Free amino acids have also been implicated alongside methylamines as playing a role in counteracting the toxic effects of urea. While the majority of the non-urea organic osmolytes are methylamines (Yancey, 1994; Yancey, 2001), some elasmobranch species require beta amino acids to achieve the optimal 2:1 ratio to urea (Steele *et al.*, 2005). The relative importance of methylamines and beta amino acids may depend on whether species are marine, euryhaline, or FW, with marine species accumulating more methylamines than beta amino acids and FW species preferentially accumulating beta amino acids (Treberg and Driedzic, 2006; Treberg *et al.*, 2006).

Variations in the plasma and cellular concentrations of urea and TMAO have also been demonstrated to have a number of other effects in elasmobranchs. The urea to TMAO ratio has been shown to affect erythrocyte cell membrane fluidity in *R. erinacea* (Barton *et al.*, 1999). Concentrations of both osmolytes have also been shown to impact on buoyancy (Withers *et al.*, 1994a; Withers *et al.*, 1994b). TMAO concentrations have also been shown to change with depth (Yancey *et al.*, 2004), although whether this is a reflection of the detrimental effect increased pressure has on protein function, or linked to lipid metabolism is unclear (Samerotte *et al.*, 2007).

It is therefore evident that osmoregulation is controlled at both the cellular and whole animal levels. Through the action of the gills, gut, rectal gland, and kidneys, elasmobranch fish have the ability to independently regulate the concentrations of Na^+, Cl^- and urea in both SW and FW environments, as part of their hyperosmoregulatory strategy. The mechanisms by which this osmoregulatory strategy is controlled are poorly understood, particularly during migration between FW and SW. However, the principle organs involved have been reasonably well studied and their modes of action are well described. In addition there are a number of other organs that are believed to play an important role in osmoregulation, such as the liver as the main site of urea production, as well as the pituitary gland, the interrenal gland, and the heart as endocrine organs effecting osmoregulatory control.

2.2 The gill

2.2.1 Gill structure

In elasmobranch fish there are usually five pairs of gills, although six and seven are not uncommon. Each gill arch is made up of lateral rods of cartilage (the gill filaments) supporting a sheet of muscular and connective tissue (the interbranchial septum). The dorsal and the ventral surfaces of each gill filament

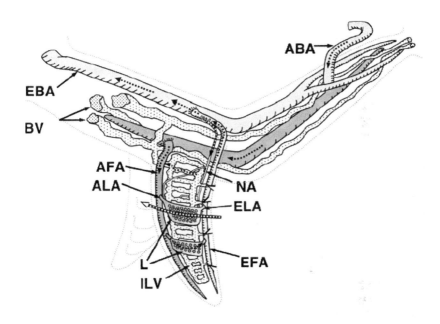

Figure 1. *Generalised blood flow through an elasmobranch gill arch and filament*

Arterio-arterial pathway: blood travels (dotted arrow) from the afferent branchial artery (ABA) to an afferent filamental artery (AFA), which runs the length of the filament. This blood is distributed to the lamellae (L) via afferent lamellar arterioles (ALA's). Lamellar blood flows through efferent lamellar arterioles (ELA's) into an efferent filamental artery (EFA). Oxygenated blood then flows to the efferent branchial artery (EBA) and on to the dorsal aorta for systemic distribution. Arteriovenous pathway: blood in the EFA can be distributed to interlamellar vessels (ILV's) via postlamellar arteriovenous anastomoses (>) or nutrient arteries (NA). The ILV's are drained by branchial veins (BV). The direction of water flow (striped arrow) over the gills is also shown, (Olson KR. 2002 Vascular anatomy of the fish gill. J Exp Zool 293: 214-231). Reprinted with permission of Wiley-Liss, Inc., a subsidiary of John Wiley &Sons, Inc.

have a row of secondary lamellae; these are the principal site of gas exchange.

The branchial vasculature in elasmobranch fish is highly complex and varies greatly from species to species. However, Evans and co-workers (2005) recently published a thorough review of the fish gill, in which detailed descriptions of the vasculature are made (see Figure 1). The entire cardiac output enters the afferent branchial arteries (ABAs) via the ventral aorta. Blood flowing through an ABA feeds two hemibranchs of a gill arch where it is oxygenated at the lamellae of the filaments (Evans et al., 2005). The vasculature which supplies the secondary epithelium can be mediated by sphincters located on the efferent primary artery, and on both afferent and efferent secondary arteries (Laurent and Dunel, 1980). Oxygenated blood flows into an efferent branchial artery (EBA), which in turn flows into the dorsal aorta for systemic distribution (Evans et al., 2005). There are two distinct but interconnected circulations within the gill filaments: the arterio-arterial pathway, which is involved in respiratory gas exchange; and the arteriovenous pathway, a non-respiratory pathway possibly involved in supplying nutrients to the epithelium and structural tissues.

2.2.2 Gill function

The elevated concentrations of urea and TMAO in the blood plasma of elasmobranchs result in a substantial concentration gradient for the diffusive efflux of these osmolytes. It is well known that elasmobranch gill epithelia are particularly impermeable to urea (Boylan, 1967; Payan et al., 1973; Wood et al., 1995; Part et al., 1998; Walsh and Mommsen, 2001). However, the large surface area combined with a huge concentration gradient means that diffusional loss of urea is greatest across the gills; indeed, this loss has been reported to be almost equivalent to the rate of urea synthesis (Carrier and Evans, 1972; Wood et al., 1995). It has been suggested that rates of urea loss are reduced through a combination of structural and active transport mechanisms. The basolateral membranes of Squalus acanthias gill epithelia have the highest cholesterol to phospholipid ratios recorded for a natural membrane (Fines et al., 2001). This could be a means of reducing the diffusion of urea into the cell as cholesterol is known to reduce urea permeability (Mourtisen and Jorgensen, 1994). Furthermore, Part et al. (1998) demonstrated that the basolateral membrane of the gill epithelia in S. acanthias was some 14 times more permeable to urea than the apical membrane. This selective permeability of urea led these researchers to postulate that the gills in elasmobranchs form an intermediary layer between the internal and external environment with respect to urea (Wood et al., 1995; Part et al., 1998). Using competitive urea transport inhibitors in vivo, Wood et al. (1995) demonstrated an increase in urea efflux from the gill of S. acanthias, suggesting the presence of a urea 'back-transporter' on the basolateral membrane. This was later supported by a similar study using an in vitro perfused gill preparation (Part et al., 1998). These two studies combined indicate the presence of a facilitated urea 'back transporter' on the basolateral membrane which could maintain the intracellular urea concentration lower than that of the blood, thus supporting the idea of the gills acting as an intermediary layer with respect to urea concentration. Further evidence for the presence of a urea transport system in the gills of elasmobranchs was provided by Fines *et al.*, (2001) who demonstrated the presence of a phloretin sensitive Na^+-urea counter-transporter directed to return urea to the blood stream. Wood *et al.*, (1995) hypothesised that local urea synthesis could also be occurring in the gills to support the 'back-transport' of urea into the blood stream by creating a higher concentration of urea in the intermediary gill layer.

Conversely to the situation for urea, there is accumulation of Na^+ and Cl^- at the gills, reported to be related to the acid-base regulatory system (Bentley *et al.*, 1976) involving the excretion of acidic (e.g. hydrogen, H^+) and basic (e.g. bicarbonate, $HCO3^-$) ions (Evans, 1982; Evans, 1984). Studies on elasmobranchs have shown consistently that acid secretion is linked to Na^+ absorption, and that base secretion is linked to Cl^- absorption. It has been suggested that there are two acid secretion mechanisms: an apical V-ATPase which is electrically linked to Na^+ absorption, and an electroneutral exchange of Na^+ and H^+ via the Na^+/H^+ exchange proteins; and two base secretion mechanisms via two apical $Cl^-/HCO3^-$ exchangers: AE1, and pendrin (Bentley *et al.*, 1976; Perry, 1997; Evans *et al.*, 2005). There is also substantial efflux of Na^+ and Cl^- across the gills, although this is still less than the rate of influx. Branchial activity of Na^+, K^+-ATPase, the active protein in Na^+ and Cl^- transport, is ten to fifteen times below that of marine teleosts, and hence there is net accumulation of Na^+ and Cl^- at the gills and no net efflux (Jampol and Epstein, 1970; Shuttleworth, 1988). Comparative studies of Raja clavata and *Scyliorhinus canicula* revealed two types of chloride cells. In one cell type the apical membrane is buried deep in a cul-de-sac and connects to the external milieu by a narrow opening; conversely, the other cell type has a protruding apical membrane (Laurent and Dunel, 1980). Both of these cell types lack the tubular system which is found in teleost chloride cells; in elasmobranchs these are functionally replaced by copious infoldings of the basolateral membrane.

Wilson and co-workers (2002) showed strong Na^+, K^+-ATPase immunoreactivity associated with the basolateral gill membrane in *S. acanthias*. High abundance of Na^+, K^+-ATPase in the gills of SW elasmobranchs not only confirms their role in acid-base regulation and possible Na^+ dependent urea transport, it also presents a possible role for the gills in excretion of Na^+ and Cl^-. Indeed, after removal of the rectal gland, *S. acanthias* was able to maintain ionic balance, although the chloride cells showed no change in number, structure, or Na^+, K^+-ATPase activity (Wilson *et al.*, 2002). This suggests that the gills, and perhaps more probably the kidney, are able to maintain ionic balance in elasmobranchs during stable environmental conditions.

It has been shown that levels and abundance of Na^+, K^+-ATPase change in relation to external salinity in certain species. In experiments carried out on the euryhaline species *D. sabina* the highest activity and relative abundance of Na^+, K^+-ATPase in the gills was seen in long term acclimated FW animals. These animals showed a reduction in both activity and abundance of Na^+, K^+-ATPase after a 7 day period at SW. Long term acclimated SW animals had the lowest activity and abundance of Na^+, K^+-ATPase of all three groups (Piermarini and Evans, 2000). In this study, in FW the elasmobranch gills are possibly acting like those of teleosts as a site of active Na⁺ and Cl⁻ uptake. This elevation in Na⁺, K⁺-ATPase abundance and activity in low salinities is presumably due to the fact that as external salinity increases, the requirement for active Na⁺ and Cl⁻ uptake across the gills will decrease, as the ion flux gradient is reversed. These results also demonstrate the capacity for modification of gill physiology and morphology to changing environmental conditions in a euryhaline elasmobranch. The discrepancy between *S. acanthias* (SW) and *D. sabina* (euryhaline) suggests that plasticity in chloride cell structure and/or abundance, and associated branchial Na⁺, K⁺-ATPase may therefore be a key factor in elasmobranch euryhalinity.

2.2.3 Control of gill function

In terms of peptide hormone control of gill function in elasmobranchs, very little is currently known. Receptors for angiotensin II (Ang II), the principle bioactive component of the renin angiotensin system (RAS), have been identified in membrane fractions prepared from gill cells of the Japanese dogfish, *Triakis scyllia* (Tierney *et al.*, 1997). Although it is highly probable that Ang II would influence the perfusion of blood through the gills due to its vasopressor activity on the vasculature of elasmobranchs (Hazon *et al.*, 1999), it is unknown if Ang II controls Na⁺, K⁺-ATPase in the gills of elasmobranchs, as has been demonstrated in the euryhaline eel (Marsigliante *et al.*, 1997). Both arginine vasotocin (AVT) and C-type natriuretic peptide (CNP) are known to be vasoactive in elasmobranchs, with AVT exerting a vasopressor effect (Hazon, unpublished) and CNP a vasodilatory effect (Bjenning *et al.*, 1992; Evans *et al.*, 1993). These two peptides may influence elasmobranch gill function by changing blood flow to the gill epithelia.

1α-hydoxycorticosterone (1α-OH-B) is the principle corticosteroid secreted from the interrenal gland in elasmobranch fish (Truscott and Idler, 1968). 1α-OH-B binding activity has been reported in the gills of the skate *Raja ocellata* (Moon and Idler, 1974), and a cytosolic receptor glycoprotein for 1α-OH-B was demonstrated in the gills of the same species (Idler and Kane, 1980). Although the role of 1α-OH-B has yet to be determined in the gills of elasmobranchs, it is clear that the steroid may influence salt and/or urea flux across the gills, particularly when considering the effects of cortisol, the major teleost corticosteroid, on chloride cell morphology and function in teleost fish (Laurent and Perry, 1990).

2.3 The gut

2.3.1 Gut structure

The oesophagus, stomach, spiral intestine, and rectum comprise the elasmobranch gut. The oesophagus of most elasmobranchs is relatively short and lined with finger-like extensions which prevent food escaping from the mouth. Elasmobranch stomachs are generally J-shaped organs, some of which have longitudinal folds (rugae) which allow expansion to accommodate gorge feeding. The stomach is comprised of two histologically distinct sections: the cardiac stomach and the pyloric stomach. The cardiac stomach can be subdivided into the proximal section with a striated muscle wall, and the distal section with a smooth muscle wall (Nilsson and Holmgren, 1988).

The valvular intestine is also relatively short, having a greatly increased surface area due to the valves. There are three basic types of intestinal valve in sharks, termed spiral, scroll, and ring. The spiral valve is found in Squalidae and Scyliorhinidae, the scroll valve is found in Carcharhinidae, and the ring valve is found in all extant lamnoids (Martin, 2003b). These increase nutrient absorption in the intestine, not only by increasing surface area, but also by increasing the length of time taken for material to pass through. Despite the relative compact nature of the elasmobranch gut, absorption efficiencies are as high as those of carnivorous teleosts: 62–83% for energy (quantifying energy lost through non-assimilated food), 76–88% for organic matter, and 76–87% for dry matter (Wetherbee and Gruber, 1993). Gross conversion efficiency for ingested food can be calculated by dividing annual production (growth, metabolism, excretion, and egestion) by annual consumption. This varies greatly depending on species and dietary composition (Wetherbee and Cortes, 2004). Estimates for the euryhaline *C. leucas* range between 5 and 12% (Schmid and Murru, 1994).

2.3.2 Gut function

(a) Dietary intake

When examining the role of the gut in elasmobranch osmoregulation, a large consideration must go to dietary composition. By definition the effects of this will vary greatly between species, and also between populations. Not only will the diet itself vary, but the requirements from that diet will vary depending on the environment in which the elasmobranch inhabits, whether the species is an active or ambush predator, and whether or not the species is ram ventilating. Many marine elasmobranch species, for example *S. canicula*, are typically gorge feeders, and as a consequence are subjected to large and infrequent salt loading during feeding events. This situation is exaggerated if the diet is also particularly rich in salts, such as one comprised largely of marine invertebrates as in *S. canicula*. Dietary intake may also be a key source of salts for FW elasmobranchs. Potamotrygonid rays experienced negative salt balance with their native ion-poor waters during periods of starvation (Wood *et al.*, 2002). FW elasmobranchs may therefore require dietary salts to maintain osmotic stasis. Metabolic urea is also important for osmoregulation, as this is directly related to food availability; this is discussed below under liver function. TMAO is also an important osmolyte, counteracting the toxic effects of urea, and in most species is primarily derived from dietary sources. It is generally accepted that most elasmobranchs lack the capacity to produce TMAO endogenously (Baker *et al.*, 1963; Goldstein *et al.*, 1967; Goldstein and Dewitt-Harley, 1973; Treberg and Driedzic, 2006; Treberg *et al.*, 2006), although there are some intriguing taxonomic exceptions (Goldstein and Funkhouser, 1972; Goldstein and Dewitt-Harley, 1973; Treberg *et al.*, 2006). It has been suggested that when TMAO in the diet is limiting, either endogenous TMAO production or endogenous betaine or sarcosine synthesis compensates for the 'methylamine gap', depending on species (Treberg *et al.*, 2006).

(b) Drinking

As marine elasmobranchs maintain their plasma osmolality iso- or slightly hyper-osmotic to the surrounding SW, and are therefore faced with a small but constant influx of water across the gills, it was thought that elasmobranch fish did not have the physiological requirement to drink (Smith, 1931b). Similarly when euryhaline fish are acclimated to FW, they face incipient water gain and therefore, as in FW teleost fish, drinking plays little if any part in osmoregulation.

However, euryhaline elasmobranchs migrating from FW to SW are faced with a very different osmoregulatory problem, and plasma osmolality must be increased rapidly to equal SW. A significant difference in drinking rate was observed in the partially euryhaline elasmobranch *S. canicula* following manipulation of environmental salinity (Hazon *et al.*, 1997). This drinking response was investigated in more detail in *S. canicula* by Anderson *et al.* (Anderson *et al.*, 2002b), and was shown to be maximal approximately 2 hours following transfer from 80 to 100% SW. The drinking response was found to be the result of extra-cellular dehydration, as occurs in teleost fish (Takei *et al.*, 1988), and not cellular dehydration which is a principle stimulus for eliciting a drinking response in mammals (Fitzsimons, 1979). Indeed, Good *et al.* (2008) recently demonstrated that 80 to 100% SW transfer in *S. canicula* induced an overcompensatory decrease in plasma volume during the first 4 hours, and could be the stimulus for a drinking response. Furthermore,, cellular dehydration induced by injection of hyper-osmotic, NaCl-rich elasmobranch Ringer caused an inhibition in drinking in *S. canicula* (Anderson *et al.*, 2002b). Drinking in elasmobranchs has also been reported in both the white-spotted bamboo shark, *Chiloscyllium plagiosum* (Taylor and Grosell, 2006), and the spiny dogfish, *S. acanthias* (De Boeck *et al.*, 2001), so it is clear that elasmobranchs do have the physiological capacity to drink under the appropriate environmental conditions. Recently both solute and water movement across the intestinal epithelia of elasmobranch fish have been reported in the white spotted bamboo shark (Taylor and Grosell, 2006; Anderson *et al.*, 2007), and water reabsorption rates in the intestine of SW adapted C. plagiosum were similar in magnitude to the basal drinking rates of both *T. scyllia* and *S. canicula*. The higher concentration of magnesium and sulphate in the intestinal fluids suggested that fish were both imbibing SW and/or actively secreting these divalent ions into the lumen of the intestine. These studies also observed the presence of bicarbonate in the intestine of bamboo sharks, regarded as a further indication that the fish has been drinking the environmental medium (Taylor and Grosell, 2006; Anderson *et al.*, 2007). However, at this stage it is not known if the presence of bicarbonate in the intestine of bamboo sharks plays an osmoregulatory and/or acid–base function (Anderson *et al.*, 2007).

(c) Control of drinking

Angiotensin II is recognised as one of the most potent dipsogenic peptide in higher vertebrates and is released in mammals in response to cellular dehydration

(Fitzsimons, 1979; Fitzsimons, 1998). Similar dipsogenic properties have been reported in both teleost (Takei *et al.*, 1979) and elasmobranch fish (Anderson *et al.*, 2001a). In both groups Ang II is released in response to extra-cellular dehydration (Takei *et al.*, 1988; Anderson *et al.*, 2002b). Circulating plasma concentrations of levels of Ang II were maximal in *S. canicula* transferred from 80 to 100% SW at the time point that coincided with the peak in drinking in these animals (Anderson *et al.*, 2002c). These data strongly implicate the involvement of Ang II in the control of drinking, at least in partially euryhaline elasmobranch fish; the control of the drinking response in fully euryhaline elasmobranches remains to be determined.

Natriuretic peptides in general are known to be antagonistic to Ang II in the physiological mechanisms they control. Indeed, in the euryhaline teleost, *Anguilla japonica*, atrial natriuretic peptide (ANP), the principle circulating natriuretic peptide, is 100 times more potent in its inhibition of drinking than Ang II is in stimulating drinking (Takei, 2000). Similarly in the elasmobranch *S. canicula* CNP was 50 times more potent in inhibition of drinking than Ang II was in stimulation (Anderson *et al.*, 2001b).

2.4 The liver

2.4.1 Liver structure

The elasmobranch liver is a large organ, often occupying nearly half of the body cavity. It consists of two lateral lobes which are united anteriorly by the cystic lobe, spanning across the body cavity posterior to the septum transversum. The gall bladder is an elongate tubular sac lying along the margin of the cystic lobe. The main lateral hepatic ducts give rise to numerous small hepatic tubules and to several larger rami. The anterior right and the anterior left rami arise from the summit of the anterior arch formed by each of the main hepatic ducts; the posterior dorsal hepatic rami arise from the hepatic ducts either at the lateral extremity of the anterior arch, or in the anterior part of their posterior course (Scammon, 1913).

The elasmobranch liver performs a number of functions for hydrodynamics and metabolism. The liver is the main store for energy reserves in the form of fatty acids, although fatty acids in some species also perform an important function in generating dynamic lift. Elasmobranchs lack the swim bladder of teleost species and are heavier than the surrounding environment. Dynamic lift is generated from the pectoral fins whilst the animal is in motion. This imposes hydrodynamic constraints on shark size as a doubling of body length equates to a square of fin surface area but a cube of body mass. This reduction in relative lift is offset by an increase in proportional liver size in larger animals which increases the relative amount of body fatty acids which are less dense than SW (Wetherbee and Nichols, 2000). An example of this can be found in the basking shark, Cetorhinus maximus: the liver from an 8.8 m, 5.9 tonne specimen accounted for nearly 25% of total body mass, yielding 2270 l of oil (Martin, 2003a).

2.4.2 Liver function

(a) Urea production

With the exception of the FW Potamotrygonid stingrays, elasmobranch fish are ureotelic with urea production largely occurring in the liver via the ornithine urea cycle (OUC), which predominates not only in elasmobranchs but also in some ureogenic teleosts and in terrestrial mammals; this subject has been extensively reviewed (Goldstein, 1967; Anderson, 1995; Anderson, 2001; Walsh and Mommsen, 2001). The major differences to mammals are that in elasmobranch fish the OUC requires glutamine as the nitrogen substrate, the enzyme carbomyl phosphate synthetase III is the rate limiting step controlling the entry of nitrogen into the cycle, and glutamine synthetase catalyses the production of glutamine from ammonia. This contrasts with mammals where the nitrogen substrate is ammonia, and carbomyl phosphate synthetase I is the enzyme controlling urea synthesis. Even the Potamotrygonid rays possess an OUC, but have been demonstrated as being ammoniotelic (Wood *et al.*, 2002).

Although the liver is generally regarded as the major site of urea production in elasmobranchs, it has recently been reported that skeletal muscle possesses an OUC, and that muscle may play a significant role in total urea production (Steele *et al.*, 2005; Kajimura *et al.*, 2006). It has also been suggested that the skeletal muscle plays an important role in scavenging muscle ammonia for urea production and ensuring that any excess nitrogen is incorporated into nitrogen metabolism for either urea synthesis or protein for growth (Steele *et al.*, 2005; Kajimura *et al.*, 2006). Furthermore, the stomach/intestine has also been implicated as a source of urea production, although the contribution to urea production is considered small compared to muscle and liver (Tam *et al.*, 2003; Kajimura *et al.*, 2006), and the physiological role may be more closely related to adjusting the osmolality of the intestinal contents (Wood *et al.*, 2007a). Total urea synthesis may also change in response to changes in environmental salinity, although the results may vary dependent on species. Acclimation of the lemon shark, *Negaprion brevirostis* to 50% SW produced no change in urea production (Goldstein *et al.*, 1968), and reduced plasma urea concentrations were attributed entirely to an increase in urea loss. However, acclimation to 50% SW induced a decrease in urea production in both the little skate, *R. erinacea* (Goldstein and Forster, 1971a), and the European lesser spotted dogfish, *S. canicula* (Hazon and Henderson, 1984). Very few studies have investigated the role of urea synthesis in elasmobranchs acclimating to environments of increased environmental salinity. However, for the FW stingray, *Himantura signifier*, acclimation to 67% SW led to an increase in activity of key enzymes involved in urea biosynthesis in the liver (Tam *et al.*, 2003); more recently, hepatic urea synthesis was shown to increase in the euryhaline bull shark *C. leucas* when acclimated to SW compared to FW (Anderson *et al.*, 2005a).

Urea synthesis in elasmobranchs may also depend on food availability: increased nitrogen conservation and elevated urea synthesis has been reported acutely, post- feeding (Wood *et al.*, 2005; Chew *et al.*, 2006; Kajimura *et al.*, 2006;

Wood *et al.*, 2007a). Conversely, urea levels have been reported to slowly decrease during starvation over a period of weeks in *Poroderma africanum* (Haywood, 1973) and *S. acanthias* (Leech *et al.*, 1979). In *S. canicula*, fish fed a high protein diet were able to respond to increased salinity challenge with an increase in urea synthesis and therefore increased plasma urea concentrations, while those fed a low protein diet could not (Armour *et al.*, 1993a). The nitrogen budget for naturally feeding *S. acanthias* suggests fish must feed every 5–6 days in order to maintain enough nitrogen for urea based osmoregulation (Kajimura *et al.*, 2006).

2.5 Kidney

2.5.1 Structure

Elasmobranch kidneys consist of a pair of elongate structures, found on either side of the dorsal aorta. In sharks, they have a thread-like appearance at the anterior end (midway along the dorsal surface of the abdominal cavity) and gradually widen posteriorly, fusing below the cloaca (Shuttleworth, 1988). Elasmobranchs possess a renal portal system in which portal veins are formed from the bifurcation of the caudal vein. Upon entering the kidney these divide to form a matrix of smaller vessels. Blood from the venous portal system mixes freely with that from the glomerular vasa efferentia before exiting the kidney through the renal vein (Hentschel, 1988). There is also anatomical evidence of a glomerular bypass vessel which permits blood to flow from the afferent to the efferent vessel, thus avoiding filtration (Brown and Green, 1992).

The elasmobranch nephron is extremely complex, consisting of four counter-current loops separated into two zones; it has been comprehensively reviewed (Hentschel *et al.*, 1993; Lacy and Reale, 1995). The bundle zone (or lateral bundle zone) is enclosed by a urea impermeable connective tissue sheath and the tubules are closely packed into discrete bundles. It is hypothesised that a counter-current exchange system operates in this region (Stolte *et al.*, 1977). The second region is the sinus zone (or mesial zone) in which different segments of the renal tubule intermingle with blood sinuses (Hentschel, 1988; Lacy and Reale, 1995). The division between the two zones is marked by large renal corpuscles. Each individual nephron forms two loops in the bundle zone and two long convolutions in the sinus region (see Figure 2) (Hentschel, 1988).

2.5.2 Kidney function

As marine elasmobranchs maintain body fluids hyperosmotic to the environment, there is a small but continual influx of water across their semi-permeable surfaces. This excess water is excreted by the kidneys, primarily through increased glomerular filtration rate (GFR) and urine flow rate (UFR) (Goldstein and Forster, 1971b; Forster *et al.*, 1972). The elasmobranch kidney cannot produce hyperosmotic urine relative to blood plasma and, coupled with the use of urea as a plasma osmolyte, the major roles of the kidney are urea retention and volume regulation.

In euryhaline elasmobranchs acclimating to brackish/FW, a major component of the reduction in plasma osmolality and urea concentrations appears to be increased renal clearance through increased GFR and UFR (Goldstein and Forster, 1971b; Forster *et al.*, 1972; Wells *et al.*, 2002; Janech *et al.*, 2006b). When euryhaline elasmobranchs are fully acclimated to FW, plasma osmolality/ urea concentrations are regulated at lower, constant values, but the increased urine flow provides the potential for increased urinary urea (and ion) loss. However, FW acclimated euryhaline elasmobranchs appear to be able to selectively reduce the urinary concentration of these solutes whereas partially euryhaline elasmobranchs have a reduced capacity to achieve this reduction

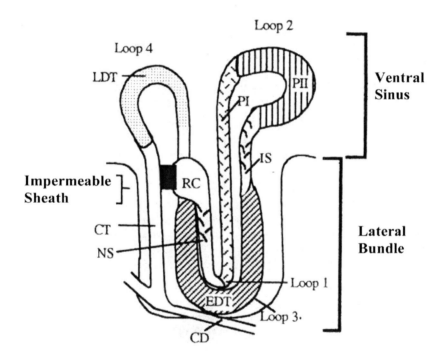

Figure 2. *Schematic diagram of a single nephron from S. canicula*
    Filtrate from the renal corpuscle/glomerulus (RC) flows through the neck segment (NS) and into loop 1 in the bundle region. Filtrate then passes through proximal segments I and II (PI and PII) of loop 2 in the sinus region. Then the filtrate passes through the intermediate segment (IS) into the early distal segment (EDT) and loop 3 in the bundle region. Filtrate then flows into the late distal segment (LDT) and loop 4 in the sinus region before entering the collecting tubule (CT). Filtrate then passes into the collecting duct (CD) (Hentschel et al. 1993). Reprinted with permission of Wiley-Liss, Inc., a subsidiary of John Wiley &Sons, Inc.

(Shuttleworth, 1988; Janech et al., 1998). Indeed, Janech et al., (2006b) concluded that euryhaline elasmobranchs acclimated to dilute environmental salinities have a remarkable functional reserve for both glomerular filtration and urinary dilution. The increased functional reserve for urinary dilution in euryhaline species may underpin the increased ability to acclimate to lower environmental salinities, compared to partially euryhaline species (Janech et al., 2006b)

One of the key roles of the elasmobranch kidney is urea retention and, as urea is reabsorbed against a sizeable concentration gradient, it has been proposed that the reabsorption mechanism is active, possibly coupled to the movement of Na^+ (Schmidt-Nielsen and Rabinowitz, 1964; Schmidt-Nielsen et al., 1972; Hays et al., 1977). Indeed, a phloretin-sensitive, Na^+-linked urea transporter has been suggested in the bundle zone of R. erinacea (Morgan et al., 2003b). However, a passive model of urea reabsorption has been proposed (Friedman and Hebert, 1990) which relies on a counter-current multiplication system and differential permeabilities of tubular segments to urea, water, and Na^+, as occurs in mammals. The renal counter-current bundles and the microvasculature of the elasmobranch nephron were examined in detail in S. canicula and R. erinacea (Hentschel et al., 1998). A single lymph capillary-like vessel was identified in close contact with the collecting tubule along the entire bundle, before merging with the venous sinusoidal capillaries of the peritubular blood circulation. It was proposed that the central vessel provided a channel for the convective flow of Na^+ Cl^- rich-fluid to the portal system, and may therefore be involved in counter-current exchange of urea, from the collecting tubule urine to the fluid in the central vessel (Hentschel et al., 1998). This exchange mechanism may account for the low urea concentration of fluid of the collecting duct as determined in micropuncture studies (Stolte et al., 1977).

The kidney of S. acanthias contains at least one protein representing a facilitated urea transporter (UT) (for review see Smith and Wright (1999)) belonging to the UT-A family of urea transporters in mammals, and there is evidence for similar urea transport proteins in R. erinacea (Smith and Wright, 1999), and D. sabina (Janech et al., 2003; Janech et al., 2006a). This is strong evidence in support of urea reabsorption occurring by facilitated diffusion (Boylan, 1972; Friedman and Hebert, 1990), although the data from R. erinacea suggests that both facilitated urea transport and Na^+-linked urea co-transport may occur, at least in this species. The model of urea reabsorption by facilitated diffusion depends on there being differential urea permeability in different regions of the elasmobranch nephron. The localisation of the Triakis urea transporter to the renal collecting duct, situated in the last segment of the bundle zone, and no other nephron segment provides direct evidence to support the facilitated diffusion theory for urea reabsorption in this species (Hyodo et al., 2004a). Furthermore, in both R. erinacea (Morgan et al., 2003a) and D. sabina (Janech et al., 2006b) expression of the renal UT was down regulated in animals exposed to reduced salinity, suggesting that decreased UT expression may play a vital role in the lower fractional reabsorption of urea and therefore decreased plasma concentration of urea when exposed to low salinities (Janech et al., 2006b).

The kidney also plays a role in the regulation of Na^+ and Cl^- plasma concentration in addition to the Na^+-linked urea transport described above. Ultra-structure studies have demonstrated that tubular cells in the early distal region of the nephron have characteristics similar to cells that are known to actively transport Na^+ (Friedman and Hebert, 1990; Lacy and Reale, 1991). Histochemical studies have only isolated Na^+, K^+-ATPase activity in the early and late distal tubules and the collecting duct (Endo, 1984; Hebert and Friedman, 1990). Isolated perfused proximal tubule preparations from *S. acanthias* have been shown to actively secrete Na^+ and Cl^- ions (Beyenbach and Fromter, 1985), and this may drive net fluid secretion (Sawyer *et al.*, 1985). Indeed, the ultrastructural studies used as evidence for active tubular reabsorption (Lacy *et al.*, 1975; Endo, 1984), could also be used to support active tubular secretion (Henderson *et al.*, 1988), as no directional element to this tubular movement was established.

2.5.3 Control of renal function

The factors controlling GFR in the elasmobranch kidney are poorly understood, although adrenaline (Brown and Green, 1987) and the endogenous peptide hormones (including vasoactive intestinal peptide (VIP) and prolactin (Yokota and Benyajati, 1988)) have all been reported to significantly increase GFR. In addition, AVT, Ang II, and natriuretic peptides (NP) have all been implicated in the control of renal function in teleost fish species (Brown *et al.*, 1980; Amer and Brown, 1995; Takei and Kaiya, 1998), although until recently their role in elasmobranch fish remained uninvestigated. To determine the actions of these individual peptides on kidney function, a perfused trunk preparation with the kidney in situ was developed for the partially euryhaline elasmobranch fish, *S. canicula* (Wells *et al.*, 2002). Addition of 10^{-9} M AVT and 10^{-10} M AVT to the in situ perfused trunk preparation caused a decrease in UFR and GFR in SW acclimated female dogfish (Wells *et al.*, 2002). Renal clearances of ions and urea were also reduced, in line with reductions in GFR. These data suggest that AVT induced a glomerular antidiuresis in *S. canicula* as previously reported for the trout (Amer and Brown, 1995). AVT is a profound vasoconstrictor in elasmobranch fish and this effect is mediated by a process of glomerular de-recruitment, in which the total number of filtering nephrons is decreased, therefore reducing the total GFR (Wells *et al.*, 2005). Similar results have also been obtained with another vasoconstrictor hormone, Ang II (Wells *et al.*, 2006), and an interaction between these two hormones remains a possibility. Conversely, perfusion of the dogfish trunk preparation with 10^{-9} M CNP resulted in an increase in urine flow rate and GFR, coupled with an increase in the clearance and excretion of urea (Wells *et al.*, 2006). CNP is the only circulating natriuretic peptide reported in elasmobranch fish (Suzuki *et al.*, 1991, 1992, 1994; Kawakoshi *et al.*, 2001), and has the opposite renal action to both AVT and Ang II, perhaps indicating a role in controlling renal function during acclimation to dilute environmental salinities. Recently Anderson *et al.*, (2006), working with the euryhaline species *C. leucas*, showed that AVT plasma concentrations increased upon acute transfer of fish to environments of increased salinity, whereas CNP levels remained unchanged (Anderson *et al.*, 2005b; Anderson *et al.*, 2006). Furthermore, AVT plasma concentrations and mRNA levels increased with environmental salinity in *T. scyllia* (Hyodo *et al.*, 2004b). These studies suggest that AVT, Ang II and CNP may play a critical role in the renal component of acclimation to environments of increased environmental salinity, and in particular during glomerular recruitment.

2.6 The rectal gland

2.6.1 Rectal gland structure

The rectal gland is a blind-ending, usually bullet-shaped tube in the dorsal mesentery, which is suspended above the valvular intestine; it is attached to the intestine postvalvularly. It produces a solution iso-osmotic to blood, essentially composed of Na^+ and Cl^-, and forms the only route for net Na^+ and Cl^- excretion in elasmobranch fish. Rectal glands vary in size and shape depending on the species of elasmobranch, and its life history. It has been reported that glands are smaller in euryhaline, and particularly in freshwater animals, than in marine species (Oguri, 1976); however, recent work has shown that in shorter FW systems, where animals are more likely to be exposed to salinity gradients, there is no significant difference in rectal gland size between FW and SW individuals (Pillans and Franklin, 2004). The adult rectal gland consists of three concentric tissue layers (the capsule, an outer layer of radial tubules, and an inner layer of branching tubules) arranged around the lumen of the central canal. The outer capsule is covered by a visceral peritoneum and is permeated with blood vessels, smooth muscle, connective tissue, and a network of nerves (Bulger, 1963).

(a) Rectal gland vasculature

The vasculature of the rectal gland has been studied using a variety of methods: vinyl acetate (Bulger, 1963), latex infusion (Hayslett *et al.*, 1974), and using scanning electron microscopy and methyl methocrylate corrosion (Kent and Olsen, 1982). The gland is supplied by the posterior-mesenteric, or rectal gland artery, which branches from the dorsal aorta. The artery enters the anterior (distal) third of the gland and splits into the anterior and posterior rami, which travel the length of the dorsal aspect of the gland (Kent and Olson, 1982). The exterior of the gland is encompassed by a network of paired circumferential arteries which branch off from the rami every 3 mm. These arteries in turn give rise to smaller branches, thus forming an arteriolar plexus in the outer capsule (Kent and Olson, 1982). The large posterior ramus continues into the postvalvular intestine.

The capsular arterioles perfuse two distinct circulations: either to the capillaries in the secretory parenchyma, or directly to the capsular venules through arteriovenous anastomoses (AVAs), thereby greatly reducing blood supply to the secretory tubules (Kent and Olson, 1982). Constrictions have been noticed in the AVAs, which supports the idea that blood flow to and around the rectal gland is tightly regulated (Kent and Olson, 1982).

The capsular venules are commonly paired on either side of the corresponding arteries and arterioles. Numerous small vessels arise from these venules and form a vascular mesh over the arterial vasculature (Kent and Olson, 1982). These venules give rise to larger veins, forming a dense venous plexus in the capsule beneath the circumferential arteries. This is drained by a series of larger veins, which travel back along the structure of the rectal gland artery to posterior cardial veins, or with the posterior arterial ramus into the postvalvular intestine (Kent and Olson, 1982).

The fine vasculature of the secretory parenchyma consists almost exclusively of capillaries or post capillary venules. These originate in the capsular arteriolar plexus and are orientated radially through the extra tubular matrix. Anastomotic branches interconnect adjacent capillaries, and these are more prevalent in the inner secretory parenchyma where the vasculature is more sinusoidal (Kent and Olson, 1982). The secretory capillaries have a fenestrated endothelium and lie in close proximity to the basal membranes of the secretory epithelial cells (Ernst *et al.*, 1981). It has been reported that blood flow in this region is parallel with secretory flow and there is therefore no counter current multiplication of electrolytes in the rectal gland (Kent and Olson, 1982). However, Newbound and O'Shea (Newbound and O'Shea, 2001) reported that flow in secretory tubules is in the opposite direction to that of the capillaries in the rectal gland of *Heterodontus portusjacksoni*, a partially euryhaline species which ventures from SW into the estuarine environment. This could therefore represent a morphological difference between euryhaline and stenohaline species, permitting counter current multiplication in the secretory tubules. However, this could also be a unique feature of H. portusjacksoni; clearly other species with varying degrees of euryhalinity must be studied. The innermost sinusoids coalesce into one of several main veins which boarder the rectal gland central duct. These eventually ramify into a single vein which exits the posterior of the gland in the tissue of the excretory duct (Kent and Olson, 1982).

In summary, blood which flows along the rectal gland artery can flow in three possible routes: it can flow directly into the postvalvular intestine via the posterior ramus, and effectively bypass the gland altogether. Secondly, the blood can enter the capsular sinusoids via the AVAs, resulting in partial blood flow to the secretory tissues of the gland. Thirdly, the blood can perfuse the capillaries of the secretory parenchyma and flow out through the central vein, resulting in maximal blood supply to the secretory tissues (Figure 3). With such large scope for variation in blood flow to the gland, it is possible that variation in blood flow is at least partly responsible for changes in rectal gland secretion rate.

Blood flow in the rectal gland has been illustrated as capable of sizeable fluctuations (Kent and Olson, 1982). This suggests a pattern of intermittent blood flow, and highlights the role of the gland in osmotic homeostasis. It is concurrent with the intermittent nature of rectal gland activity (Burger, 1967), suggesting minimal blood flow to the gland during periods of inactivity. This theory was proven experimentally using microsphere studies of blood flow and relating them to in vivo rates of rectal gland secretion (Kent and Olson, 1982).

(b) Rectal gland secretory tissue

The rectal gland is comprised of a complex mixture of connective, nerve, and smooth muscle tissue, and at least three types of epithelia: secretory tubule, central duct and endothelium (Valentich *et al.*, 1996). The middle secretory parenchyma consists of radially orientated tubules, and an extra tubular matrix of connective tissue interspersed with capillaries and nerve fibres (Bulger, 1963). Occasionally a single tubule may transverse the entire region, but more commonly a single tubule will diverge into three to five branches as it radiates from the central canal. This results in tubules being tightly packed in the peripheral portion of the parenchyma (Bulger, 1963). The tubules are lined with a single type of columnar cell and have a narrow lumen in this region of the secretory tissue (Eveloff *et al.*, 1979). The extra tubular matrix is compact with capillaries closely associated with, and running parallel to the tubules.

In the inner layer of the parenchyma, tubules are more randomly orientated and have larger tubular lumens. In this area the capillaries are often replaced by venous sinuses, and the matrix is less compact (Bulger, 1963). Nerve fibres with VIP immunoreactivity are closely associated with the tubular cells in *S. acanthias* (Stoff *et al.*, 1988). These nerve fibres are well ordered in the peripheral parenchyma, and ramify extensively in the venous sinusoids of the inner parenchyma (Bulger, 1963). This suggests a greater degree of neural influence, and hence an increased potential for the subsequent modification of rectal gland secretory output in this region. In the caudal end of the gland, where it is embedded in the postvalvular intestine, the secretory parenchyma is reduced and ductal epithelium predominates (Bulger, 1963).

The secretory tubules of the rectal gland generally consist of a single type, and a single layer of columnar epithelium (Eveloff *et al.*, 1979), which have a selective barrier to urea in the basolateral membrane (Zeidel *et al.*, 2005). Two varieties of cells have been categorised: 'light' and 'dark' cells, based on the density of the cytoplasmic matrix (Bulger, 1963). It remains unclear whether these are different types of cell, or if they represent different states of activity. The secretory cells have two distinctive features: numerous mitochondria and extensive basolateral membrane infoldings (Ernst *et al.*, 1981). Recent studies on the euryhaline species *C. leucas* have shown no significant differences in the numbers of mitochondria or basolateral infoldings between FW and SW acclimated animals (Pillans *et al.*, 2008).

There are generally between one and five parallel strands of tight (occluding) junctions which separate adjacent cells. These junctions are relatively shallow but have a very high length density. The values vary according to species and life history, but a typical value is seen in *S. acanthias* of 86 ± 5.7 m cm^{-2} (Forrest *et al.*, 1982). The network of junctions provide an extensive, selective, paracellular diffusional pathway which is important in Na$^+$ secretion, as well as restricting the diffusion of other ions into the lumen of the tubule (Forrest *et al.*, 1982). The length density of the junctions in *S. acanthias* is greater in the inner secretory parenchyma (102 ± 4.7 m cm^{-2}) than in the outer region (80 ± 6.7 m cm^{-2}), which was thought to indicate differences in regional secretory activity (Forrest *et al.*, 1982). The anatomy of the junctions remains unchanged in 68% SW acclimated *S. acanthias*, as well as during maximal stimulation of perfused glands (Forrest *et al.*, 1982). Secretion rate is therefore independent of junction morphology in this partially euryhaline species. However, the depth of the tight junctions has been shown to be 52% greater in SW acclimated *C. leucas* (a fully euryhaline elasmobranch), compared to animals from FW (Pillans *et al.*, 2008). Given the role of tight junctions in ion fluxes within the tissue, this plasticity in junction morphology may represent a fundamental difference between partially and fully euryhaline species.

2.6.2 Control of rectal gland secretion

(a) Endocrine Control

The fact that the rectal gland is often unaffected by nerve blockage suggests that stimuli affecting rectal gland secretion are typically carried in the blood, such as hormonal cues or ion concentrations. A hormonal signal is consistent with the constant lag time between external stimuli and increases in rectal gland secretion

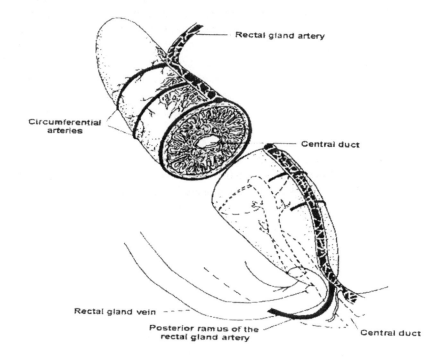

Figure 3.
    Schematic diagram of the vascularisation of the rectal gland of *S. acanthias* (Kent and Olsen 1982) used with permission of The American Physiological Society.

rates, which have been seen in a variety of experiments (Erlij and Rubio, 1986; Anderson et al., 1995; Anderson et al., 2002a). It has been theorised that rectal gland secretion rate correlates to the concentration of Cl⁻ ions in the arteriovenous blood and/or changes in the degree of perfusion of blood through the rectal gland (Burger, 1962). This was questioned by the findings of work on perfused rectal glands of S. canicula which showed no change in blood flow even after a twenty-fold increase in Na^+ secretion (Solomon et al., 1984; Shuttleworth and Thompson, 1986). However, it has been shown that blood flow to the secretory epithelia of the rectal gland is greater in fish acclimating to reduced salinities than those seen in fish acclimating to increased salinities, or long term acclimated to SW (Anderson et al., 2002a), reflecting the greater requirement for active secretion. Indeed, the number of red blood cells in the interstitial tissue of FW acclimated C. leucas (which conserve Na^+ and Cl⁻) was 72% lower than in SW acclimated animals (which actively secrete Na^+ and Cl⁻) (Pillans et al., 2008). It has also been shown that intravascular volume expansion (that occurs during acclimation to reduced salinity (Good et al., 2008)) is a potent, and possibly the primary stimulus for rectal gland secretion (Erlij and Rubio, 1986). For vertebrates in general, release of natriuretic peptides from the heart is directly associated with blood volume expansion. CNP is the principle circulating natriuretic peptide in elasmobranches (Loretz and Pollina, 2000; Kawakoshi et al., 2001). Natriuretic peptide like-binding sites have been demonstrated in both the capsular and sub-capsular regions of the rectal gland of S. canicula (Masini et al., 1994); a NPR-B type natriuretic peptide receptor has been cloned from the rectal gland of S. acanthias (Aller et al., 1999). CNP stimulated salt secretion from cultured rectal gland cells (Karnaky et al., 1992), in addition to in vitro preparations (Solomon et al., 1992; Anderson et al., 2002a). CNP is therefore believed to be the hormonal factor controlling stimulation of rectal gland stimulation in response to volume load (Solomon et al., 1985; Loretz and Pollina, 2000).

In addition to stimulation, the possibility of direct hormonal inhibition of rectal gland secretion in elasmobranchs has been investigated. Anderson et al., (2002a) reported a significant decrease in rectal gland secretion rate in S. canicula acclimated to experimentally increased salinity of 120% SW, compared to fish acclimated to 100% SW. This response is presumably due to the requirement of maintaining increased plasma Na^+ and Cl⁻ to increase osmolality in acclimating to 120% SW. Circulating levels of Ang II have been demonstrated to increase in S. canicula following transfer from 80 to 100% SW, and this increase was the result of hypo-volaemia (Anderson et al., 2002b). Ang II like binding sites and angiotensin converting enzyme like activity have been reported in the rectal gland of S. canicula (Masini et al., 1994; Hazon et al., 1997). However, perfusion of the isolated rectal gland of S. canicula with 10^{-9} M Ang II affected neither secretion rate nor vascular perfusion of the secretory epithelia in the isolated rectal gland of S. canicula (Anderson et al., 2002a). The reported inhibition in 120% SW from the rectal gland of S. canicula would appear to result from other endocrine or neuroendocrine factors, as reported in some other species (see below).

As rectal gland activity has been linked to feeding activity/dietary salt intake, there has been considerable interest regarding the possibility that a peptide derived from the gut is involved in control of rectal gland secretion rate. Interestingly, VIP has been reported to act as a potent secretagogue in *S. acanthias* (Stoff *et al.*, 1979), but induced no response in *S. canicula* or R. clavata (Shuttleworth and Thorndyke, 1984; Thorndyke and Shuttleworth, 1985; Anderson *et al.*, 1995). A stimulatory gut peptide for rectal gland secretion in *S. canicula* was initially isolated, but not sequenced, and named 'rectin' (Shuttleworth and Thorndyke, 1984). Anderson *et al.*, (1995) purified and sequenced a stimulatory peptide (most probably 'rectin') from the intestine of *S. canicula* and showed this factor to be the previously identified intestinal peptide, scyliorhinin II. To date, this discrepancy has yet to be fully explained and at best can be described as a species difference.

1α-OH-B receptors have been identified in the rectal gland of R. ocellata (Idler and Truscott, 1966; Moon and Idler, 1974), and surgical removal of interrenal tissue in R. ocellata caused a decrease in secretion by the rectal gland, which could be reversed by injection of 1α-OH-B (Holt and Idler, 1975). 1α-OH-B has been implicated in a variety of osmoregulatory processes, including rectal gland secretion (Holt and Idler, 1975), and may have a potential mineralocorticoid role in the retention of Na^+ from renal and extra-renal sites in elasmobranch fish (Armour *et al.*, 1993b).

(b) Neuroendocrine control

Although endocrine factors are regarded as most important in controlling rectal gland secretion, the extensive ramification of nerve fibres in the inner secretory parenchyma of the rectal gland of *S. acanthias* (Kent and Olson, 1982), the recorded release of VIP from nerves within the rectal gland of *S. acanthias* (Silva *et al.*, 1987; Chipkin *et al.*, 1988), and the stimulatory effect of VIP on the rectal gland of *S. acanthias* (Stoff *et al.*, 1977; Silva *et al.*, 1987), suggest that neural influences may be more prevalent, at least in this species. VIP found in the rectal gland nerves of *S. acanthias* stimulates Cl⁻ secretion by activating adenylate cyclase (Stoff *et al.*, 1979). The rectal gland of *S. acanthias* also contains inhibitory neuropeptides including somatostatin, bombesin, cholecystokinin and neuropeptide Y (Holmgren and Nilsson, 1983; Bjenning and Holmgren, 1988; Silva *et al.*, 1993). Somatostatin has a direct inhibitory effect on rectal gland cells both proximally and distally to the release of cAMP (Stoff *et al.*, 1979; Silva *et al.*, 1985), while bombesin inhibits indirectly through the release of somatostatin (Silva *et al.*, 1990). The method of inhibition by cholecystokinin has yet to be defined. The inhibitory action of neuropeptide Y does not affect adenylate cyclase activity, having a direct effect on Cl⁻ secretion at a site distal to the generation of cAMP. Neuropeptide Y also inhibits VIP-stimulated transport related oxygen consumption by Na^+, K^+-ATPase (Silva *et al.*, 1993).

(c) Rectal gland cell volume

Rectal gland cell volume expansion has been illustrated as a major stimulus of rectal gland secretion (Solomon *et al.*, 1984). Cell volume in the epithelial cells of the secretory tubules is regulated by the structural organisation of actin within the cell (Henson *et al.*, 1997). Transient loss of cytoskeletal (F-actin) organisation at the basolateral cell face, induced by hypotonicity, brings about the selective efflux of organic osmolytes. This produces a regulatory volume decrease in the rectal gland cells of *S. acanthias* (Ziyadeh and Kleinzeller, 1991). The cytoskeleton may also be important in mediating the response of the rectal gland to CNP: CNP stimulation of the rectal gland in *S. acanthias* was highly dependent on the action of the actin cytoskeleton and myosin light chains, although stimulation with VIP (via the cAMP cascade) was virtually unaffected by similar cytoskeletal effects (Silva and Epstein, 2002).

(d) Other factors

The role of blood acid-base status as a stimulus for rectal gland activity has received recent attention. In vivo studies in *S. acanthias* showed a linear relationship between extracellular pH and secretion rate, where increased blood pH increased secretory flow (Wood *et al.*, 2007b). Although acid-base status is the only parameter of the secretory fluid which is modified (Shuttleworth *et al.*, 2006; Wood *et al.*, 2007b), this is not believed to have any significant impact in whole animal acid-base balance (Wood *et al.*, 2007b); it is more likely that this phenomenon occurs in response to the alkaline tide associated with feeding (Wood *et al.*, 2005; Wood *et al.*, 2007b), and removal of the associated salt load.

One further influence on rectal gland secretions has been proposed. Elasmobranch rectal glands are surrounded by a band of smooth muscle fibres just below the capsule (Bulger, 1963; Evans and Piermarini, 2001) and, although not localised to this band, rectal glands are responsive to smooth muscle signalling agents (Evans and Piermarini, 2001). Therefore, there is scope for smooth muscle contractions having some influence on rectal gland secretory output.

2.6.3 Mechanism of secretion

The mechanisms involved in ion transport in the tissues of the rectal gland have been well documented (Shuttleworth, 1988; Silva *et al.*, 1997; Olson, 1999). Localised on the basolateral membrane of the epithelial cells of the secretory tubules is the protein Na^+, K^+-ATPase (Dubinsky and Monti, 1986). This actively pumps Na^+ into the extracellular space, as well as transporting K^+ into the secretory cell. Also located on the basolateral membrane is the Na^+K^+-$2Cl^-$ cotransporter. The action of this protein is passive, as it is driven by the inward Na^+ gradient set up by the action of Na^+, K^+-ATPase. Along this concentration gradient Na^+ enters the cell facilitating the coupled translocation of K^+ and Cl^- into the intracellular space. Na^+, K^+-ATPase then actively pumps Na^+ back out of the cell (Haas and Forbush, 1998). The internal accumulation of excess K^+ is prevented by passive flow through the basolateral potassium specific channel, thereby maintaining equilibrium (Riordan *et al.*, 1994).

These processes result in a high concentration of Cl^- in the secretory cells and a high Na^+ concentration in the intercellular space. Located on the apical membrane of the secretory cells are Cl^--selective channels. Through these channels Cl^- ions move passively into the lumen of the secretory tubule, so as to restore the intercellular electrochemical equilibrium. The Na^+K^+-

2Cl⁻ cotransporter is stimulated by a fall in intracellular Cl⁻ concentration pursuant to increased Cl⁻ efflux across the apical membrane. Na⁺ then passively moves paracellularly through the Na⁺-selective tight junctions into the lumen to balance the electrical potential created by the movement of Cl⁻ ions (Olson, 1999).

In contrast to the situation described in the gills, activity and abundance of Na⁺, K⁺-ATPase in the rectal gland is lowest in long term acclimated FW animals. Levels in acclimated and wild caught SW animals are relatively constant (Piermarini and Evans, 2000; Pillans *et al.*, 2005). This is due to a relative influx of Na⁺ and Cl⁻ across semi-permeable membranes in SW, and an efflux in FW. Hence there is a reduced requirement for rectal gland secretion of Na⁺ and Cl⁻ in more dilute environments.

The rate of cellular secretion is controlled by regulating the permeability of the Cl⁻-selective channel in the apical membrane of the secretory tubule cells (Riordan *et al.*, 1994). This is achieved through alterations in the intracellular concentrations of cAMP, which is stimulated by hormones such as VIP and scyliorhinin II (Forrest, 1996). The activity of the Na⁺K⁺-2Cl⁻ cotransporter is mediated by intracellular Cl⁻ concentration: elevating intracellular Cl⁻ concentration, or preventing it from decreasing (i.e. not permitting Cl⁻ secretion into the lumen), blocks the activation of the cotransporter in response to secretory stimuli. Cellular Cl⁻ therefore regulates its own rate of entry via the Na⁺K⁺-2Cl⁻ cotransporter (Lytle and Forbush, 1996).

2.7 Perspectives

Although there has been significant progress in our understanding of osmoregulation in elasmobranch fish, there is still much to be discovered. It is now apparent that many species thought initially to be stenohaline marine species can acclimate to environments of varying salinities, if not full FW, and can therefore be better classified as partially euryhaline (Hazon *et al.*, 2003). In most cases the detailed ecology of these elasmobranch species is unknown, but the advancement of tagging techniques means that, in the near future, it will be possible to tag individual fish and record their movements through environments of differing salinities. These techniques will also be invaluable for a more detailed understanding of fully euryhaline species that migrate between FW and SW. Theses species may frequently interact with humans, and a greater understanding of both the physiology and ecology is essential to promote scientifically derived management policies that are not based on the uninformed, unjustified, negative public perspective common for many species.

In terms of the physiology of euryhaline species, one of the key differences between fully and partially euryhaline species appears to be that fully euryhaline fish maintain relatively high concentrations of urea in FW. The reason for this remains unclear, but may be related to some elasmobranch enzymes requiring urea for optimal function (Yancey and Somero, 1978). Euryhaline elasmobranch fish in FW maintain plasma osmolalities more than double those of FW teleosts, which emphasises the osmo-, and ionoregulatory problems of inhabiting FW. Therefore, in terms of renal physiology, euryhaline elasmobranch fish acclimated to FW must reabsorb filtered urea (and Na⁺ and Cl⁻) and simultaneously excrete large volumes of dilute urine. The mechanism by which this occurs still requires to be fully elucidated, although the findings of a renal functional reserve for the Atlantic stingray and the identification of a number of renal urea transporters are clearly important. To date, most studies on euryhaline elasmobranchs have been conducted on SW fish acclimating to FW. There is an urgent need for studies on FW to SW acclimation, when Na$^+$, Cl$^-$ and urea levels must all increase rapidly in order to achieve a hyperosmotic osmoregulatory strategy. The control and interactions of the gut and drinking, the kidney in terms of Na$^+$, Cl$^-$ and urea reabsorption, and the liver or other extra-hepatic sources of urea production, largely remains a mystery.

Another factor that is becoming increasingly important is the interaction of dietary protein and salt intake on the capacity of elasmobranchs to osmoregulate. This is especially important as many elasmobranchs do not feed in captivity, or have been starved prior to experimentation. The effects of different diet compositions and/or the possibility of irregular gorge feeding can have a profound effect on the osmoregulatory process in some species. For example, Mackenzie an co-workers (MacKenzie *et al.*, 2002) showed that a high salt intake in *S. canicula* could have a marked effect on both Na$^+$- K$^+$-ATPase activity, and also on the gene expression of Na$^+$, K$^+$-ATPase subunits. Similarly, the concept that at least some elasmobranch species must eat at a 5 daily frequency to maintain urea homeostasis raises questions of how the control of osmoregulation changes from a well fed to a starved fish, depending on food availability. Wood and colleagues (Wood *et al.*, 2005) have reported marked post-prandial conservation of nitrogen in *S. acanthias*, reflecting the requirement of urea synthesis for osmoregulation and protein growth in fish that are severely nitrogen limited due to their sporadic feeding in nature.

Very little is known regarding the control of blood volume in elasmobranch fish (Anderson *et al.*, 2007; Good *et al.*, 2008), although it is now apparent that euryhaline fish maintain extremely close control on blood volume even during rapid acclimation from SW to FW and vice versa; this may be another crucial factor that defines the difference between fully and partially euryhaline species. How the control of blood volume relates to the coordinated function of osmoregulatory organs during acclimation to different salinity challenges is also very unclear, and may involve multiple endocrine factors. In conclusion, while considerable progress has been made in understanding osmoregulation in elasmobranch fish at the level of mechanisms of osmoregulatory organ action, considerably less is known about the co-ordination of osmoregulatory organ function and control at the whole animal Our understanding to date is based on only a few species and, as more species are investigated, it is apparent that there may be a range of partially euryhaline species that display different osmoregulatory capacities, depending on environmental salinity.

References

Acher, R. (1996). Molecular evolution of fish neurohypophysial hormones: neutral and selective evolutionary mechanisms. Gen Comp Endocrinol 102: 157–172.

Acher, R., Chauvet, J., Chauvet, M.-T. and Rouille, Y. (1999). Unique evolution of neurohypophysial hormones in cartilaginous fishes: possible implications for urea-based osmoregulation. J Exp Zool 284: 475–484.

Aller, S. G., Lombardo, I. D., Bhanot, S. and Forrest, J. N. (1999). Cloning, characterization, and functional expression of a CNP receptor regulating CFTR in the shark rectal gland. Am J Physiol 276: C442–C449.

Amer, S. and Brown, J. A. (1995). Glomerular actions of arginine vasotocin in the in-situ perfused trout kidney. Am J Physiol 38: R775–R780.

Anderson, P. M. (1995). Urea cycle in fish: molecular and mitochondrial studies. In: Wood, C. M. and Shuttleworth, T. J. (eds) Ionoregulation: Cellular and molecular approaches to fish ionic regulation. Academic Press, New York: 57–83.

Anderson, W. G., Conlon, J. M. and Hazon, N. (1995). Characterization of the endogenous intestinal peptide that stimulates the rectal gland of *Scyliorhinus canicula*. Am J Physiol 268: R1359–R1364.

Anderson, W. G., Tierney, M. L., Takei, Y. and Hazon, N. (1995). Natriuretic hormones in elasmobranch fish; possible interactions with other endocrine systems. Physiol Zool 68: 184.

Anderson, P. M. (2001). Urea and glutamine synthesis: environmental influences on nitrogen excretion. In: Wright, P. A. and Anderson, P. M. (eds) Nitrogen excretion. Academic Press, San Diego: 239–277.

Anderson, W. G., Takei, Y. and Hazon, N. (2001a). The dipsogenic effect of the renin-angiotensin system in elasmobranch fish. Gen Comp Endocrinol 124 (3): 300–307.

Anderson, W. G., Takei, Y. and Hazon, N. (2001b). Possible interaction between the renin angiotensin system and natriuretic peptides on drinking in elasmobranch fish. In: Goos, H. J. T., Rastogi, R. K., Vaudry, H. and Pierantoni, R. (eds) Perspective in Comparative Endocrinology: Unity and Diversity. Monduzzi Editore, Bologna, Italy: 753–758.

Anderson, W. G., Good, J. P. and Hazon, N. (2002a). Changes in chloride secretion rate and vascular perfusion in the rectal gland of the European lesser spotted dogfish in response to environmental and hormonal stimuli. J Fish Biol 60: 1580–1590.

Anderson, W. G., Takei, Y. and Hazon, N. (2002b). Osmotic and volaemic effects on drinking rate in elasmobranch fish. J Exp Biol 205: 1115–1122.

Anderson, W. G., Wells, A., Takei, Y. and Hazon, N. (2002c). The control of drinking in elasmobranch fish with special reference to the renin-angiotensin system. In: Flik, G. and Hazon, N. (eds) Osmoregulation and drinking in aquatic and terrestrial animals. BIOS Scientific Publishers Ltd, Oxford, UK: 19–30.

Anderson, W. G., Good, J. P., Pillans, R. D., Hazon, N. and Franklin, C. E. (2005a). Hepatic urea biosynthesis in the euryhaline elasmobranch *Carcharhinus leucas.* J Exp Zool 303A: 917–921.

Anderson, W. G., Hyodo, S., Tsukada, T., Meischke, L., Pillans, R. D., Good, J. P., Takei, Y., Cramb, G., Franklin, C. E. and Hazon, N. (2005b). Sequence, circulating levels, and expression of C-type natriuretic peptide in a euryhaline elasmobranch, *Carcharhinus leucas.* Gen Comp Endocrinol 144: 90–98.

Anderson, W. G., Pillans, R. D., Hyodo, S., Tsukada, T., Good, J. P., Takei, Y., Franklin, C. E. and Hazon, N. (2006). The effects of freshwater to seawater transfer on circulating levels of angiotensin II, C-type natriuretic peptide and arginine vasotocin in the euryhaline elasmobranch, *Carcharhinus leucas.* Gen Comp Endocrinol 147: 39–46.

Anderson, W. G., Taylor, J. R., Good, J. P., Hazon, N. and Grosell, M. (2007). Body fluid volume regulation in elasmobranch fish. Comp Biochem Physiol 148 A: 3–13.

Armour, K. J., O'Toole, L. B. and Hazon, N. (1993a). The effect of dietary protein restriction on the secretory dynamics of 1α-hydroxycorticosterone and urea in the dogfish, *Scyliorhinus canicula*: a possible role for 1α-hydroxycorticosterone in sodium retention. J Endocrinol 138: 275–282.

Armour, K. J., O'Toole, L. B. and Hazon, N. (1993b). Mechanisms of ACTH- and angiotensin II-stimulated I α-hydroxycorticosterone secretion in the dogfish, *Scyliorhinus canicula.* J Mol Endocrinol 10: 235–244.

Baker, J. R., Chaykin, S. and Struempler, A. (1963). A comparative study of trimethylamine-N-oxide biosynthesis. Biochim Biophys Acta 71: 58–64.

Ballantyne, J. S., Moyes, C. D. and Moon, T. W. (1987). Compatible and counteracting solutes and the evolution of ion and osmoregulation in fishes. Can J Zool 65: 1883–1888.

Barton, K. N., Buhr, M. M. and Ballantyne, J. S. (1999). Effects of urea and trimethylamine N-oxide on fluidity of liposomes and membranes of an elasmobranch. Am J Physiol 276: R397–R406.

Bentley, P. J., Maetz, J. and Payan, P. (1976). A study of the unidirectional fluxes of Na[+] and Cl[-] across the gills of the dogfish *Scyliorhinus canicula* (Chondrichthyes). J Exp Biol 64: 629–637.

Bernier, N. J., Gilmour, K. M., Takei, Y. and Perry, S. F. (1999). Cardiovascular control via angiotensin II and circulating catecholamines in the spiny dogfish, *Squalus acanthias.* J Comp Physiol 169 B: 237–248.

Beyenbach, K. W. and Fromter, E. (1985). Electrophysiological evidence for Cl secretion in shark renal proximal tubules. Am J Physiol 248: F282–F295.

Bjenning, C. and Holmgren, S. (1988). Neuropeptides in the fish gut. An immunohistochemical study of evolutionary patterns. Histochemistry 88: 155–163.

Bjenning, C., Takei, Y., Watanabe, T. X., Nakajima, K., Sakakibara, S. and Hazon, N. (1992). A C-type natriuretic peptide is a vasodilator in vivo and in vitro in the common dogfish. J Endocrinol 133: R1–R4.

Boyd, T. A., Cha, C. J., Forster, R. P. and Goldstein, L. (1977). Free amino acids in tissues of the skate *Raja erinacea* and the stingray *Dasyatis sabina*: effects of environmental dilution. J Exp Zool 199: 435–442.

Boylan, J. W. (1967). Gill permeability in *Squalus acanthias*. In: Gilbert, P. W., Mathewson, R. F. and Rall, D. P. (eds) Sharks, Skates and Rays. John Hopkins University Press, Baltimore: 197–206.

Boylan, J. W. (1972). Model for passive urea reabsorption in elasmobranch kidney. Comp Biochem Physiol 42 (1A): 27–30.

Brooks, D. R., Thorson, T. B. and Mayes, M. A. (1981). Fresh-water stingrays (Potamotrygonidae) and their helminth parasites: testing hypotheses of evolution and co-evolution. Proc Willi Hennig Soc 1: 147–175.

Brown, J. A., Oliver, J. A., Henderson, I. W. and Jackson, B. A. (1980). Angiotensin and single nephron glomerular function in the trout *Salmo gairdneri*. Am J Physiol 239: R509–R514.

Brown, J. A. and Green, C. (1987). Single nephron function of the lesser spotted dogfish, *Scyliorhinus canicula*, and the effects of adrenaline. J Exp Biol 129: 265–278.

Brown, J. A. and Green, C. (1992). Glomerular bypass shunts and distribution of glomeruli in the kidney of the lesser spotted dogfish, *Scyliorhinus canicula*. Cell Tissue Res 269: 299–304.

Bulger, R. E. (1963). Fine structure of the rectal (salt secreting) gland of the spiny dogfish, *Squalus acanthias*. Anat Rec 147: 95–127.

Burger, J. W. (1962). Further studies on the function of the rectal gland in the spiny dogfish. Physiol Zool 35: 205–217.

Burger, J. W. (1967). Problems in the electrolyte economy of the spiny dogfish, *Squalus acanthias*. In: Gilbert, P. W., Mathewson, R. F. and Rall, D. P. (eds) Sharks, Skates and Rays. John Hopkins University Press, Baltimore: 177–185.

Capra, M. F. and Satchell, G. H. (1977). The adrenergic responses of isolated saline perfused prebranchial arteries and gills of the elasmobranch *Squalus acanthias*. Gen Pharmacol 8: 67–71.

Carrier, J. C. and Evans, D. H. (1972). Ion, water and urea turnover rates in nurse shark, *Ginglymostoma cirratum* Comp Biochem Physiol 41: 761–764.

Carroll, S., Hazon, N. and Eddy, F. B. (1995). Drinking rates and Na+ effluxes in response to temperature change in two species of marine flatfish: dab, *Limanda limanda* and plaice, *Pleuronectes platessa*. J Comp Physiol 164 B: 579–584.

Cerra, M. C., Tierney, M. L., Takei, Y., Hazon, N. and Tota, B. (2001). Angiotensin II binding sites in the heart of *Scyliorhinus canicula*: An autoradiographic study. Gen Comp Endocrinol 121: 126–134.

Chauvet, J., Rouille, Y., Chauveau, C., Chauveau, M. T. and Acher, R. (1994). Special evolution of neurohypophysial hormones in cartilagenous fishes: asvatocin and phasvatocin, two oxytocin-like peptides isolated from the spotted dogfish (*Scyliorhinus canicula*). Proc Natl Acad Sci USA 91:

11266–11270.

Chester-Jones, I. (1957). The adrenal cortex. Cambridge University Press.

Chew, S. F., Poothodiyil, N. K., Wong, W. P. and Ip, Y. K. (2006). Exposure to brackish water, upon feeding, leads to enhanced conservation of nitrogen and increased urea synthesis and retention in the Asian freshwater stingray *Himantura signifer*. J Exp Biol 209: 484–492.

Chipkin, S. R., Stoff, J. S. and Aronin, N. (1988). Immunohistochemical evidence for the neural mediation of VIP activity in the dogfish rectal gland. Peptides 9: 119–124.

Choe, K. P. and Evans, D. H. (2003). Compensation for hypercapnia by a euryhaline elasmobranch: Effect of salinity and roles of gills and kidneys in freshwater. J Exp Zool 297A: 52–63.

Compagno, L. J. V. and Roberts, T. R. (1982). Freshwater stingrays (Dasyatidae) of Southeast Asia and New Guinea, with a description of a new species Himantura and reports of unidentified species. Environ Biol Fish 7: 321–339.

Conlon, J. M. and Thim, L. (1988). Isolation of the tachykinin, des[ser1pro2] scyliorhinin-II from the intestine of the ray, *Torpedo marmorata*. Gen Comp Endocrinol 71: 383–388.

Cooper, A. R. and Morris, S. (2004). Osmotic, sodium, carbon dioxide and acid-base state of the Port Jackson shark, *Heterodontus portusjacksoni*, in response to lowered salinity. J Comp Physiol 174 B: 211–222.

Cooper, A. R. and Morris, S. (2004). Haemoglobin function and respiratory status of the Port Jackson shark, *Heterodontus portusjacksoni*, in response to lowered salinity. J Comp Physiol 174 B: 223–236.

Cornelius, F. (1995). Hydrophobic ion interaction on Na^+ activation and dephosphorylation of reconstituted Na^+,K^+-ATPase. Biochim Biophys Acta 1235: 183–196.

Cornelius, F. (1995). Phosphorylation/dephosphorylation of reconstituted shark Na^+,K^+-ATPase: one phosphorylation site per alpha beta promoter. Biochim Biophys Acta 1235: 197–204.

Davies, D. T. and Rankin, J. C. (1973). Adrenergic receptors and vascular responses to catecholamines of perfused dogfish gills. Comp Gen Pharmacol 60: 830–840.

De Boeck, G., Grosell, M. and Wood, C. (2001). Sensitivity of the spiny dogfish (*Squalus acanthias*) to waterborne silver exposure. Aquat Toxicol 54: 261–275.

De Vlaming, V. L., Sage, M. and Beitz, B. (1975). Pituitary, adrenal and thyroid influences on osmoregulation in the euryhaline elasmobranch, *Dasyatis sabina*. Comp Biochem Physiol 52 A: 505–513.

DeVries, R. and DeJaeger, S. (1984). The gill of the spiny dogfish, *Squalus acanthias*: respiratory and non-respiratory function. Am J Anat 169: 1–29.

Dubinsky, W. P. and Monti, L. B. (1986). Resolution of apical from basolateral membrane of shark rectal gland. Am J Physiol 251: C721–C726.

Endo, M. (1984). Histological and enzymatic studies on the renal tubules of some marine elasmobranchs. J Morphol 182: 63–69.

Erlij, D. and Rubio, R. (1986). Control of rectal gland secretion in the dogfish (*Squalus acanthias*) - Steps in the sequence of activation. J Exp Biol 122: 99–112.

Ernst, S. A., Hootman, S. R., Schreiber, J. H. and Riddle, C. V. (1981). Freeze-fracture and morphometric analysis of occluding junctions in rectal glands of elasmobranch fish. J Membrane Biol 58: 101–114.

Evans, D. H. (1982). Mechanisms of acid extrusion by two marine fishes: the teleost *Opsanus beta* and the elasmobranch *Squalus acanthias*. J Exp Biol 97: 289–299.

Evans, D. H. (1984). The roles of gill permeability and transport mechanisms in euryhalinity. In: Hoar, W. S. and Randall, D. J. (eds) Fish Physiology. Academic Press, New York: 239–283.

Evans, D. H., Toop, T., Donald, J. and Forrest, J. N. (1993). C-Type Natriuretic Peptides Are Potent Dilators of Shark Vascular Smooth-Muscle. J Exp Zool 265: 84–87.

Evans, D. H. and Piermarini, P. M. (2001). Contractile properties of the elasmobranch rectal gland. J Exp Biol 204: 59–67.

Evans, D. H., Piermarini, P. M. and Choe, K. P. (2005). The multifunctional fish gill: dominant site of gas exchange, osmoregulation, acid-base regulation, and excretion of nitrogenous waste. Physiol Rev 85: 97–177.

Eveloff, J., Karnaky, K. J., Silva, P., Epstein, F. H. and Kinter, W. B. (1979). Elasmobranch rectal gland cell autoradiographic localization of (3H) ouabain sensitive Na,K-ATPase in rectal gland of the dogfish *Squalus acanthias*. J Cell Biol 83: 16–32.

Fenstermacher, J., Sheldon, F., Ratner, J. and Roomet, A. (1972). The blood to tissue distribution of various polar materials in the dogfish, *Squalus acanthias*. Comp Biochem Physiol 42 A: 195–204.

Fines, G. A., Ballantyne, J. S. and Wright, P. A. (2001). Active urea transport and an unusual basolateral membrane composition in the gills of a marine elasmobranch. Am J Physiol 280: R16–R24.

Fitzsimons, J. T. (1979). The Physiology of Thirst and Sodium Appetite. Cambridge University Press, Cambridge, UK.

Fitzsimons, J. T. (1998). Angiotensin, thirst, and sodium appetite. Physiol Rev 78: 583–686.

Forrest, J. N., Boyer, J. L., Ardito, T. A., Murdaugh, H. V. and Wade, J. B. (1982). Structure of tight junctions during Cl- secretion in the perfused rectal gland of the dogfish shark. Am J Physiol 242: C388–C392.

Forrest, J. N. (1996). Cellular and molecular biology of chloride secretion in the shark rectal gland: Regulation by adenosine receptors. Kidney Int 49: 1557–1562.

Forster, R. P., Goldstein, L. and Rosen, J. K. (1972). Intrarenal control of urea reabsorption by renal tubules of the marine elasmobranch, *Squalus acanthias*.

Comp Biochem Physiol 42 A: 3–12.

Forster, R. P. and Goldstein, L. (1976). Intracellular osmoregulatory role of amino acids and urea in marine elasmobranchs. Am J Physiol 230: 925–931.

Frick, N. T. and Wright, P. A. (2001). Nitrogen metabolism and excretion in the mangrove killifish *Rivulus marmoratus* I. The influence of environmental salinity and external ammonia. J Exp Biol 205: 79–89.

Friedman, P. A. and Hebert, S. C. (1990). Diluting segment in kidney of dogfish shark. I. Localization and characterization of chloride absorption. Am J Physiol 258: R398–R408.

Goldstein, L. (1967). Urea biosynthesis in elasmobranchs. In: Gilbert, P. W., Mathewson, R. F. and Rall, D. P. (eds) Sharks, Skates and Rays. John Hopkins University Press, Baltimore: 207–214.

Goldstein, L., Hartman, S. C. and Forster, R. P. (1967). On origin of trimethylamine oxide in Spiny Dogfish *Squalus acanthias*. Comp Biochem Physiol 21: 719–722.

Goldstein, L., Oppelt, W. W. and Maren, T. H. (1968). Osmotic regulation and urea metabolism in the lemon shark *Negaprion brevirostris*. Am J Physiol 215: 1493–1497.

Goldstein, L. and Forster, R. P. (1971a). Osmoregulation and urea metabolism in the little skate *Raja erinacea*. Am J Physiol 220: 742–746.

Goldstein, L. and Forster, R. P. (1971b). Urea biosynthesis and excretion in freshwater and marine elasmobranchs. Comp Biochem Physiol 39 (2B): 415–421.

Goldstein, L. and Funkhouser, D. (1972). Biosynthesis of trimethylamine oxide in Nurse shark, *Ginglymostoma cirratum*. Comp Biochem Physiol 42 (1A): 51–57.

Goldstein, L. and Dewitt-Harley, S. (1973). Trimethylamine oxidase of Nurse shark liver and its relation to mammalian mixed-function amine oxidase. Comp Biochem Physiol 45 (4B): 895–903.

Good, J. P., Wells, A. and Hazon, N. (2008). Measurement of blood volume in the elasmobranch fish *Scyliorhinus canicula* following acute and long-term salinity transfers. J Fish Biol 73(6): 1301–1313.

Griffith, R. W. (1991). Guppies, toadfish, lungfish, coelacanths and frogs - A scenario for the evolution of urea retention in fishes. Environ Biol Fish 32: 199–218.

Gunning, M., Solomon, R. J., Epstein, F. H. and Silva, P. (1997). Role of guanylyl cyclase receptors for CNP in salt secretion by shark rectal gland. Am J Physiol 273: R1400–R1406.

Haas, M. and Forbush, B. (1998). The Na-K-Cl cotransporters. Bioenerg Biomem 30: 161–172.

Hays, R. M., Levine, S. D., Myers, J. D., Heinemann, H. O., Kaplan, M. A., Franki, N. and Berliner, H. (1977). Urea transport in dogfish kidney. J Exp Zool 199: 309–315.

Hayslett, J. P., Schon, D. A., Epstein, M. and Hogben, C. A. M. (1974). In vitro perfusion of the dogfish rectal gland. Am J Physiol 226: 1188–1192.

Haywood, G. P. (1973). Hypo-osmotic regulation coupled with reduced metabolic urea in the dogfish *Poroderma africanum*: an analysis of serum osmolarity, chloride, and urea. Mar Biol 23: 121–127.

Hazon, N. and Henderson, I. W. (1984). Secretory dynamics of 1a-hydroxycorticosterone in the elasmobranch fish, *Scyliorhinus canicula*. J Endocrinol 103: 205–211.

Hazon, N. and Henderson, I. W. (1985). Factors affecting the secretory dynamics of 1α-hydroxycorticosterone in the dogfish, *Scyliorhinus canicula*. Gen Comp Endocrinol 59: 50–55.

Hazon, N., Balment, R. J., Perrott, M. and O'Toole, L. B. (1989). The renin-angiotensin system and vascular and dipsogenic regulation in elasmobranchs. Gen Comp Endocrinol 74: 230–236.

Hazon, N., Tierney, M., Hamano, K., Ashida, K. and Takei, Y. (1995). Endogenous angiotensins, angiotensin-II competitive binding inhibitors and converting enzyme inhibitor in elasmobranch fish. Neth J Zool 45: 117–120.

Hazon, N., Cerra, M. C., Tierney, M. L., Tota, B. and Takei, Y. (1997). Elasmobranch renin angiotensin system and the angiotensin receptor. Proc Int Cong Comp Endocrinol 13: 1307–1312.

Hazon, N., Tierney, M. L., Anderson, G., MacKenzie, S., Cutler, C. and Cramb, G. (1997). Ion and water balance in elasmobranch fishes. In: Hazon, N., Eddy, B. and Flik, G. (eds) Ionic Regulation in Animals. Springer-Verlag, Berlin, Heidelberg: 70–86.

Hazon, N., Tierney, M. L. and Takei, Y. (1999). Renin-angiotensin system in elasmobranch fish: A review. J Exp Zool 284: 526–534.

Hazon, N., Wells, A., Pillans, R. D., Good, J. P., Anderson, W. G. and Franklin, C. E. (2003). Urea based osmoregulation and endocrine control in elasmobranch fish with special reference to euryhalinity. Comp Biochem Physiology B 136: 685–700.

Hebert, S. C. and Friedman, P. A. (1990). Diluting segment in kidney of dogfish shark.2. Electrophysiology of apical membranes and cellular resistances. Am J Physiol 258: R409–R417.

Henderson, I. W., O'Toole, L. B. and Hazon, N. (1988). Kidney function. In: Shuttleworth, T. J. (eds) Physiology of Elasmobranch Fishes. Springer Verlag, Berlin: 201–214.

Henson, J. H., Roesener, C. D., Gaetano, C. J., Mendola, R. J., Forrest, J. N., Holy, J. and Kleinzeller, A. (1997). Confocal microscopic observation of cytoskeletal reorganizations in cultured shark rectal gland cells following treatment with hypotonic shock and high external K[+]. J Exp Zool 279: 415–424.

Hentschel, H. (1988). Renal blood vascular system in the elasmobranch, *Raja erinacea* Mitchill, in relation to kidney zones. Am J Anat 183: 130–147.

Hentschel, H., Mahler, S., Herter, P. and Elger, M. (1993). Renal tubule of dogfish, *Scyliorhinus canicula* - a comprehensive study of structure with emphasis on intramembrane particles and immunoreactivity for H^+-K^+-adenosine triphosphatase. Anat Rec 235: 511–532.

Hentschel, H. and Zierold, K. (1993). Morphology and element distribution of magnesium-secreting epithelium: the proximal tubule segment PII of dogfish, *Scyliorhinus canicula* (L.). Eur J Cell Biol 63: 32–42.

Hentschel, H., Storb, U., Teckhaus, L. and Elger, M. (1998). The central vessel of the renal countercurrent bundles of two marine elasmobranchs - dogfish (*Scyliorhinus canicula*) and skate (*Raja erinacea*) - as revealed by light and electron microscopy with computer-assisted reconstruction. Anat Embryol 198: 73–89.

Holmgren, S. and Nilsson, S. (1983). Bombesin-, gastrin/cck-, 5-hydroxytryptamine-, neurotensin-, somatostatin-, and VIP-like immunoreactivity and catecholamine fluorescence in the gut of the elasmobranch, *Squalus acanthias*. Cell Tiss Res 234: 595–618.

Holmgren, S., Axelsson, M. and Farrell, A. P. (1992). The effect of catecholamines, substance-p and vasoactive intestinal polypeptide on blood-flow to the gut in the dogfish *Squalus acanthias*. J Exp Biol 168: 161–175.

Holt, W. F. and Idler, D. R. (1975). Influence of the interrenal gland on the rectal gland of a skate. Comp Biochem Physiol 50 C (NC1): 111–119.

Honn, K. V. and Chavin, W. (1976). In vitro trophic action of ACTH and insulin upon adrenocortical enzymes of the Squaliform elasmobranch *Ginglymostoma cirratum* (Bonnaterre). Gen Comp Endocrinol 29: 360–368.

Hyodo, S., Katoh, F., Kaneko, T. and Takei, Y. (2004a). A facilitative urea transporter is localized in the renal collecting tubule of the dogfish *Triakis scyllia*. J Exp Biol 207: 347–356.

Hyodo, S., Tsukada, T. and Takei, Y. (2004b). Neurohypophysial hormones of dogfish, Triakis scyllium: structures and salinity-dependent secretion. Gen Comp Endocrinol 138: 97–104.

Idler, D. R. and Truscott, B. (1966) I α-Hydroxycorticosterone from cartilaginous fish: a new adrenal steroid in blood. J Fish Res Bd Canada 23: 615–619.

Idler, D. R. and Kane, K. M. (1980) Cytosol receptor glycoprotein for 1-alpha-hydroxycorticosterone in tissues of an elasmobranch fish (*Raja ocellata*). Gen Comp Endocrinol 42: 259–266.

Jampol, L. M. and Epstein, F. M. (1970). Sodium-potassium-activated adenosinetriphosphate and osmotic regulation by fishes. Am J Physiol 218: 607–611.

Janech, M. G., Fitzgibbon, W. R., Miller, D. H., Lacy, E. R. and Ploth, D. W. (1998). Effect of low salinity on the renal function of *Dasyatis sabina*, a marine euryhaline elasmobranch. J Invest Med 46: 63A–63A.

Janech, M. G., Fitzgibbon, W. R., Chen, R. H., Nowak, M. W., Miller, D. H., Paul, R. V. and Ploth, D. W. (2003). Molecular and functional characterization of a urea transporter from the kidney of the Atlantic stingray. Am J Physiol 284: F996–F1005.

Janech, M. G., Fitzgibbon, W. R., Nowak, M. W., Miller, D. H., Paul, R. V. and Ploth, D. W. (2006a). Cloning and functional characterization of a second urea transporter from the kidney of the Atlantic stingray, *Dasyatis sabina*.

Am J Physiol 291: R844–R853.

Janech, M. G., Fitzgibbon, W. R., Ploth, D. W., Lacy, E. R. and Miller, D. H. (2006b). Effect of low environmental salinity on plasma composition and renal function of the Atlantic stingray, a euryhaline elasmobranch. Am J Physiol 291: F770–F780.

Kajimura, M., Walsh, P. J., Mommsen, T. P. and Wood, C. M. (2006). The dogfish shark (*Squalus acanthias*) increases both hepatic and extrahepatic ornithine urea cycle enzyme activities for nitrogen conservation after feeding. Physiol Biochem Zool 79: 602–613.

Karnaky, K. J., Stidham, J. D., Nelson, D. S., McCraw, A. S., Valentich, J. D., Kennedy, M. P. and Currie, M. G. (1992). C-type natriuretic peptide is a potent secretagogue for the cultured shark (*Squalus acanthias*) rectal gland. Bull Mt Des Mar Lab 31: 122–123.

Kawakoshi, A., Hyodo, S. and Takei, Y. (2001). CNP is the only natriuretic peptide in an elasmobranch fish, *Triakis scyllia*. Zool Sci 18: 861–868.

Kawauchi, H. (1992). Advances of fish pituitary hormone research. Trends Comp Physiol Biochem 8: 81–86.

Kent, B. and Olson, K. R. (1982). Blood flow in the rectal gland of *Squalus acanthias*. Am J Physiol 243: R296–R303.

Kime, D. E. (1987). The steroids. In: Chester-Jones, I., Ingleton, P. M. and Phillips, J. G. (eds) Fundamentals of comparative vertebrate Endocrinology. Plenum Press, New York: 3–56.

Klesch, W. and Sage, M. (1975). The stimulation of corticosteroidogenesis in the interrenal of the elasmobranch *Dasyatis sabina* by mammalian ACTH. Comp Biochem Physiol 52 A: 145–146.

Kobayashi, H. and Takei, Y. (1996). The Renin-Angiotensin System: Comparative Aspects. Springer-Verlag, Berlin, Heidelberg.

Lacy, E. R., Schmidt-Nielsen, B., Galaske, R. G. and Stolte, H. (1975). Configuration of the skate (*Raja erinacea*) nephron and ultrastructure of two segments of the proximal tubule. Bull Mt Des Mar Lab 15: 54–56.

Lacy, E. R., Castellucci, M. and Reale, E. (1987). The elasmobranch renal corpuscle: Fine structure of Bowman's capsule and the glomerular capillary wall. Anat Rec 218: 294–305.

Lacy, E. R. and Reale, E. (1989). Granulated peripolar epithelial cells in the renal corpuscle of marine elasmobranch fish. Cell Tiss Res 257: 61–67.

Lacy, E. R. and Reale, E. (1990). The presence of a juxtaglomerular apparatus in elasmobranch fish. Anat Embryol 182: 249–262.

Lacy, E. R. and Reale, E. (1991). Fine structure of the elasmobranch renal tubule: intermediate, distal and collecting duct segments of the little skate. Am J Anat 192(4): 478–497.

Lacy, E. R. and Reale, E. (1995). Functional morphology of the elasmobranch nephron and retention of urea. In: Wood, C. M. and Shuttleworth, T. J. (eds) Cellular and Molecular Approaches to Fish Ionic Regulation. Academic Press, New York: 107–146.

Laurent, P. and Dunel, S. (1980). Morphology of gill epithelia in fish. Am J Physiol 238: R147–R159.

Laurent, P. and Perry, S. F. (1990). Effects of cortisol on gill chloride cell morphology and ionic uptake in the fresh-water trout, *Salmo gairdneri*. Cell Tiss Res 259: 429–442.

Lea, M. and Hillman, S. (1990). Effects of osmolality and solutes on performance of shark heart mitochondria. J Exp Zool 255: 9–15.

Leech, A. R., Goldstein, L., Cha, C. J. and Goldstein, J. M. (1979). Alanine biosynthesis during starvation in skeletal muscle of the spiny dogfish, *Squalus acanthias*. J Exp Zool 207: 73–80.

Lewiston, N., Newman, A., Robin, E. and Holtzman, D. (1979). Shark heart mitochondria: Effects of external osmolality on respiration. Science 206: 75–76.

Loretz, C. A. and Pollina, C. (2000). Natriuretic peptides in fish physiology. Comp Biochem Physiol 125 A: 169–187.

Lytle, C. and Forbush, B. (1996). Regulatory phosphorylation of the secretory Na-K-Cl cotransporter: Modulation by cytoplasmic Cl. Am J Physiol 39: C437–C448.

MacKenzie, S., Cutler, C., Hazon, N. and Cramb, G. (2002). The effects of dietary sodium loading on the activity and expression of Na, K-ATPase in the rectal gland of the European dogfish (*Scyliorhinus canicula*). Comp Biochem Physiol 131 B: 185–200.

Marsigliante, S., Muscella, A., Vinson, G. P. and Storelli, C. (1997). Angiotensin II receptors in the gill of sea water- and freshwater-adapted eel. J Mol Endocrinol 18: 67–76.

Martin, R. A. (2003a). Does liver size limit shark body size [on line]. Available from: www.elasmo-research.org/education/topics/p_liver_size.htm (Accessed June 2005).

Martin, R. A. (2003b). No guts, no glory [on line]. Available from: www.elasmo-research.org/education/white_shark/digestion.htm (Accessed June 2005).

Masini, M. A., Uva, B., Devecchi, M. and Napoli, L. (1994). Renin-like activity, angiotensin I-converting enzyme-like activity, and osmoregulatory peptides in the dogfish rectal gland. Gen Comp Endocrinol 93: 246–254.

McKendry, J. E., Bernier, N. J., Takei, Y., Duff, D. W., Olson, K. R. and Perry, S. F. (1999). Natriuretic peptides and the control of catecholamine release in two freshwater teleost and a marine elasmobranch fish. Fish **Physiol** Biochem 20: 61–77.

Metcalfe, J. D. and Butler, P. J. (1986). The functional anatomy of the gills of the dogfish (*Scyliorhinus canicula*). J Zool Lond 208 A: 519–530.

Moon, T. W. and Idler, D. R. (1974). Binding of 1 alpha-hydroxycorticosterone to tissue soluble-proteins in Skate *Raja ocellata*. Comp Biochem Physiol 48 (4B): 499–506.

Morgan, J. D., Wilson, J. M. and Iwama, G. K. (1997). Oxygen consumption and Na^+,K^+-ATPase activity of the rectal gland and gill tissue in the spiny dogfish, *Squalus acanthias*. Can J Zool 75: 820–825.

Morgan, R. L., Ballantyne, J. S. and Wright, P. A. (2003a). Regulation of a renal urea transporter with reduced salinity in a marine elasmobranch, *Raja erinacea*. J Exp Biol 206: 3285–3292.

Morgan, R. L., Wright, P. A. and Ballantyne, J. S. (2003b). Urea transport in kidney brush-border membrane vesicles from an elasmobranch, *Raja erinacea*. J Exp Biol 206: 3293–3302.

Mourtisen, O. G. and Jorgensen, K. (1994). Dynamic order and disorder in lipid bilayers. Chem Phys Lipids 73: 3–25.

Newbound, D. R. and O'Shea, J. E. (2001). The microanatomy of the rectal salt gland of the Port Jackson shark, *Heterodontus portusjacksoni* (Meyer) (Heterodontidae): Suggestions for a counter-current exchange system. Cells Tissues Organs 169: 165–175.

Nilsson, S. and Holmgren, S. (1988). The autonomic nervous system of elasmobranchs: structure and function. In: Shuttleworth, T. J. (eds) Physiology of Elasmobranch Fishes. Springer-Verlag, London: 157–163.

Oguri, M. (1976). Rectal glands of marine and freshwater sharks: Comparative histology. In: Thorson, T. B. (eds) Investigations of the Ichthyofauna of Nicaraguan Lakes. School of Life Sciences, Lincoln: 613–614.

Olivereau, M. and Ball, J. N. (1970) Pituitary influences on osmoregulation in teleosts. Mem Soc Endocrinol 18: 57–85.

Olson, K. R. and Kent, B. (1980). The microvasculature of the elasmobranch gill. Cell Tiss Res 209: 49–63.

Olson, K. R. (1999). Rectal gland and volume homeostasis. In: Hamlett, W.C. (eds) Sharks, Skates and Rays. John Hopkins University Press, Baltimore: 329– 352.

Opdyke, D. F. and Holcombe, R. (1976). Response to angiotensin I and II and to AI-converting enzyme inhibitor in a shark. Am J Physiol 231: 1750–1753.

Opdyke, D. F., Carroll, R. G., Keller, N. E. and Taylor, A. A. (1981). Angiotensin-II releases catecholamines in dogfish. Comp Biochem Physiol 70: 131–134.

O'Toole, L. B., Armour, K. J., Decourt, C., Hazon, N., Lahlou, B. and Henderson, I. W. (1990), Secretory patterns of 1-alpha-hydroxycorticosterone in the isolated perifused interrenal gland of the dogfish, *Scyliorhinus canicula*. J Mol Endocrinol 5: 55–60.

Part, P., Wright, P. A. and Wood, C. M. (1998). Urea and water permeability in dogfish (*Squalus acanthias*) gills. Comp Biochem Physiol 119 A: 117–123.

Payan, P., Forster, R. P. and Goldstein, L. (1973). Gills and kidneys in ureosmotic regulation in euryhaline skates. Am J Physiol 224: 367–372.

Perlman, D. F. and Goldstein, L. (1988). Nitrogen Metabolism. In: Shuttleworth, T.J. (eds) Physiology of Elasmobranch Fishes. Springer-Verlag, London: 253–276.

Perrott, M. N., Grierson, C. E., Hazon, N. and Balment, R. J. (1992). Drinking behaviour in sea water and fresh water teleosts, the role of the renin-angiotensin system. Fish Physiol Biochem 10: 161–168.

Perry, S. F. (1997). The chloride cell: Structure and function in the gills of freshwater fishes. Ann Rev Physiol 59: 325–347.

Peterson, T. V. and Benjamin, B. A. (1992). The heart and control of renal excretion: neural and endocrine mechanisms. FASEB 6: 2923–2932.

Piermarini, P. M. and Evans, D. H. (1998). Osmoregulation of the Atlantic stingray (*Dasyatis sabina*) from the freshwater lake Jesup of the St. Johns River, Florida. Physiol Zool 71: 553–560.

Piermarini, P. M. and Evans, D. H. (2000). Effects of environmental salinity on Na$^+$/K$^+$-ATPase in the gills and rectal gland of a euryhaline elasmobranch (*Dasyatis sabina*). J Exp Biol 203: 2957–2966.

Pillans, R. P. and Franklin, C. E. (2004). Plasma osmolyte concentrations of bull sharks *Carcharhinus leucas*, captured along a salinity gradient. Comp Biochem Physiol 138 A: 363–371.

Pillans, R. P., Good, J. P., Anderson, W. G., Hazon, N. and Franklin, C. E. (2005). Freshwater to seawater acclimation of juvenile bull sharks (*Carcharhinus leucas*): plasma osmolytes and Na$^+$/K$^+$-ATPase activity in gill, rectal gland, kidney and intestine. J Comp Physiol 175 B: 37–44.

Pillans, R. D., Good, J. P., Anderson, W. G., Hazon, N. and Franklin, C. E. (2008). Rectal gland morphology of freshwater and seawater acclimated bull sharks *Carcharhinus leucas*. J Fish Biol 72(7): 1559–1571.

Pillans, R. D., Anderson, W. G., Good, J. P., Hyodo, S., Takei, Y., Hazon, N. and Franklin, C. E. (2006). Plasma and erythrocyte solute properties of juvenile bull sharks, *Carcharhinus leucas*, acutely exposed to increasing environmental salinity. J Exp Mar Biol Ecol 331: 145–157.

Ramos, C. (2004). The structure and ultrastructure of the sinus venosus in the mature dogfish (*Scyliorhinus canicula*): the endocardium, the epicardium and the subepicardial space. Tissue Cell 36: 399–407.

Riordan, J. R., Forbush, B. and Hanrahan, J. W. (1994). The molecular basis of chloride transport in shark rectal gland. J Exp Biol 196: 405–418.

Samerotte, A. L., Drazen, J. C., Brand, G. L., Seibel, B. A. and Yancey, P. H. (2007). Correlation of trimethylamine oxide and habitat depth within and among species of teleost fish: An analysis of causation. Physiol Biochem Zool 80: 197–208.

Saunders, B. (2002). Merck Source Resource Library [on line]. Merck Source. Available from: www.mercksource.com/ppdocs/us/common/dorlands/dorland/images (Accessed June 2005).

Sawyer, D. B., Cliff, W. H., Wilhelm, M. M., Fromter, R. O. and Beyenbach, K. W. (1985). Proximal tubules of the glomerular shark kidney secrete fluid via secretion of NaCl. Fed Proc 44: 1898–1898.

Scammon, R. E. (1913). The development of the elasmobranch liver. I. The early development of the liver. II The development of the liver ducts and gall-bladder. Am J Anat 14: 333–409.

Schmid, T. H. and Murru, F. L. (1994). Bioenergetics of the bull shark, *Car-*

charhinus leucas, maintained in captivity. Zool Biol 13: 177–185.

Schmidt-Nielsen, B. and Rabinowitz, L. (1964). Methylurea and acetamide: Active reabsorption by elasmobranch renal tubules. Science 146 (365): 1587–1588.

Schmidt-Nielsen, B., Truniger, B. and Rabinowi, L. (1972). Sodium-linked urea transport by renal tubule of spiny dogfish, *Squalus acanthias*. Comp Biochem Physiol 42 (1A): 13–25.

Schofield, J. P., Stephen, D., Jones, C. and Forrest, J. N. (1991). Identification of C-type natriuretic peptide in heart of spiny dogfish shark (*Squalus acanthias*). Am J Physiol 261 (4 Pt2): F734–F739.

Shuttleworth, T. J. (1983). Haemodynamic effects of secretory agents on the isolated elasmobranch rectal gland. J Exp Biol 103: 193–204.

Shuttleworth, T. J. and Thorndyke, M. C. (1984). An endogenous peptide stimulates secretory activity in the elasmobranch rectal gland. Science 225 (4659): 319–321.

Shuttleworth, T. J. and Thompson, J. L. (1986). Perfusion secretion relationships in the isolated elasmobranch rectal gland. J Exp Biol 125: 373–384.

Shuttleworth, T. J. (1988). Salt and water balance - extrarenal mechanisms. In: Shuttleworth, T. J. (ed) Physiology of Elasmobranch fishes. Springer-Verlag, Berlin, Heidelberg: 170–199.

Shuttleworth, T. J., Thompson, J., Munger, R. S. and Wood, C. M. (2006). A critical analysis of carbonic anhydrase function, respiratory gas exchange, and the acid-base control of secretion in the rectal gland of *Squalus acanthias*. J Exp Biol 209: 4701–4716.

Silva, P., Stoff, J., Field, M., Fine, L., Forrest, J. N. and Epstein, F. H. (1977). Mechanism of active chloride secretion by shark rectal gland: role of Na-K-ATPase in chloride transport. Am J Physiol 233: F298–F306.

Silva, P., Stoff, J. and Epstein, F. H. (1979). Indirect evidence for enhancement of Na-K-ATPase activity with stimulation of rectal gland secretion. Am J Physiol 237: F468–F472.

Silva, P., Epstein, J. A., Stevens, A., Spokes, K. and Epstein, F. H. (1983). Ouabain binding in rectal gland of *Squalus acanthias*. J Memb Biol 75: 105–114.

Silva, P., Stoff, J. S., Leone, D. R. and Epstein, F. H. (1985). Mode of action of somatostatin to inhibit secretion by shark rectal gland. Am J Physiol 249: R329–R334.

Silva, P., Stoff, J. S., Solomon, R. J., Lear, S., Kniaz, D., Greger, R. and Epstein, F. H. (1987). Atrial natriuretic peptide stimulates salt secretion by shark rectal gland by releasing VIP. Am J Physiol 252: F99–F103.

Silva, P., Lear, S., Reichlin, S. and Epstein, F. H. (1990). Somatostatin mediates bombesin inhibition of chloride secretion by rectal gland. Am J Physiol 258: R1459–R1463.

Silva, P., Epstein, F. H., Karnaky, K. J., Reichlin, S. and Forrest, J. N. (1993). Neuropeptide-Y inhibits chloride secretion in the shark rectal gland. Am J

Physiol 265: R439–R446.

Silva, P., Solomon, R. J. and Epstein, F. H. (1996). The rectal gland of *Squalus acanthias*: A model for the transport of chlorine. Kidney Int 49: 1552–1556.

Silva, P., Solomon, R. J. and Epstein, F. H. (1997). Transport mechanisms that mediate the secretion of chloride by the rectal gland of *Squalus acanthias*. J Exp Zool 279: 504–508.

Silva, P., Solomon, R. J. and Epstein, F. H. (1999). Mode of activation of salt secretion by C-type natriuretic peptide in the shark rectal gland. Am J Physiol 277: R1725–R1732.

Silva, P. and Epstein, F. H. (2002) Role of the cytoskeleton in secretion of chloride by shark rectal gland. J Comp Physiol 172 B: 719–723.

Smith, H. W. (1931a). The absorption and excretion of water and salts by the elasmobranch fishes I. Fresh water elasmobranchs. Am J Physiol 98(2): 279–295.

Smith, H. W. (1931b). The absorption and excretion of water and salts by the elasmobranch fishes II. Marine elasmobranchs. Am J Physiol 98(2): 296–310.

Smith, C. P. and Wright, P. A. (1999). Molecular characterization of an elasmobranch urea transporter. Am J Physiol 276: R622–R626.

Solomon, R., Taylor, M., Stoff, J. S., Silva, P. and Epstein, F. H. (1984). In vivo effect of volume expansion on rectal gland function I. humoral factors. Am J Physiol 246: R63–R66.

Solomon, R., Taylor, M., Dorsey, D., Silva, P. and Epstein, F. H. (1985). Atriopeptin stimulation of rectal gland function in *Squalus acanthias*. Am J Physiol 249: R348–R354.

Solomon, R., Protter, A., McEnroe, G., Porter, J. G. and Silva, P. (1992). C-type natriuretic peptides stimulate chloride secretion in the rectal gland of *Squalus acanthias*. Am J Physiol 262: R707–R711.

Solomon, R., Solomon, H., Wolff, D., Hornburg, S., Brignull, H., Landsberg, J., Silva, M., Epstein, F. H. and Silva, P. (1992). Chloride secretion in the rectal gland of *Squalus acanthias* the role of C-type natriuretic peptide (CNP). Bull Mt Des Mar Lab 31: 62–64.

Solomon, R., Castelo, L., Franco, E., Taylor, M., Silva, P. and Epstein, F. H. (1995). Preliminary data on intracellular signalling mechanisms in the rectal gland of *Squalus acanthias*: a pharmalogical approach. Bull Mt Desert Isl Biol Lab 34: 47–48.

Solomon, R., Nathanson, M., Taylor, M., Silva, P. and Epstein, F. H. (1995). An increase in intracellular calcium is associated with inhibition and not stimulation of the rectal gland of *Squalus acanthias*. Bull Mt Desert Isl Biol Lab 34: 42–43.

Steele, S. L., Yancey, P. H. and Wright, P. A. (2005). The little skate *Raja erinacea* exhibits an extrahepatic ornithine urea cycle in the muscle and modulates nitrogen metabolism during low-salinity challenge. Physiol Biochem Zool 78: 216–226.

Stoff, J. S., Hallac, R., Rosa, R., Silva, P., Fischer, J. and Epstein, F. H.

(1977). The role of vasoactive intestinal peptide (VIP) in the regulation of active chloride secretion in the rectal gland of *Squalus acanthias*. Bull Mt Desert Isl Biol Lab 17: 66.

Stoff, J. S., Silva, P., Field, M., Forrest, J., Stevens, A. and Epstein, F. H. (1977). Cyclic AMP regulation of active chloride transport in the rectal gland of marine elasmobranchs. J Exp Zool 199: 443–448.

Stoff, J. S., Rosa, R., Hallac, R., Silva, P. and Epstein, F. H. (1979). Hormonal regulation of active chloride transport in the dogfish rectal gland. Am J Physiol 237: F138–F144.

Stoff, J. S., Silva, P., Lechan, R., Solomon, R. and Epstein, F. H. (1988). Neural control of shark rectal gland. Am J Physiol 255: R212–R216.

Stolte, H., Galaske, R. G., Eisenbach, G. M., Lechene, C., Schmidt-Nielsen, B. and Boylan, J. W. (1977). Renal tubule ion transport and collecting duct function in the elasmobranch little skate, *Raja erinacea*. J Exp Zool 199: 403–410.

Sulikowski, J. A., Treberg, J. R. and Howell, H. (2003). Fluid regulation and physiological adjustments in the winter skate, *Leucoraja ocellata*, following exposure to reduced environmental salinities. Environ Biol Fish 66: 339–348.

Suzuki, R., Takahashi, A., Hazon, N. and Takei, Y. (1991). Isolation of high-molecular-weight C-type natriuretic peptide from the heart of a cartilaginous fish (European dogfish, *Scyliorhinus canicula*). Febs Letts 282: 321–325.

Suzuki, R., Takahashi, A. and Takei, Y. (1992). Different molecular forms of C-type natriuretic peptide isolated from the brain and heart of an elasmobranch, *Triakis scyllia*. J Endocrinol 135: 317–323.

Suzuki, R., Togashi, K., Ando, K. and Takei, Y. (1994). Distribution and molecular forms of C-type natriuretic peptide in plasma and tissue of a dogfish, *Triakis scyllia*. Gen Comp Endocrinol 96: 378–384.

Takei, Y., Hirano, T. and Kobayashi, H. (1979). Angiotensin and water-intake in the Japanese eel, *Anguilla japonica*. Gen Comp Endocrinol 38: 466–475.

Takei, Y., Okubo, J. and Yamaguchi, K. (1988). Effects of cellular dehydration on drinking and plasma angiotensin-II level in the eel, *Anguilla japonica*. Zool Sci 5: 43–51.

Takei, Y., Hasegawa, Y., Watanabe, T. X., Nakajima, K. and Hazon, N. (1993). A novel angiotensin I isolated from an elasmobranch fish. J Endocrinol 139: 281–285.

Takei, Y. and Kaiya, H. (1998). Antidiuretic effect of eel ANP infused at physiological doses in conscious, seawater-adapted eels, *Anguilla japonica*. Zool Sci 15: 399–404.

Takei, Y. (1999). Structural and functional evolution of the natriuretic peptide system in vertebrates. Internat Rev Cytology, 194: 1–66.

Takei, Y. (2000). Comparative physiology of body fluid regulation in vertebrates with special reference to thirst regulation. Jap J Physiol 50: 171–186.

Tam, W. L., Wong, W. P., Loong, A. M., Hiong, K. C., Chew, S. F., Ballantyne, J. S. and Ip, Y. K. (2003). The osmotic response of the Asian freshwater stingray (*Himantura signifer*) to increased salinity: a comparison with the marine (*Taeniura lymma*) and Amazonian freshwater (*Potamotrygon motoro*) stingrays. J Exp Biol 206: 2931–2940.

Taylor, J. R. and Grosell, M. (2006). Evolutionary aspects of intestinal bicarbonate secretion in fish. Comp Biochem Physiol 143 A: 523–529.

Thorndyke, M. C. and Shuttleworth, T. J. (1985). Biochemical and physiological studies on peptides from the elasmobranch gut. Peptides 6: 369–372.

Thorson, T. B. (1970). Freshwater stingrays, Potamotrygon spp.: failure to concentrate urea when exposed to a saline medium. Life Sci 9: 893–900.

Thorson, T. B., Cowan, C. M. and Watson, D. E. (1973). Body fluid solutes of juveniles and adults of the euryhaline bull shark *Carcharhinus leucas* from freshwater and saline environments. Physiol Zool 46: 29–42.

Thorson, T. B., Wooton, R. M. and Georgi, T. A. (1978). Rectal gland of freshwater stingrays, Potamotrygon spp. (Chondrichthyes: Potamotrygonidae). Biol Bull 154: 508–516.

Tierney, M. L., Takei, Y. and Hazon, N. (1997). The presence of angiotensin II receptors in elasmobranchs. Gen Comp Endocrinol 105: 9–17.

Tierney, M. L., Takei, Y. and Hazon, N. (1998). A radioimmunoassay for the determination of angiotensin II in elasmobranch fish. Gen Comp Endocrinol 111: 299–305.

Tota, B. (1999). Heart. In: Hamlett, W.C. (eds) Sharks, Skates and Rays. John Hopkins University Press, Baltimore: 238–272.

Treberg, J. R. and Driedzic, W. R. (2006). Maintenance and accumulation of trimethylamine oxide by winter skate (*Leucoraja ocellata*): reliance on low whole animal losses rather than synthesis. Am J Physiol 291: R1790–R1798.

Treberg, J. R., Speers-Roesch, B., Piermarini, P. M., Ip, Y. K., Ballantyne, J. S. and Driedzic, W. R. (2006). The accumulation of methylamine counteracting solutes in elasmobranchs with differing levels of urea: a comparison of marine and freshwater species. J Exp Biol 209: 860–870.

Truscott, B. and Idler, D. R. (1968). Widespread occurrence of a corticosteroid 1alpha-hydroxylase in interrenals of Elasmobranchii. J Endocrinol 40: 515–5126.

Valentich, J. D., Karnaky, K. J. and Ecay, T. W. (1996). Ultrastructural and cytochemical characterization of cultured dogfish shark rectal gland cells. Am J Physiol 40: C1993–C2003.

Walsh, P. J. and Mommsen, T. P. (2001). Evolutionary considerations of nitrogen metabolism and excretion. In: Wright, P. A. and Anderson, P. M. (eds) Nitrogen excretion. Academic Press, San Diego: 1–30.

Walsh, P. J., Kajimura, M., Mommsen, T. P. and Wood, C. M. (2006). Metabolic organization and effects of feeding on enzyme activities of the dogfish shark (*Squalus acanthias*) rectal gland. J Exp Biol 209: 2929–2938.

Wells, A. (2002). The endocrine control of renal function in elasmobranch fish. Ph.D thesis, University of St Andrews, St Andrews.

Wells, A., Anderson, W.G. and Hazon, N. (2002). Development of an in situ perfused kidney preparation for elasmobranch fish: action of arginine vasotocin. Am J Physiol 282: R1636–R1642.

Wells, A., Anderson, W. G. and Hazon, N. (2003). Evidence for an intrarenal renin-angiotensin system in the European lesser-spotted dogfish. J Fish Biol 63: 1337–1340.

Wells, A., Anderson, W. G. and Hazon, N. (2005). Glomerular effects of AVT on the in situ perfused trunk preparation of the dogfish. Ann NY Acad Sci 1040: 515–517.

Wells, A., Anderson, W. G., Cains, J. E., Cooper, M. W. and Hazon, N. (2006). Effects of angiotensin II and C-type natriuretic peptide on the in situ perfused trunk preparation of the dogfish, *Scyliorhinus canicula*. Gen Comp Endocrinol 145: 109–115.

Wetherbee, B. M. and Gruber, S. H. (1993). Absorption efficiency of the lemon shark *Negaprion brevirostris* at varying rates of energy intake. Copeia 2: 416–425.

Wetherbee, B. M. and Nichols, P. D. (2000). Lipid composition of the liver oil of deep-sea sharks from the Chatham Rise, New Zealand. Comp Biochem Physiol 125 B: 511–521.

Wetherbee, B. M. and Cortes, E. (2004). Food consumption and feeding habits. In: Carrier, J. C., Musick, J. A. and Heithaus, M. R. (eds) Biology of sharks and their relatives. CRC Press, London: 225–246.

Wilson, E. D., McGuinn, M. R. and Goldstein, L. (1999). Trimethylamine oxide transport across plasma membranes of elasmobranch erythrocytes. J Exp Zool 284: 605–609.

Wilson, J. M., Morgan, J. D., Vogl, A. W. and Randall, D. J. (2002). Branchial mitochondria-rich cells in the dogfish *Squalus acanthias*. Comp Biochem Physiol 132 A: 365–374.

Withers, P. C., Morrison, G. and Guppy, M. (1994a). Buoyancy role of urea and TMAO in an elasmobranch fish, the Port-Jackson shark, *Heterodontus portusjacksoni*. Physiol Zool 67: 693–705.

Withers, P. C., Morrison, G., Hefter, G. T. and Pang, T. S. (1994b) .Role of urea and methylamines in buoyancy of elasmobranchs. J Exp Biol 188: 175–189.

Wood, C. M., Part, P. and Wright, P. A. (1995). Ammonia and urea metabolism in relation to gill function and acid-base-balance in a marine elasmobranch, the spiny dogfish (*Squalus acanthias*). J Exp Biol 198: 1545–1558.

Wood, C. M., Matsuo, A. Y. O., Gonzalez, R. J., Wilson, R. W., Patrick, M. L. and Luis Val, A. (2002). Mechanisms of ion transport in Potamotrygon, a stenohaline freshwater elasmobranch native to the ion-poor blackwaters of the Rio Negro. J Exp Biol 205: 3039–3054.

Wood, C. M., Kajimura, M., Mommsen, T. P. and Walsh, P. J. (2005). Alkaline tide and nitrogen conservation after feeding in an elasmobranch (*Squalus acanthias*). J Exp Biol 208: 2693–2705.

Wood, C. M., Kajimura, M., Bucking, C. and Walsh, P. J. (2007a). Osmo-regulation, ionoregulation and acid-base regulation by the gastrointestinal tract after feeding in the elasmobranch (*Squalus acanthias*). J Exp Biol 210: 1335–1349.

Wood, C. M., Munger, R. S., Thompson, J. and Shuttleworth, T. J. (2007b). Control of rectal gland secretion by blood acid-base status in the intact dogfish shark (*Squalus acanthias*). Resp Physiol Neurobiol 156: 220–228.

Wright, D. E. (1973). The structure of the gills of the elasmobranch *Scyliorhinus canicula*. Z Zellforch 144: 489–509.

Wright, P., Anderson, P., Weng, L., Frick, N., Wong, W. P. and Ip, Y. K. (2004). The crab-eating frog, Rana cancrivora, up-regulates hepatic carbam-oyl phosphate synthetase I activity and tissue osmolyte levels in response to increased salinity. J Exp Zool 301A: 559–568.

Yancey, P. H. and Somero, G. N. (1978). Urea-requiring lactate dehydrogenases of marine elasmobranch fish. J Comp Physiol 125: 135–141.

Yancey, P. H. and Somero, G. N. (1979). Counteraction of urea destabilization of protein structure by methylamine osmoregulatory compounds of elasmo-branch fishes. Biochem J 183: 317–323.

Yancey, P. H. and Somero, G. N. (1980). Methylamine osmoregulatory solutes of elasmobranch fishes counteract urea inhibition of enzymes. J Exp Zool 212: 205–213.

Yancey, P. H., Clark, M. E., Hand, S. C., Bowlus, R. D. and Somero, G. N. (1982). Living with water stress: evolution of osmolyte systems. Science 217: 1214–1222.

Yancey, P. H. (1994). Compatible and counteracting solutes. In: Strange, K. (ed) Cellular and Molecular physiology of Cell Volume Regulation. CRC Press, Boca Raton: 81–109.

Yancey, P. H. (2001). Nitrogen compounds as osmolytes. In: Wright, P. A. and Anderson, P. M. (eds) Fish Physiology. Academic Press, San Diego: 309 –341.

Yancey, P. H., Samerotte, A. L., Brand, G. L. and Drazen, J. C. (2004). Increasing contents of TMAO with depth within species as well as among spe-cies of teleost fish. Int Comp Biol 44: 669–669.

Yancey, P. H. (2005). Organic osmolytes as compatible, metabolic and counter-acting cytoprotectants in high osmolarity and other stresses. J Exp Biol 208: 2819–2830.

Yokota, S. D. and Benyajati, S. (1988). Hormonal control of renal function in the spiny dogfish (*Squalus acanthias*). FASEB 2: A949–A949.

Young, J. Z. (1981). The Life of Vertebrates. Oxford University Press, London.

Zeidel, J. D., Mathai, J. C., Campbell, J. D., Ruiz, W. G., Apodaca, G. L., Riordan, J. and Zeidel, M. L. (2005). Selective permeability barrier to urea in shark rectal gland. Am J Physiol 289: F83–F89.

Ziyadeh, F. N. and Kleinzeller, A. (1991). Determinants of regulatory volume decrease in rectal gland cells of *Squalus acanthias*. Bull Mt Des Mar Lab 30: 78–79.

Chapter 3

The molecular basis of osmoregulation, and ion and water transport in teleostean fish

Christopher P. Cutler, Stephan Brezillion, Songul Bekir, Robert Sterling and Gordon Cramb

Keywords: Ion transport, genes, Na⁺,K⁺-ATPase, chloride cation cotransporters (CCC), cystic fibrosis transmembrane conductance regulator (CFTR) chloride channels, K⁺ channels, H⁺-ATPases, Na⁺ channels, aquaourins, basolateral tubular network (BTN)

Abstract

Teleostean phylogengy has been diverging for millions of years and is complicated by several genome wide gene duplication events, and independent evolution of salinity tolerance in a number of teleosts. This presents a uniquely complicated situation for the study of the genes and proteins involved in osmoregulatoin, with teleosteans showing multiple isoforms of many ion transporters compared to mammals. The characteristics of fish ion and water transport gene/protein isoforms are described in fish tissues including the Na⁺,K⁺-ATPase, Cl⁻ cation cotransporters (CCC), cystic fibrosis transmembrane conductance regulator (CFTR) chloride channels, K⁺ channels, H⁺-ATPases, Na⁺ channels versus ion exchangers, and aquaourins. The role that these proteins and/or isoforms play in the main osmoregulatory tissues is examined including the gill, intestine and kidney then examined. Differences between freshwater and seawater-adapted gills are discussed, and particular attention is paid to the potential roles that the basolateral tubular network (BTN) of branchial chloride cells in fluid movements and osmoregulation. In the gastrointestinal tract, the changing salinity gradient across the gut is discussed in context with the location of transporters along the length of the gut, and the role of transporters in the absorption and secretion of salts, and water movements, are explored. Finally, recent information on kidney ion and water transporters is examined in the light of some older data in the literature.

3.1 Introduction

In recent years there have been a number of excellent reviews covering various aspects of osmoregulation and ion and water transport in teleostean fish (Claiborne *et al.*, 2002; Ando *et al.*, 2003; Hirose *et al.*, 2003; Perry *et al.*, 2003b; Evans *et al.*, 2005; Grosell, 2006; Marshall and Grosell, 2006; Cutler *et al.*, 2007a; Hoffmann *et al.*, 2007; Hwang and Lee, 2007). This review will focus on the more recent molecular aspects such as the role that isoforms of various ion and water transporters play in osmoregulatory processes and the issues arising from this relatively new information.

3.1.1 Some general considerations

One of the central issues currently facing fish molecular physiologists is that the data concerning osmoregulatory mechanisms comes from a number of different species across the breadth of the teleostean phylogeny. As teleost fish are relatively ancient, there is a considerable amount of diversity between phylogentically older and more recently derived species. One example of this diversity is for instance the fact that some teleosts are stenohaline freshwater or seawater species. For osmoregulatory studies, of particular interest are the euryhaline fish that inhabit either environment. A related issue for the study of osmoregulation in fish, concerns the impact of diversity on the development of adaptation strategies during evolution. For example, euryhalinity has probably developed independently several times in species from different parts of the teleost phylogeny (Evans *et al.*, 2005). It is therefore probable that the mechanisms allowing successful acclimation of fish to either freshwater or seawater were somewhat different each time euryhalinity was acquired (see below). The physiological diversity among fish species indicates that any one species does not necessarily provide a good guide as to what physiological mechanisms will be present in other species from different branches of the teleostean phylogeny. Now that the genomes of several teleost fish have been sequenced, the best strategy for future DNA sequencing efforts should be to choose the relatively inexpensive approach of sequencing the transcriptomes (cDNAs of all expressed genes) of as many species as possible from across the teleost spectrum, rather than concentrating on sequencing the whole genome of one or two species, as is currently being contemplated (Burnett *et al.*, 2007).

Another complicating factor for molecular physiological studies is the notion that teleost fish underwent a genome wide duplication event that probably led to the 'teleost radiation', producing the great number of currently extant species (Cutler and Cramb, 2001; Hoegg *et al.*, 2004). This duplication event presumably led to the ancestors of modern teleostean species, from Osteoglossomorphs (i.e. bony tongue species) onwards, to originally have two copies of every gene, in comparison to older ray-finned fish species existing before the duplication (i.e. bowfins, gars, sturgeon and bichirs). Following the genome duplication, many of the additional gene duplicates were lost, with estimates of around 10% remaining in fugu (*Takifugu rubripes*) and 20% in zebrafish (*Danio rerio*; Fishman, 2001). Evidence from the authors' laboratories suggests that the (relatively ancient teleost) European eel (*Anguilla anguilla*) may well have retained more than 20% of its duplicate genes (based on published and unpublished data; Cutler and Cramb, 2001). Prior to the teleost-specific genome duplication, the presence of duplicate gene/protein isoforms was already an issue in earlier vertebrate species due to two other genome duplication events. These early duplication events have resulted in up to four copies of each gene in, for example, mammalian species. The teleost-specific genome duplication event may have led to the presence of up to eight isoforms of any gene/protein, in comparison to a single copy usually found in non-vertebrate species such as the tunicate *Ciona intestinalis* (Hoegg and Meyer, 2007). The result of the additional pairs of teleostean gene duplicates is that these isoforms have developed different functions or patterns of expression or regulation, in comparison to their single mammalian homologous counterparts (neo- or sub-functionalization; Cutler and Cramb, 2001). Additionally, due to the diversification of teleost species following genome duplication, pairs of duplicate genes may have diverged in different ways in different teleost species making it difficult to make any assumptions across species regarding the function or regulation of any particular isoform. It is not yet clear, as there is currently insufficient sequence data, but the level of divergence of some duplicated pairs of genes may, in some cases, make it impossible to tell which duplicate corresponds to which, in comparison to copies of those genes found in other teleost species. In such cases it may only be possible to tell which duplicate genes correspond to each other across different teleost species, by using each gene's chromosomal location and it's relationship to other syntenic genes or gene clusters. As recently highlighted in a review by Hwang and Lee (2007), the presence of multiple isoforms of most proteins in teleostean fish, and the fact that these isoforms could vary in number and behave significantly differently between species, makes analysis of experimental results in any area of physiology difficult.

It should also be remembered that teleosts as a group have been diverging for a similar amount of time, and may therefore, be genetically as diverse as tetrapods (around 350 compared to 360–370 million years respectively; Munar and Hedges, 1998; Meyer and Van de Peer, 2005). Many osmoregulatory studies that have been performed recently, have been carried out ignoring the fact that multiple gene/protein isoforms may exist, and this can clearly lead to misinterpretation of the data produced. Similarly, Hwang and Lee (2007) also drew attention to another problem that may lead to the generation of erroneous data, namely, the use of heterologous antibodies in Western blot analysis and/or immunohistochemistry. The antibodies used have often been produced against mammalian antigens. Clearly, when they are used in fish, there is a considerable danger of cross-reaction of the antibodies to other protein isoforms (any antibody able to bind antigens across species is also likely to bind antigens across isoforms) and may also allow binding to more than one isoform simultaneously. Exactly which isoforms are, or are not, being detected is therefore difficult to know when heterologous antibodies are used. If the field of comparative physiology in general, and fish osmoregulation in particular, is to move forward, studies need to initially determine what protein/gene isoforms are present in the model species employed. Molecular tools, such as, species- and isoform-specific homologous antibodies could then be produced for more accurate experimentation.

3.1.2 The general osmoregulatory mechanism in teleostean fish

Teleostean fish in freshwater (FW) have body fluids that are hyper-osmotic to the external environment, and continuously gain water by endosmosis across their permeable body surfaces, principally the gills, and lose small amounts of ions (such as Na^+ and Cl^- ions) through the production of urine. As with terrestrial vertebrates, water homeostasis is achieved by excreting excess water through the production of relatively large quantities of dilute urine in the kidney, and additionally ions are absorbed across the gills or from the diet.

Marine teleosts or euryhaline teleosts acclimated to seawater (SW), face the opposite osmoregulatory challenge to their FW counterparts, in that they are constantly losing water to the external hyper-osmotic environment across permeable body surfaces such as the gills. This situation would quickly lead to severe dehydration but fish counteract this problem by the use of a regulated drinking response. Imbibed SW is first partially desalinated in the esophagus before entering the intestine. The absorption of water across the intestinal epithelium into body fluids takes place with the concomitant uptake of salts. Osmotic equilibrium is maintained due to the excretion of excess Na^+ and Cl^- ions across the surface of the gill. Some salts are also lost via urine production, but renal output is reduced to the minimum required to eradicate other waste products (other than Na^+ and Cl^- ions). Renal output is reduced because teleostean fish cannot produce urine with a significantly higher osmotic concentration than that of plasma, and greater output would otherwise result in a significant water loss (see Marshall and Grosell, 2006, for a more in depth overview).

As a consequence of the osmoregulatory mechanisms outlined above, the organs with the greatest osmoregulatory role are the gills, gastrointestinal tract and the kidneys. This review will focus on ion and water transporters in these tissues and the role these processes play in osmotic homeostasis. Additionally certain aspects of the related areas of acid-base regulation will be included where appropriate.

3.2 Ion and water transporter isoforms in teleostean fish

3.2.1 Na^+,K^+-ATPase

The 'sodium pump' or Na^+,K^+-ATPase is an ubiquitous enzyme found throughout the animal kingdom, that transports Na^+ and K^+ ions and thereby maintains gradients for these ions across the membrane of cells. It is composed of 2 main subunits, α and β and an additional accessory or regulatory γ subunit (see reviews; Bystriansky and Caplan, 2007; Franzin *et al.*, 2007; Lingrel *et al.*, 2007; Vagin et. al., 2007). The nomenclature for teleostean sodium pump subunit isoforms has borrowed its framework from mammals, where there exist four α-subunit isoforms (α 1-4), 4 β-subunit isoforms (β 1-3 and $\beta4\beta m$; Crambert *et al.*, 2002) and the γ–subunit, a member of the FXYD family of 12 isoforms (FXYD 1-8; Sweadner and Rael, 2000; Geering, 2005; Garty and Karlish, 2006; Geering, 2006; Tipsmark, 2008) many of which have been shown to be sodium pump regulatory subunits.

In teleostean fish, sodium pump α subunit isoforms were first identified by molecular cloning in white sucker (*Catostomus commersoni*; Schoenrock *et al.*, 1991). Subsequently, 3 α-subunit isoforms have been identified in the eel (Anguilla anguilla), orthologues of the α1 and α3 isoforms (Cutler *et al.*, 1995a; Cutler and Cramb, 2001) and an as yet uncharacterized α isoform (G. Cramb personal communication). Eel α1 and α3 isoforms are ubiquitously expressed including in the gill, kidney and gastrointestinal tract. Additionally, multiple isoforms have since been discovered in other species following access to expressed sequence tag (EST) and genome databases. In zebrafish (*Danio rerio*) there were 9 α subunit isoforms identified, 6 α1 isoforms (α1a.1-5 and α1b), 1 α2 isoform and 2 α3 (α3a and α3b) isoforms (Cutler and Cramb, 2001; Rajarao *et al.*, 2001; Blasiole *et al.*, 2002; Canfield *et al.*, 2002). Five of the α1 isoforms (α1a.1-5 come from the local tandem duplication of a single α1 gene (Blasiole *et al.*, 2002). Expression of the zebrafish genes has predominantly been studied during embryogenesis. In salmonids, up to 5 α isoforms are expressed (α1a-c, α2 and α3; D'Cotta *et al.*, 1996; D'Cotta *et al.*, 2000; Cutler and Cramb, 2001; Seidelin *et al.*, 2001; Richards *et al.*, 2003; Gharbi *et al.*, 2005; Bystriansky *et al.*, 2006; Bystriansky *et al.*, 2007). In Rainbow trout (*Oncorhynchus mykiss*), α1b and c, and α3 isoforms are expressed unbiquitously, whereas the α1a isoform is confined to gill and heart tissues and the α2 isoform to muscle, brain and eye (Richards *et al.*, 2003). Three α– isoforms have been identified in Antarctic nototheniids (*Trematomus bernacchii*; α1-3; Guynn *et al.*, 2002) and all three isoforms were expressed ubiquitously. Two α isoforms have also been described in tilapia (*Oreochromis mossambicus*; α1 and α3; Feng *et al.*, 2002) both of which were ubiquitously expressed but with only low levels of the α3 isoform in intestine. Two isoforms were also found in killifish (*Fundulus heteroclitus*; α1 and α2; Semple *et al.*, 2002). The killifish α1 isoform was expressed ubiquitously whereas the α2 was only found in brain, heart, muscle and spleen. Finally, single α isoforms have been isolated from sea bream (*Sparus sarba*; Deane and Woo, 2004; where it is expressed in gill and kidney), and eel electroplax (*Electrophorus electicus*; Kaya *et al.*, 1997).

The sodium pump β-subunit in teleosts was initially cloned and identified in the eel (β1; Cutler *et al.*, 1995b) and subsequently 6 β subunit isoforms, including 2 β1 (β1 and β233; Cutler *et al.*, 2000), 2 β2 (β185 and β185b), 1 β3 and a β4 (β179) isoform were shown to exist in this species (Cutler *et al.*, 1997a; Cutler *et al.*, 1997b; Cutler and Cramb, 2001). The β1 and β233 were expressed ubiquitously. In zebrafish, up to 8 β subunit isoforms may exist, although to date only 6 of these gene sequences have been shown to be expressed (Appel *et al.*, 1996; Cutler and Cramb, 2001; Rajarao *et al.*, 2001; Canfield *et al.*, 2002; Rajarao *et al.*, 2002). These include 4 β1 isoforms (2 putative) and, 2 β2 and β3 isoforms. Expression of the zebrafish genes has predominantly been studied during embryogenesis. Four β subunit isoforms have been demonstrated in salmonids including 2 β1 isoforms (β1a and β1b), and a β2 and a β3 (β3b) isoform (Cutler and Cramb, 2001; Seidelin *et al.*, 2001; Gharbi *et al.*, 2005). One β1 isoform is expressed in the Atlantic salmon gill (*Salmo salar*; Seidelin *et al.*, 2001). A single β isoform has also been identified in sea bream (*Sparus sarba*) where expression has been found in gill and kidney (Deane and Woo, 2004).

Homologues of the sodium pump γ subunit (FXYD genes) have recently been identified in various teleostean fish (Sweadner and Rael, 2000; Tipsmark, 2008). Orthologues of FXYD2, 5, 6, 7, and 8 have been shown to exist in Atlantic salmon and zebrafish. Similarly orthologues of FXYD5, 6, 7, and 8 were identified in rainbow trout and medaka (*Oryzias latipes*) genomes. Orthologues of FXYD9 (previously identified in zebrafish; Sweadner and Rael, 2000) and two new FXYD isoforms (FXYD11 and 12) were identified in all four species. The FXYD genes in Atlantic salmon were expressed ubiquitously but FXYD2 was predominantly expressed in kidney; FXYD5 in kidney with lower levels in gill and intestine; FXYD6 and 7 were mainly expressed in brain; FXYD8 mainly in muscle; FXYD9 at highest levels in heart but with significant expression in gill kidney and intestine; FXYD11 was predominantly found in gill; and FXYD12 was expressed mainly in kidney and intestine.

3.2.2 Chloride cation cotransporters

The chloride-cation cotransporters (CCC) are a family of genes responsible for electroneutral cotransport of Na^+ and/or K^+ and Cl^- ions across the plasma membrane (see reviews, Gamba, 2005; Gimenez, 2006). Three major classes of CCC exist; those transporting Na^+, K^+, $2Cl^-$ (NKCC), those transporting NaCl (NCC) and those transporting KCl (KCC). In mammals two isoforms of NKCC have been identified, NKCC1, a protein located in the basolateral membranes of cells, that is usually involved in trans-epithelial ion secretion and/or cell volume regulation, and NKCC2, an apically located protein usually concerned with trans-epithelial ion absorption processes. The presence of NKCC cotransporters in teleostean fish was initially suggested by Musch *et al.*, (1982). Four CCC isoforms were reported to exist in the eel (cot1-4; Cutler *et al.*, 1996). Partial sequences of NKCC1 were identified in rainbow trout and Atlantic salmon (Tipsmark *et al.*, 2002). NKCC1 from both species was expressed in the gill. In eel, two NKCC1 isoforms were described (NKCC1a and 1b, previously cot 1 and cot3; Cutler and Cramb, 2002a). Eel NKCC1a is expressed ubiquitously but with high levels found in gill, intermediate levels in kidney and low levels found in the intestine. NKCC1b is predominantly expressed in brain but is also expressed in the gill at low levels (see Figure 1). Two NKCC1 isoforms have also been identified in tilapia (NKCC1α and β; NCBI accession numbers AY513737 and AY513738. A NKCC1 isoform has been cloned from sea bass (*Dicentrarchus labrax*) and is expressed in gill, kidney and intestine (Lorin-Nebel *et al.*, 2006). In killifish, a NKCC1 isoform has also been cloned (partial sequence) that is expressed in the gill (Scott *et al.*, 2004). Isoforms of NKCC2 have also been identified in eel (NKCC2α and β, previously cot6 and cot2; Cutler and Cramb, 2001; Cutler and Cramb, 2008). NKCC2α shows a similar tissue distribution of expression to mammalian NKCC2, being found predominantly in the eel kidney.

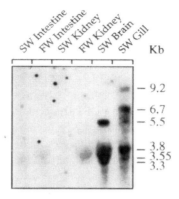

Figure 1.
  Northern blot of eel (Anguilla anguilla) NKCClb mRNA in RNA from tissues of seawater-
(SW) and freshwater- (FW) acclimated fish. Messenger RNA sizes shown are in kilobases (Kb).

NKCC2β was expressed instead in the eel intestine and urinary bladder. A partial sequence of a NKCC2 isoform has also been cloned from killifish (Scott *et al.*, 2004), and a NKCC2 gene has also been cloned from tilapia (NCBI accession number AY513739). The first teleostean fish NCC isoform identified was from the winter flounder (*Pseudopleuronectes americanus*), and this isoform is expressed in a wide range of tissues including intestine, urinary bladder and kidney (Gamba *et al.*, 1993). Two eel NCC isoforms were also subsequently characterized (NCC2α and β, previously cot5 and cot4; Cutler and Cramb, 2001; Cutler and Cramb, 2008). Eel NCCα is expressed, in a similar fashion to mammalian NCC, in kidney (although it can be also detected by PCR in eel gill; data not shown), NCCβ is detected in a wider range of tissues (than NCCα including intestine and oesophagus, with lower levels found in gill and kidney.

3.2.3 Chloride and potassium ion channels

The cystic fibrosis transmembrane conductance regulator (CFTR) Cl⁻ ion channel gene product (for CFTR reviews see Okiyoneda and Lukacs, 2007; Aleksandrov *et al.*, 2007; Cheung and Deber, 2008) was first suggested to be involved in teleostean osmoregulatory processes due to the similarity of its characteristics with those of the channel responsible for chloride efflux in killifish opercular mitochondrial-rich cells (Marshall, 1995). Information confirming the presence of an orthologue of CFTR in teleostean fish, occurred initially in the eel due to molecular cloning of a partial CFTR cDNA (Cutler *et al.*, 1996). Subsequently the first full-length teleost CFTR cDNA sequence was published from killifish (Singer *et al.*, 1998). The eel CFTR orthologue exhibits a limited range of expression, with high levels only in gill, with lower levels in kidney (and levels only detectable by PCR in intestine; Cutler and Cramb, 2001), in comparison to killifish CFTR. Killifish CFTR itself, is expressed at high levels in gill, operculum, brain and intestine (Singer *et al.*, 1998). Two highly homologous CFTR isoforms were subsequently demonstrated in Atlantic salmon (CFTR I and II; Chen *et al.*, 2001), both of which are expressed in gill (Singer *et al.*, 2002; Nilsen *et al.*, 2007). A partial CFTR cDNA sequence has also been determined for striped bass (*Morone saxatilis*), and in this species, CFTR mRNA expression is also found in the gill (Madsen *et al.*, 2007). An inwardly rectifying potassium channel (eKir) has also been isolated from the eel (*Anguilla japonica*) and this channel exhibits mRNA expression in the gill, posterior intestine and kidney (Suzuki *et al.*, 1999).

3.2.4 Bicarbonate transporters

Many different proteins can transport bicarbonate and to date these have been best studied in mammals (for review see Sterling and Casey, 2002; Alper, 2006). In teleosteans, initial studies focused on the chloride-bicarbonate exchangers (anion exchanges; AE1-4; genes SLC4A1-3, 9). These transporters are known to exchange chloride and bicarbonate ions across the plasma membrane. The first teleost AE was the trout band 3 homologue (AE1) identified from erythrocytes (Hubner, 1992). In eel, cDNA fragments were subsequently isolated from the intestine and these encoded three isoforms which are homologous to AE1 and 2 (EAE1-3; Cutler and Cramb, 2001). Preliminary studies indicated that EAE 1 is an orthologue of trout AE1 and its mRNA is expressed at high levels in gill, kidney, heart and brain, and with only just detectable levels of expression in the intestine, oesophagus and liver. EAE2 is a duplicate isoform of AE1, and is expressed at high levels in kidney, oesophagus and stomach, with intermediate levels in heart and lower levels in brain, eye, intestine and gill. EAE3 is orthologous to mammalian AE2, and had high levels of expression in the gill, with intermediate levels in kidney and lower levels in intestine, liver, skeletal muscle and heart. Anion exchanger isoforms have also been studied in zebrafish. Zebrafish AE1 is expressed in erythrocytes and in head kidney (Paw *et al.*, 2003). Zebrafish also express two copies of AE2 during development. Zebrafish AE2.1 is expressed in renal and neural tissues (Smuckler *et al.*, 2005). Zebrafish AE2.2 is expressed in brain, eye, skin and vasculature (Smuckler *et al.*, 2008).

Other members of the SLC4 gene family include the sodium bicarbonate cotransporters (NBC), which were initially identified and cloned from the kidneys of the salamander (*Ambystoma tigrinum*) and various isoforms have now been identified in mammals that show 30–35% amino acid homology with mammalian AEs (NBC1-4; Romero *et al.*, 1997; Romero and Boron, 1999; Sterling and Casey, 2002). Some mammalian NBC isoforms have been shown to be electrogenic, transporting more bicarbonate than Na^+ ions. In teleosteans, a partial cDNA that is an orthologue of NBC1 was identified (SLC4A4) from the eel, and mRNA encoding this protein is expressed at highest levels in the intestine, with intermediate levels in kidney and lower levels in the gill (Cutler and Cramb, 2001). A full-length cDNA

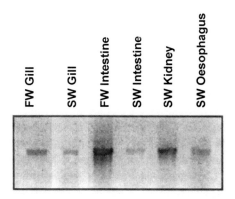

Figure 2.
An agaraose gel showing RT-PCR amplification of a fragment of the eel (Anguilla anguilla) sodium-dependant chloride-bicarnonate exchanger (NCBE) orthologue in the tissues of seawater-acclimated yelloe eel, except where marked FW (freswhwater eel).

has also been isolated from Osorezan dace (*Tribolodon hakonensis*; Hirata *et al.*, 2003). Dace NBC1 mRNA is expressed predominantly in the gill, and functional expression of the protein revealed that this isoform is also electrogenic, similar to mammalian NBC1. A full-length cDNA of NBC1 from rainbow trout was also obtained along with a partial cDNA from American eel (*Anguilla rostrata*; Perry *et al.*, 2003a). Trout NBC1 exhibits mRNA expression in gill, kidney, stomach and intestine with low levels in liver. Unlike in the European eel, in American eel, NBC1 mRNA expression is not detectable in the gill. Recently, a NBC1 orthologue was also isolated from a euryhaline pufferfish species (*Takifugu obscurus*; Kurita *et al.*, 2008). Pufferfish NBC1 mRNA is expressed in gill, kidney, intestine, skin, liver and spleen and is also found to represent an electrogenic transporter. Another related member of the SLC4 mammalian gene family is the sodium-dependent chloride bicarbonate exchanger (NCBE; Sterling and Casey, 2002). A partial cDNA of an orthologue of NCBE was recently cloned from the European eel and this is expressed in gill, kidney, intestine and oesophagus (see Figure 2).

A second gene family also exists that is capable of bicarbonate and/or chloride transport, namely members of the SLC26 gene family (Sterling and Casey, 2002). Expression of one family member, called pendrin (SLC26A4), has been shown to be expressed in rainbow trout, using microarrays (Bobe *et al.*, 2006). Recently, duplicate copies of another SLC26 protein in mammals called, PAT1 (SLC26A6), have been cloned from a euryhaline pufferfish species (SLC26A6A and B; *Takifugu obscurus*; Kurita *et al.*, 2008). Both pufferfish isoforms appear to be electrogenic chloride-bicarbonate exchangers. SLC26A6A exhibited mRNA expression in intestine and kidney, whereas SLC26A6B is additionally expressed in liver.

3.2.5 Proton and/or sodium exchangers, ATPases or channels

The first sodium and/or hydrogen transporters to be identified in teleostean fish were the sodium hydrogen exchangers (NHE; gene family SLC9) that as the name suggests, exchange Na^+ ions for hydrogen ions across the plasma membrane of cells. Up to 11 NHE (NHE1-11) family members have now been identified in various species (for reviews see Claiborne et al., 2002; Orlowski and Grinstein, 2004; Bret et al., 2005). Most widely studied in teleostean fish are homologues of NHE1-3. The first NHE to be identified was NHEβ from trout erythrocytes (Borgese et al., 1992). NHEβ is essentially similar to mammalian NHE1 isoforms (Noel and Pouyssegur, 1995). NHE1 orthologues have also been identified in long-horned sculpin (Myoxocephalus octodecimspinosus) where NHE1 mRNA expression is found in gill, intestine, kidney and bladder (Claiborne et al., 1999). A partial NHE1 cDNA was cloned from killifish and that was shown to have mRNA expression in the gill (Claiborne et al., 1999). NHE1 sequences have also been isolated from carp (Cyprinus carpio; genebank accession no. AJ006916), and European flounder (Platichthys flesus; genebank accession no. AJ006918). Two partial, apparently duplicate cDNA copies of NHE1 have also been identified in European eel (Cutler and Cramb, 2001). A further NHE1 orthologue was isolated from winter flounder erythrocytes (Pseudopleuronectes americanus; Pedersen et al., 2003). Sequences of teleost NHE2 isoforms have been isolated from long-horned sculpin, killifish and European eel (Claiborne et al., 1999; Cutler and Cramb, 2001; Claiborne et al., 2002). A teleost NHE3 isoform has also been isolated from Osorezan dace and this exhibited mRNA expression in gill, kidney and posterior intestine (Hirata et al., 2003). A NHE3 gene has also been identified in long-horned sculpin and in this species NHE3 shows mRNA expression in the gill (Lanier and Claiborne, 2004). A further study has investigated the expression of various NHEs (1-8) in zebrafish, as these sequences were found in its genome, and consequently expressed sequences have been detected by reverse transcriptase polymerase chain reaction (RT-PCR). In zebrafish, NHE1 is expressed primarily in erythrocytes, NHE2 and 3b are expressed in the gill, NHE3a and 3b are expressed in kidney, low levels of NHE5 and 6 are expressed in brain and gill, NHE2 and 7 are expressed in testis, and finally, NHE8 is ubiquitously expressed (Yan et al., 2007).

Another proton transporter thought to be involved in osmoregulatory processes is the vacuolar ATPase (V-ATPase, V-type ATPase or H^+-ATPase) that transports protons across membranes against its concentration gradient using energy from ATP. V-ATPase is a multi-subunit complex (related to ATP synthase/F-ATPase of mitochondria and chloroplasts) localized to both intracellular membranes and the plasma membrane (for reviews see Beyenbach and Wieczorek, 2006). In teleostean fish, the first V-ATPase subunit identified was that of the B subunit from rainbow trout, and this subunit shows ubiquitous mRNA expression in different tissues including gill, kidney and intestine (Perry et al., 2000). Two duplicate B subunit isoforms have been cloned from the eel swimbladder (Niederstatter and Pelster, 2000; Cutler and Cramb, 2001). A partial cDNA sequence was identified in Atlantic salmon that exhibits mRNA expression in the gill (Seidelin *et al.*, 2001). Likewise a V-ATPase B subunit sequence was cloned from Osorezan dace, and its mRNA is also expressed in the gill (Hirata *et al.*, 2001). Finally, a V-ATPase A subunit has been identified in killifish, where expression was shown in the gill using a homologous antibody raised against part of the deduced amino acid sequence of the protein (Katoh *et al.*, 2003).

Sodium channel activity has been reported in the gills of some freshwater teleostean fish and has been attributed to an amiloride- or phenamil-sensitive eNaC-like channel (Reid *et al.*, 2003; Parks *et al.*, 2007; for a current review of the eNaC family of channels see Drummond *et al.*, 2008). However, studies of the fugu or zebrafish genomes reveal no signs of orthologues of any of the subunits of eNaC (personal observation and see Hwang *et al.*, 2007). The closest family members (to eNaC) that are present in the fugu or zebrafish genomes are the acid-sensing ion channels (ASIC). However studies investigating their tissue distribution have so far failed to realize any expression of these channels in the gill (Paukert *et al.*, 2004).

3.2.6 Aquaporin water and small solute channels

The main category of water transporters that have been characterized to date are members of the MIP/aquaporin (AQP) water channel gene family. Members of the MIP/AQP family were originally identified and characterized in mammals (Gorin *et al.*, 1984; Preston and Agre, 1991; see reviews Nejsum, 2005; Agre, 2006; Krane and Goldstein, 2007; Rojek *et al.*, 2008). In mammals, the AQPs are a large gene family of 13 members, which have been grouped into 3 broad sub-families. These include the 'water-selective' AQPs which comprise AQPs 0-2 and AQPs 4-6 (although AQP0 is also permeable to glycerol; Ishibashi *et al.*, 2000), the aquaglyceroporin group which contains AQPs 3, 7, 9 and 10 that are permeable to water and/or glycerol and/or urea (Echevarria *et al.*, 1996; Yang and Verkman, 1997; Ishibashi *et al.*, 1997; Ishibashi *et al.*, 1998), and finally AQP8, and the superaquaporins, AQPs 11 and 12 which are an anomalous group of channels with lower amino acid homology. AQP8 is permeable to water and/or urea and possibly ammonia (Yang *et al.*, 2006; Saparov *et al.*, 2007), AQP11 is permeable to water but not glycerol, and the transport properties of AQP12 are unknown (Ishibashi *et al.*, 2000; Morishita *et al.*, 2004; Tenckhoff *et al.*, 2005).

In teleostean fish, the expression of orthologues of AQP3 and duplicate copies of AQP1 (AQP1 and AQP1dup) were initially reported in the European eel (Cutler and Cramb, 2000). Subsequently, an orthologue of AQP0 was identified in killifish lens (Virkki *et al.*, 2001), and further homologues of AQP3 or 1 were identified in Japanese dace and eel (Hirata *et al.*, 2003; Aoki *et al.*, 2005), tilapia (Watanabe *et al.*, 2005), sea bream (Sparus auratus; Fabra *et al.*, 2005; Raldua *et al.*, 2008) and sea bass (Giffard-Mena *et al.*, 2007). Recently partial amino acid sequences of Atlantic salmon and two duplicate isoforms of rainbow trout AQP3 were published (Cutler *et al.*, 2007). Sequence data indicates there may be as many as three subtly different AQP3 isoforms expressed in teleostean fish (Cutler *et al.*, 2007). A novel aquaglyceroporin (sbAQP) was recently identified in sea bream (Santos *et al.*, 2004) and its orthologue has also been identified in the European eel (AQPe; Martinez *et al.*, 2005a; Martinez 2005b), although genomic databases suggest these AQPs represent homologues of mammalian AQP10.

European eel AQP3 mRNA is expressed in gill, intestine, oesophagus and eye, with low levels in kidney (Cutler *et al.*, 2002b; Cutler *et al.*, 2007). Osorezan dace AQP3 only shows mRNA expression in the gill (Hirata *et al.*, 2003), whereas, tilapia AQP3 is expressed in a wider range of tissues, namely the brain, pituitary, kidney, spleen, intestine, skin, eye and gill (Watanabe *et al.*, 2005). Sea bass AQP3 shows mRNA expression in the gill, anterior gut and kidney (Giffard-Mena *et al.*, 2007). Japanese eel AQP1 minor sequence variants (S- and L-AQP1), are both expressed in heart, intestine, spleen and swim bladder (Aoki *et al.*, 2005). European eel AQP1 shows mRNA expression in brain, eye, heart, and intestine at high levels, with intermediate levels in pancreas, oesophagus and stomach and with low levels in gill, kidney, and skeletal muscle (Martinez *et al.*, 2005b). Eel AQP1dup has a much more restricted tissue distribution of expression, with mRNA only found in kidney and oesophagus, although expression is also seen sporadically in intestine in certain animals (Martinez *et al.*, 2005b; Martinez *et al.*, 2005c). AQP1dup expression is also detectable in the gill using RT-PCR (data not shown). In sea bream, saAQP1 mRNA is ubiquitously expressed as assessed by RT-PCR (Fabra *et al.*, 2005). The sea bream AQP1 duplicate isoform, saAQP1o, is expressed mainly in ovary, but also in posterior intestine, gills and kidney (Fabra *et al.*, 2005). Sea bass AQP1 is expressed in brain, gill, kidney and posterior gut (Giffard-Mena *et al.*, 2007). The sea bream aquaglyceroporin, sbAQP, shows high levels of mRNA expression in intestine, and low levels in gill and kidney (Santos *et al.*, 2004). European eel AQPe is also expressed in intestine but has higher levels of expression in kidney than sbAQP, but no detectable expression in gill (Martinez *et al.*, 2005a; Martinez *et al.*, 2005b). Expression of a trout AQP4 sequence has been demonstrated in ovarian tissue, in rainbow trout, using microarrays (Bobe *et al.*, 2004). Similarly a European eel AQP4 clone was isolated and expression of this gene is indicated in intestine, gill, kidney and brain on microarrays (Kalujnaia *et al.*, 2007). Additionally RT-PCR shows that eel AQP4 is also expressed in oesophagus (data not shown). The European eel has a second copy of AQP4 (AQP4b) that is expressed in oesophagus and kidney (data not shown). There have also been further aquaporins found in the European eel and their expression was assessed by RT-PCR. Two copies of AQP8 (8 and 8b) are expressed in European eel intestine. Duplicate copies of AQP9 were also found in European eel. Eel AQP9 is expressed in gill, intestine, kidney and oesophagus, and eel AQP9b, in intestine, kidney and oesophagus. Lastly, European eel AQP7 is expressed in kidney, gill, intestine and oesophagus (data not shown).

3.3. Gills

3.3.1 Seawater teleostean fish

In sea water (SW) adapted teleosteans, the excess Na^+ and Cl^- ions imbibed during the SW drinking response (with subsequent absorbance of the salts across the surface of the intestine into body fluids), are predominantly excreted from the gills. The generally accepted mechanism for the extrusion of sodium chloride across the gills has been established for some time. Salt excretion is mediated by large mitochondrial-rich (MR) cells, often also known as chloride cells (See Figure 3).

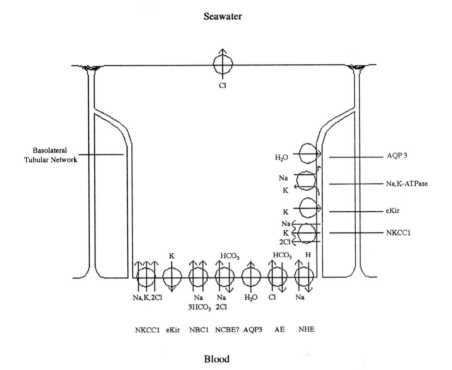

Figure 3. *Cartoon model of a marine teleost gill 'chloride cell' showing the main solute transporters and their common abbreviations.*

These cells usually occur (in SW-adapted fish), alone or in complexes, in the primary epithelium of the gill filament located between the secondary lamellae (often at the trailing edge of the flament). The excretion mechanism is essentially similar to that often employed in mammalian cells where stimulation of secretion results in the opening of potassium channels that hyperpolarize the membrane potential creating a driving force for chloride exit through apically located chloride channels. Reduction of the intracellular chloride concentration leads to a stimulation of a basolaterally located $Na^+,K^+,2Cl^-$ cotransporter (NKCC1) bringing into the cell further chloride and K^+ ions (as well as Na^+ ions). The sodium ions are expelled across basolateral surfaces of the cells by the enzyme, Na^+,K^+-ATPase. Sodium ions in the lateral spaces diffuse passively through the paracellular space, across tight junctions and into the external environment, following the secreted chloride ions and down the electrochemical gradient (see Hirose *et al.*, 2003, Evans *et al.*, 2005, Marshall and Grosell, 2006, and Hwang and Lee, 2007, for reviews of the mechanism).

One of the issues that has often been overlooked in recent years is the role of the structure (internal to the chloride cell) known as the basolateral tubular network (BTN). This is a network of tubules that is present in chloride cells, that is thought to be an internalized extension of the basolateral plasma membrane. The BTN usually occupies the majority of chloride cells, with only a relatively small intracellular space underneath the apical membrane being free of BTN (see Hirose *et al.*, 2003). There are several possible roles that the BTN may play, for which there are varying degrees of evidence. 1) The BTN may exist merely to extend the surface area of the basolateral membrane to allow additional space for transport proteins. Chloride cells have been shown in many studies to posses large quantities of ion transporting enzymes such as Na^+,K^+-ATPase (in comparison to surrounding pavement surface epithelial cells for example) and additional space may be required for that purpose. 2) As the BTN is interspersed with numerous mitochondria in chloride cells, it may be that the BTN exists to allow closer proximity of these ATP generating centers, with the large quantities of Na^+,K^+-ATPase enzymes that require ATP. Other possibilities exist that have been expounded to some extent previously (see Isaia, 1984) that do not exclude, and are additional to, the first two roles above. Before moving on to those possibilities the concept of standing gradients needs to be outlined. Firstly, as suggested by Diamond and Bossert (1967), the long narrow paracellular spaces or basolateral infoldings of epithelial cells are usually associated with standing gradients of solutes (creation of a local areas with significantly higher levels of solutes i.e., hyperosmotic fluids). The standing gradients are used to produce iso-osmotic or hyperosmotic fluid transport. 3) For example if this was the case in chloride cells, then the enzyme Na^+,K^+-ATPase would create a local area with high or hyperosmotic levels of Na^+ ion-rich fluid in its lumen. The presence of hyperosmotic fluid in the BTN would tend to draw in water by osmosis. This would tend to distend the BTN but would create hydrostatic pressure that would force the fluid along towards the end of the tubules. As the BTN may open into the paracellular space (for example see the schematic diagram of a chloride cell in Zadunaisky, 1997) as well as the basal side of the cell, if this is indeed the case, this mechanism would continuously pump hyperosmotic or iso-osmotic sodium rich fluid into the paracellular spaces. Why would this be important for transport? Well, Na^+ ions are thought to diffuse passively from the paracellular space out across tight junctions into the external SW. However the level of plasma Na^+ in a marine teleost is around 150-200 meq l^{-1}, whereas Na^+ in SW is around 450–500 meq l^{-1}. The reason for the outward diffusion of Na^+ ions is thought to be a blood positive transepithelial potential difference generated by chloride transport/excretion (Marshall and Grosell, 2006). However, the potential difference required to result in a net outward movement of sodium is thought to be around +29 mV (inside/blood positive), but most measurements on various teleostean species have determined figures of a less positive value. This discrepancy has been put down to experimental errors associated with the complexity of gill morphology (Marshall and Grosell, 2006), which may well be true, but if the BTN produces a standing gradient of Na$^+$ion-rich fluid that flows continuously into the paracellular space on the lateral sides of chloride cells, it would have two potential effects. 1) It would raise the local Na$^+$ ion concentration, reducing the potential difference necessary to produce a net Na$^+$ ion efflux. 2) Unless an anion, such as bicarbonate was also transported into, or was allowed to diffuse into the BTN lumen, an elevated potential difference within the lumen of the BTN and the paracellular space would be generated (due to the electrogenic nature of the Na$^+$,K$^+$-ATPase). This locally increased positive potential difference (compared to the SW) would also help to drive Na$^+$ ion efflux. Fluid flow from the BTN, due to net osmosis into the BTN following the Na$^+$ transport, may also be a necessary component of this putative BTN transport mechanism. However, Na$^+$,K$^+$-ATPase in the BTN would presumably only be able to continue to function if K$^+$ ions were allowed to leak into the BTN from the cytoplasm through K$^+$ ion channels. Without this the level of K$^+$ ions would probably be reduced to the point where this would limit the rate of both Na$^+$,K$^+$-ATPase and NKCC transport (also shown to be present in the BTN: see Cutler and Cramb, 2002a; Marshall et al., 2002). A build up of positive charge inside the BTN would increase the potential difference across the BTN membrane and if the membrane potential reached the equilibrium potential for potassium, this would prevent K$^+$ ions from leaving the chloride cell down their electrochemical gradient into the BTN lumen, also reducing the availability of K$^+$ ions for Na$^+$,K$^+$-ATPase and NKCC. Fluid flow out of the BTN would consequently reduce this problem. One issue for any speculation concerning BTN fluid flow, is that the BTN is open at the basal side of chloride cells. This might allow diffusion of K$^+$ and Cl$^-$ ions from serosal extracellular fluid into the BTN lumen, although ion diffusion would be opposed by any bulk fluid flow from the BTN to the serosal side. Clearly the function of the BTN is likely to be complex but is probably also going to be essential for a proper understanding of how chloride cells function.

The possibility of fluid flow from the BTN basally and possibly laterally suggests a potential role for AQP3 that is expressed in the branchial chloride cell BTN (Lignot et al., 2002a). Although AQP3 mRNA levels and protein are decreased in SW fish (compared to FW fish), much of the decrease appeared to occur in non-chloride cells (Cutler et al., 2002b; Lignot et al., 2002a), although this has been disputed in other studies concerning Japanese eel (Tse et al., 2006). The presence of AQP3 in chloride cell BTN membranes potentially serves two related purposes. Firstly, it would allow water from the cytoplasm into the BTN lumen by osmosis, diluting the contents, expanding the BTN volume and potentially producing/increasing fluid flow through the BTN. Secondly removal of water from the cytoplasm would cause cytoplasmic shrinkage. Chloride cell shrinkage has been shown to stimulate both NKCC activity and ion excretion (short circuit current; Zadunaisky, 1996; Zadunaisky, 1997; Hoffmann et al., 2002; Hoffmann et al., 2007). Consequently any water flowing into the BTN through AQP3 is likely to have the secondary effect of stimulating Cl$^-$ ion efflux and consequently, NaCl excretion.

The central mechanism of Cl$^-$ ion excretion from marine teleost gill chloride cells is now established, and as mentioned above involves the actions of Na$^+$,K$^+$-

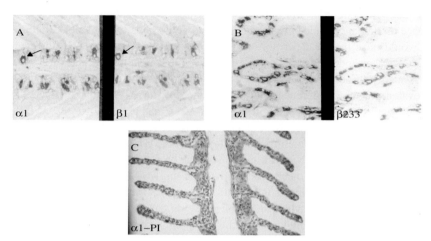

Figure 4. *Sections through the gill of a seawater acclimated eel (Anguilla anguilla) stained with sheep anti-eel isoform-specific Na,K-ATPase primary polyclonal antisera and a horseradish peroxidase secondary antibody (brown precipitate; x250).*

(**a**) *Serial longitudinal sections stained with either an α1-specific or β1-specific antisera.* (**b**) *Serial cross-sections through the primary filament epithelium, stained with either an α1-specific or β233-specific antisera.* (**c**) *A longitudinal control section incubated with pre-immune serum from the sheep prior to immunization with the Na,K-ATPase α1 antigen.*

ATPase (see Figure 4), NKCC1, and CFTR chloride and possibly e-Kir potassium ion channels.

One method to indicate the likely role of transporters isoforms is to utilize euryhaline fish species and determine whether isoforms are up- or down- regulated during or after transfers of fish from FW-SW or SW-FW. One of the best studied euryhaline models where these transporters have been studied is the eel. In European eel, following SW transfer of FW eels, Na^+,K^+-ATPase α1, β1 and β233 mRNA levels are upregulated 21 days after transfer depending on the developmental status of the fish (Figure 5; Cutler *et al.*, 1995a; Cutler *et al.*, 1995b; Cutler *et al.*, 2000; Tse *et al.*, 2006). Additionally, NKCC1a is upregulated during SW acclimation (Cutler and Cramb, 2002). The situation for eel CFTR is less clear. In European eel CFTR expression has been shown to remain unchanged during salinity acclimation (Cutler and Cramb, 2001), whereas in other studies using heterologous PCR primers to amplify Japanese eel CFTR, an increase in mRNA was seen over the first 7 days of SW acclimation (Tse *et al.*, 2006). eKir was shown in Japanese eel gill to be upregulated following SW-transfer (Suzuki *et al.*, 1999; Tse *et al.*, 2006). Similar studies have also been performed in other species. Following salinity transfer, studies have shown increases in Na^+,K^+-ATPase mRNA (Seidelin *et al.*, 2001; Singer *et al.*, 2002; Deane and Woo, 2004; Scott *et al.*, 2004), protein (Lee *et al.*, 2000; Tipsmark *et al.*, 2002; Lin *et al.*, 2003) or both (D'Cotta *et al.*, 2000; Lin *et al.*, 2004; Lin *et al.*, 2006; Tang and Lee, 2007). In salmonids, there is also a switch over in expression of Na^+,K^+-ATPase α1a and α1b isoforms following SW-acclimation (Richards *et al.*, 2003; Bystriansky *et al.*, 2006). Similarly, gill NKCC

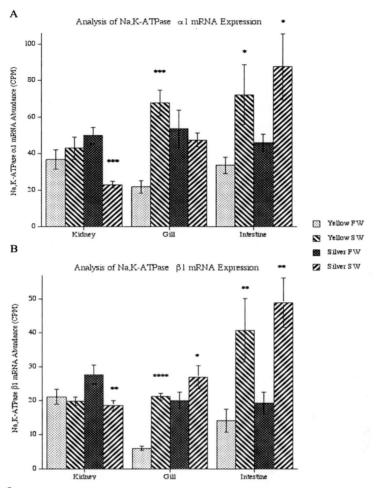

Figure 5.
*Quantification of Na,K-ATPase α1 (a) and β1 (b) mRNA abundance in total RNA samples (10μg) from the kidney, gills and intestine of yellow or silver eels (Anguilla anguilla) acclimated from FW to FW or to SW fro 21 days (n=6). Statistical analysis was peformed on log$_{10}$ transformed data using ANOVA with Fisher's post ad hoc testing. * P≤0.05, ** P≤0.01, ***P≤0.005 and ****P≤0.0001. Error bars are standard errors.*

mRNA abundance (Scott *et al.*, 2004; Tipsmark *et al.*, 2004) and protein (Tipsmark *et al.*, 2002; Wu *et al.*, 2003; Scott *et al.*, 2004; Tipsmark *et al.*, 2004; Hiroi and McCormick, 2007; Tang and Lee, 2007) have been shown to be upregulated following salinity transfer in several other teleostean fish. Although, NKCC protein detection was achieved using a heterologous antibody that would likely bind any NKCC or possibly NCC isoform. CFTR mRNA abundance (Singer *et al.*, 1998; and Scott *et al.*, 2004) and protein (Scott *et al.*, 2004; Tang and Lee, 2007) in the gills of other teleostean fish was also upregulated following salinity transfer.

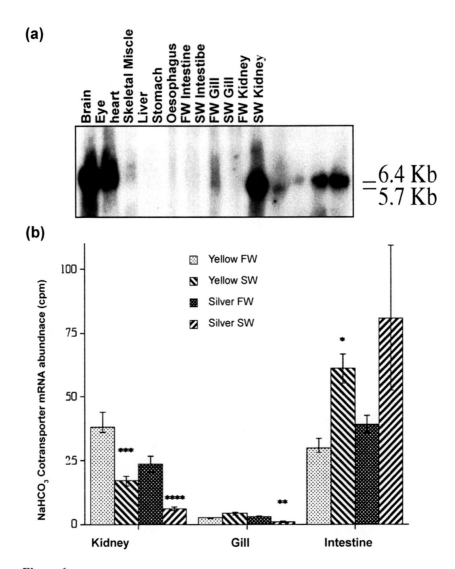

Figure 6.
(a) *Northern blot showing the tissue distribution of the eel (Anguilla anguilla) NBC1 sodium bicarbonate transporter mRNA expression in a seawater-acclimated (SW) yellow eel fish except where labeled FW (freshwater eel). 10μg of total RNA was used for each sample.* (b) *Quantification of eel NBCl mRNA abundance in total RNA samples (10μg) from the kidney, gills and intestine of six (per group) yellow or silver eels acclimated from FW to FW (FW) or FW to SW (SW) for 21 days. Statistical analysis was performed on log_{10} transformed data using ANOVA with Fisher's post ad hoc testing, where * P≤05, ** P≤01 *** P≤.001, and **** P≤0.0001. Error bars are standard errors.*

Another aspect of ion transport by marine teleostean MR or chloride cells is the role of bicarbonate transport in chloride efflux. It has previously been suggested that chloride cells of teleostean fish possess chloride-bicarbonate exchangers (AE; Zadunaisky et al., 1995; Zadunaisky, 1996; Zadunaisky, 1997; Marshall and Bryson, 1998) due to 4,4'-diisothiocyano-2,2'-disulfonic acid stilbene (DIDS) sensitivity of chloride cell short-circuit current. As suggested above, the European eel possesses several AEs expressed in the gill (Cutler and Cramb, 2001) and heterologous antibody studies have also indicated AE1 expression in tilapia, coho salmon (*Oncorhynchus kisutch*) and fugu gill (Wilson et al., 2000; Wilson et al., 2002a; Tang and Lee, 2007). However, the anion exchangers are not the only DIDS-sensitive bicarbonate transporters. Firstly, there are sodium-bicarbonate cotransporters (NBC1) expressed in teleost gill (see Figure 6; Cutler and Cramb, 2001; Hirata et al., 2003; Perry et al., 2003a; Kurita et al., 2008), these are thought to be DIDS-sensitive (Hirata et al., 2003; Perry et al., 2003a), and electrogenic (Hirata et al., 2003; Kurita et al., 2008) and have been shown to be expressed in Na^+,K^+-ATPase rich MR-like gill cells (Hirata et al., 2003). The presence of NBC1 on at least some chloride-like cells may explain the stimulation of ion secretion found previously (Zadunaisky et al., 1995; Zadunaisky, 1996; Zadunaisky, 1997), as the sodium-bicarbonate cotransporter would likely respond to additional serosal extracellular bicarbonate, transporting these ions into the chloride cells in an electrogenic fashion, thereby hyperpolarizing the membrane potential and increasing the driving force for apical chloride efflux. A basolateral chloride-bicarbonate exchanger (as suggested by Zadunaisky et al., 1997) if active, would likely take chloride out of the cell in exchange for the elevated extracellular bicarbonate, reducing mucosal chloride efflux. The sodium-bicarbonate cotransporter is though, not the only candidate bicarbonate transporter expressed in the gill. An orthologue of the sodium-dependent chloride-bicarbonate exchanger (NCBE) is also expressed in European eel gill (see Figure 2). Mammalian NCBE is also DIDS-sensitive and can be electrogenic (Sterling and Casey, 2002) and therefore this transporter might also be responsible for stimulation of short-circuit current due to additional extracellular bicarbonate, although the most likely candidate is NBC1.

Several lines of evidence also point to the presence of sodium-hydrogen exchangers in both the apical (not shown in Figure 3) and basolateral membranes of marine teleost branchial MR cells (Marshall and Bryson, 1998; Claiborne et al., 1999; Claiborne et al., 2002; Lanier and Claiborne, 2004; Tse et al., 2006). Some evidence suggests a basolateral exchanger may be involved in ion excretion (Zadunaisky et al., 1995; Zadunaisky, 1996; Zadunaisky, 1997), sodium-hydrogen exchangers are most likely present for the purposes of acid-base regulation and would operate at an osmoregulatory cost, as Na^+ ions would be brought into the cell and would need to be expelled by Na^+,K^+-ATPase (Claiborne et al., 2002).

As mentioned above, European eel AQP3 is expressed in branchial chloride cells but is also located in cells of the epithelium covering the branchial arch (Lignot et al., 2002a; Lignot et al., 2002b). European eel AQP3 gill mRNA and protein expression was significantly down-regulated with acclimation of fish from

FW to SW, although the reason for this decrease is still unclear. The decrease in AQP3 branchial mRNA expression does correlate with changes in gill water permeability and the change was mimicked by infusions of the 'SW-acclimating' hormone, cortisol, into FW eels (Cutler et al., 2007b). Sea bass AQP3 mRNA was also found in gill and this was significantly upregulated following acclimation of fish from SW to FW in a similar fashion to eel AQP3 (Giffard-Mena et al., 2007). Small amounts of sea bream aquaporin sbAQP mRNA are also found in the gill and expression was also localized to chloride cells (Santos et al., 2004). Small amounts of AQP1 (European eel and sea bass), and AQP1dup, 4, 7 and 9 (European eel) mRNAs are also expressed in the gill (data not shown; Giffard-Mena et al., 2007).

3.3.2 Freshwater teleostean fish

Freshwater teleostean fish have essentially the opposite osmoregulatory problems compared to marine fish. They need to conserve or gain Na^+ and Cl^- ions and prevent water loading due to osmosis across body surfaces. Apart from the diet, the gill is the main location that teleostean fish can acquire Na^+ and Cl^- ions. The mechanism used to obtain these ions is however still controversial, and almost certainly, differences between proposed mechanisms represent species differences between members of this taxonomic group. For branchial Cl^- ion absorption, several different mechanisms have been suggested and these may even involve different types of MR cells (Hwang and Lee, 2007). The most common gill Cl^- ion uptake mechanism proposed involves apically located chloride-bicarbonate exchangers, and several AE isoforms are expressed in teleost gill (see above; also see Tresguerres et al., 2006 for review). One feature of this transport is that due to the bicarbonate transport, AE activity is also associated with acid-base regulation. Another is that various isoforms of the enzyme, carbonic anhydrase (CA), that converts CO_2 and H_2O to H^+ and $HCO3^-$ ions via carbonic acid, have been shown in mammals, to be coupled to AEs or other anion exchanger isoforms (SLC4 and SLC26; Sterling and Casey, 2002; Alvarez et al., 2005). There are three different possibilities for the role of CA in chloride absorption that depend on the level of association of CA with gill AEs. Firstly, CA may just raise the 'global' intracellular bicarbonate concentration inside MR cells increasing the bicarbonate gradient with the external FW and therefore potentially stimulating chloride uptake. Secondly, (as recently suggested by Tresguerres et al., 2006), if CA is in close proximity to apical AEs it may continuously, significantly raise the local bicarbonate concentration stimulating chloride influx. Thirdly, if CA is directly coupled to the AEs, the CA may directly and continuously 'load' the bicarbonate binding site of AEs with bicarbonate. The significance of this later possibility is that the overall cell bicarbonate concentration may then become irrelevant to Cl^- ion uptake, which would then be solely dependent on the external chloride concentration. The extent to which this third possibility would occur, would be dependent on how well/completely CA was able to keep the AE bicarbonate binding site occupied. A mechanism to prevent a build up of the protons also generated by CA would also be needed.

Additional supplies of bicarbonate ions within MR cells, may also be supplied by either chloride-bicarbonate exchangers or sodium-bicarbonate cotransporters located in the basolateral membrane (Perry et al., 2003; Parks et al., 2007). The basolateral exit pathway for Cl^- ions from MR cells into interstitial body fluids is unknown, but might involve either Cl^- ion channels or anion exchangers (Claiborne et al., 2002; Hirose et al., 2003; Evans et al., 2005; Marshall and Grosell, 2006; Hwang and Lee, 2007; Parks et al., 2007).

Other mechanisms for chloride uptake into gill cells from the external FW environment may include apically located NKCC2 or NCC cotransporters. NKCC2 is expressed in the gill of some teleostean fish species (Wu et al., 2003; Hiroi et al., 2005), however the role of NKCC2 in chloride uptake is still unclear (Hwang and Lee, 2007). As mentioned above, NCCα and β (but not NKCC2α and β) are expressed at low levels in European eel gill (Cutler et al., 2008), although a role for NCC in chloride uptake in the eel is unlikely as eels are thought not to absorb Cl^- ions in FW (Getman, 1950). The presence of NCC has also been established in tilapia gill MR cells and zebrafish skin ionocytes, but its exact role in gill chloride uptake is still unclear (Hwang and Lee, 2007).

A similarly controversial situation exists regarding the absorption of Na^+ ions from FW through teleost gill cells. On the one hand, sodium absorption across the apical membrane of gill cells has been suggested to involve an electrogenic V-type ATPase activity that excretes protons across the membrane, supplied by the CA hydration of CO_2. This electrogenic proton excretion would hyperpolarize the membrane potential creating additional driving force for Na^+ ion entry through apical sodium channels (see Hirose et al., 2003; Evans et al., 2005; Marshall and Grosell, 2006; Hwang and Lee, 2007).

The current problem for this model of Na^+ ion uptake is that the apically located sodium channel is yet to be identified and fully characterized, and the presence of the often postulated eNaC teleostean fish orthologue appears impossible due to the apparent absence of any eNaC subunit genes in the teleostean fish genome (see above). The alternate model proposed for apical sodium uptake is a sodium-hydrogen exchanger, such as NHE2 or 3 (Claiborne et al., 2002). Again protons driving hydrogen ion excretion may be produced by the hydration of CO2 by CA. As with anion exchangers, CA has also been shown to be bound to NHEs (Li et al., 2002; Li et al., 2006). Again this may merely create a local elevated hydrogen ion concentration in the vicinity of NHEs, but if CA loaded protons into the hydrogen ion binding site of NHEs, then the overall intracellular proton concentration may then become irrelevant to Na^+ ion uptake, which would be solely dependent on the external sodium concentration. The extent to which this possibility would occur, would be dependent on how well/completely CA was able to keep the NHE proton binding site occupied. A mechanism to prevent a build up of the bicarbonate ions also generated by CA would again also be needed.

3.4 Intestine

The teleost intestine plays a role in osmoregulation mainly in seawater fish. In the marine environment, fish drink seawater to replace water lost by osmosis across permeable body surfaces to the external milieu. Consequently the gastrointestinal tract has to firstly desalinate imbibed fluid in the oesophagus, where salts are absorbed by both secondary active and passive processes (Parmalee and Renfro, 1983). As the water permeability of the oesophagus is extremely low, only small net effluxes of water occur due to osmosis. These processes together lead to an overall dilution of the esophageal fluid concentration to around one half to one third of the initial osmolality (Hirano and Mayer-Gostan, 1976; Kirsch, 1978; Kirsch and Meister, 1982; Parmalee and Renfro, 1983; Nagashima and Ando 1993). Very little further change in concentration occurs as the luminal fluid passes through the stomach (Hirano, 1974). When the ingested fluid reaches the anterior intestine, the process of desalination (to iso-osmotic levels) is complete in some teleost species (Hickman, 1968; Shehadah and Gordon, 1969; Kirsch and Meister, 1982; Parmalee and Renfro, 1983). Once reaching the intestine, most of the remainder of the salts and water are absorbed (Skadhauge, 1969; Hirano and Mayer-Gostan, 1976). Salts are actively absorbed in the intestine, and fluid uptake continues until the Na^+ and Cl^- ion concentrations are reduced to around 30–90 meq l^{-1} (Skadhauge, 1969; Parmalee and Renfro, 1983). As the net uptake of divalent ions is very low (10–15% of the Mg^{2+} and SO_4^{2-}), these ions become concentrated 2- to 4- fold (Pelis and Renfro, 2003; Marshall and Grosell, 2006). Additionally, other solutes such as bicarbonate are actively secreted into the intestinal lumen (Pelis and Renfro, 2003; Grosell et al., 2005). The concentration of Ca^{2+} and Mg^{2+} ions, elevation of the HCO_3^- concentration and the absorption of water, lead to the precipitation of carbonates that are found in the marine teleostean intestinal lumen (Walsh et al., 1991; Wilson et al., 1996; Wilson, 1997). The precipitation of carbonates reduces the overall osmotic concentration of dissolved solutes in the intestinal lumen, allowing greater water absorption (Wilson et al., 2002b). Although 60%–85% of the imbibed water is absorbed, the final osmolality of the fluid reaching the rectum remains iso-osmotic to that of body fluids (Ando et al., 2003; Marshall and Grosell, 2006).

3.4.1 Ion absorption

The mechanisms of salt and water uptake in the intestine of seawater fish probably involves a considerable number of different transporters and the extent to which each element of the overall transport mechanism is used, varies by species (for other reviews see Ando et al., 2003; Grosell, 2006; Marshall and Grosell, 2006). Again, as in the gill, euryhaline fish species have often been studied, as the contrasting increase in salt and water absorption between the FW- and SW-acclimated intestine, allows the transporters/isoforms involved to be identified. The transport mechanisms are best considered in two parts, sodium-coupled transport and bicarbonate-associated transport. Sodium-coupled chloride transport occurs through apically (mucosal) located CCC cotransporters, such as NKCC2 and/or NCC. Both of these cotransporters use the favourable Na^+ ion gradient to absorb Cl^- (and K^+ ions with NKCC2) from the intestinal lumen. Numerous studies have suggested their involvement in teleostean intestinal ion absorption (Frizzell et al., 1979; Field et al., 1980; Musch et al., 1982; Ando, 1985; Halm et al., 1985). The extent to which each CCC isoform (NKCC2 and/or NCC) is used is species-dependent. In winter flounder, NCC is expressed along the length of the intestine suggesting this transporter plays a prominent role in sodium chloride uptake (Gamba et al., 1993). By contrast in the European eel, NCCβ is only expressed at a significant level in the posterior intestine/rectum. NKCC2β instead shows high levels of mRNA expression in the anterior and middle intestine and decreased levels in the posterior intestine/rectum (Cutler and Cramb, 2008). The apparent transition from NKCC2 to NCC along the length of the SW eel intestine is in agreement with thermodynamic considerations, as the potassium concentration decreases as fluid travels along the intestine (due to absorption), making the activity of a NCC cotransporter more efficient (Loretz, 1995). Once inside the surface epithelial cells, Na^+ ions are thought to be expelled basolaterally through the considerable amounts of Na^+,K^+-ATPase located in these cells (see Figures 7 and 8, and Cutler et al., 2000). Both NKCC2β and Na^+,K^+-ATPase mRNA levels are upregulated during the SW-acclimation of FW eels (dependent on the developmental status of the eel), although NCC mRNA levels are unchanged (Cutler et al., 2000; Cutler and Cramb, 2008; see also Figure 5). The chloride efflux pathway from intestinal surface epithelial cells is unknown, but may involve a potassium chloride cotransporter (KCC) or Cl^- ion channels (Marshall and Grosell, 2006).

Most studies investigating sodium chloride absorption by the intestine of seawater fish have shown that significantly more chloride ions are absorbed from the lumen than sodium ions (Marshall and Grosell, 2006). This is of course partly a consequence of the fact that seawater contains more chloride than sodium ions (Karnaky, 1998). However absorption of the additional Cl^- ions allows more water to be absorbed from imbibed fluid and estimates suggest that 30%–70% of Cl^- ions (depending on the species) are absorbed from intestinal luminal fluid via apically located anion exchangers in surface epithelial cells (Grosell et al., 1999; Grosell and Jensen, 1999; Grosell et al., 2001; Grosell et al., 2004; Grosell, 2006; Marshall and Grosell, 2006). However, the transporters involved in intestinal anion transport are yet to be fully determined. The chloride ions are thought to be exchanged for bicarbonate ions across the apical surface of epithelial cells. One class of transporters that may be involved in this chloride-bicarbonate exchange is the anion exchangers (AEs), and as noted above, three AE isoforms are expressed in the European eel intestine (Cutler and Cramb 2001; see Grosell, 2006, for other evidence for apical AEs). Furthermore antibodies have been used to localize AE to the apical pole of mudskipper intestinal surface epithelial cells, although this study used heterologous antibodies (Wilson et al., 2002b). Another transporter that may be involved in chloride absorption is the sodium-dependent chloride-bicarbonate exchanger (NCBE) that is expressed in European eel intestine (see Figure 2).

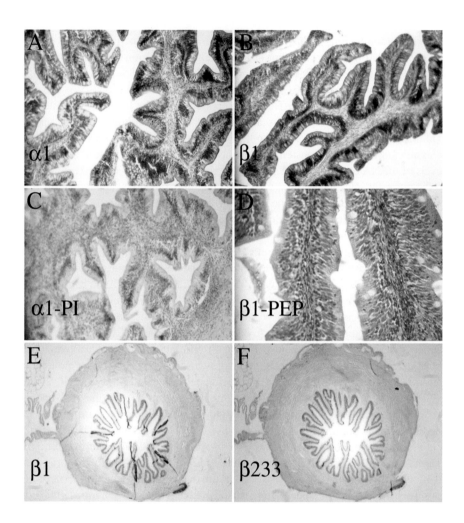

Figure 7.

Imunohistochemicallocalization of different Na.K-ATPase subunit isoforms using homologous sheep anti-eel Na,K-ATPase polyclonal antisera in cross-sections of seawater eel (Anguilla anguilla) anterior intestine (a–d). Sections were stained using horse raddish peroxidase-coupled secondary antibodies yielding a brown precipitate and were otherwise processed similar to Cutler et al., 2000.
(a,b) *Incubated with Na,K-ATPase αl and βl subunit-isoform-specific antisera respectively (x 100).*
(c) *Incubation of sections with pre-immune serum from eel Na,K-ATPase al immunized sheep, (x 100).*
(d) *Incubated with Na,K-ATPase βl antisera pre-treated with peptide antigen (x250). (e,f) Transverse-sections of freshwater eel intestine incubated with Na,K-ATPase βl and β233 antisera (x25).*

alpha 1   beta 1   beta 233

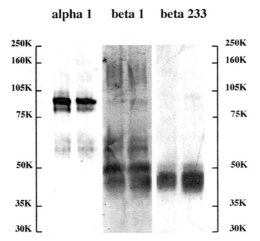

Figure 8. *Western blots performed using sheep anti-eel Na,K-ATPase isoform-specific polyclonal antisera.*

Anti-Na,K-ATPase α1 and β1 antisera were raised against NH₂-HKNANSEESKHLLV-COOH and NH₂-DAAKVREIKYYGIQE-COOH MAP peptides derived from eel (Anguilla anguilla) amino acid sequences respectively. Blotting was performed essentially as in Cutler et al., 2000, using membrane fractions produced from intestinal epithelial scrapes. Sizes shown are in kilodaltons (kDa).

Sodium-dependent bicarbonate transport has also been demonstrated in Japanese eel intestine (Ando and Subramanyam, 1990). Recently, the expression of two PAT-1 type electrogenic chloride-bicarbonate exchangers (SLC26A6A and B) were characterized in euryhaline pufferfish intestine (Kurita *et al.*, 2008). Both transporters were localized to the apical membrane of intestinal surface epithelial cells and expression of SLC26A6A was highly induced following transfer to SW.

The source of bicarbonate to be exchanged for chloride across the apical membrane of intestinal surface epithelial cells has also still to be fully determined. As in the gill, intracellular CA may be responsible for producing bicarbonate ions for exchange with chloride (Grosell, 2006). However the presence of electrogenic sodium bicarbonate cotransporters in eel intestine (NBC1; see Figure 6) and in the basolateral membranes of euryhaline pufferfish surface intestinal epithelial cells (Kurita *et al.*, 2008), suggests that some of the bicarbonate transported probably comes from extracellular (interstitial) sources. The presence of electrogenic sodium bicarbonate cotransporters in SW teleost intestine, suggests a possible link between bicarbonate transport and sodium coupled chloride transport through apical CCC transporters. NBC1 electrogenic activity would hyperpolarize the membrane potential which may increase the driving force for basolateral Cl⁻ ion exit, reducing the intracellular chloride concentration, providing additional driving force for NKCC2 or NCC ion absorption. However, the presence of other electrogenic bicarbonate transporters such as NCBE or the SLC26A6 anion exchangers would tend to depolarize the membrane potential and reduce the effect of any NBC1 hyperpolarization. Clearly the role of bicarbonate transporters in intestinal chloride absorption is complex and may very well differ along the length of the intestine as well as among different teleostean species.

3.4.2 Ion secretion

One interesting feature of seawater teleost intestine is the trade-off between the need to absorb ions and water for osmoregulatory purposes, against the need to secrete ions, as occurs in the intestines of other vertebrates (Takei and Yuge, 2007). The transporters and components of the transport regulatory system normally associated with intestinal ion secretion in mammals are, the NKCC1 secretory-cotransporter, CFTR chloride ion channels, and guanylin peptide hormones and receptors (Takei and Yuge, 2007). The NKCC1a isoform is expressed in the middle region of European eel intestine (Cutler and Cramb, 2002a). CFTR ion channels have been localized to surface epithelial cells of killifish intestine (Marshall *et al.*, 2002), although only a very low level of CFTR mRNA expression could be detected in the European eel intestine even using RT-PCR (data not shown). Additional confirmation of a secretory mechanism in teleost intestine is also derived from the expression of members of the guanylin family of peptide hormones and their receptors, in European and Japanese eel intestine, as guanylin stimulates intestinal fluid secretion in other organisms (Comrie *et al.*, 2001a; Comrie *et al.*, 2001b; Yuge *et al.*, 2003; Yuge *et al.*, 2006; Yuge and Takei, 2007; Takei and Yuge, 2007). The mechanisms that regulate whether the intestine is absorbing ions and water, or secreting them is not yet fully understood, but it seems clear that teleostean fish intestine has the capacity to do both, as in other vertebrate species.

3.4.3 Water absorption

In addition to ion absorption or secretion, the teleost intestine also absorbs (and/or may secrete) water. There are two possible mechanisms that may be used to absorb water from the lumen of seawater teleostean fish following the drinking of the external milieu. Those are either through the paracellular pathway between surface epithelial cells or through a transcellular pathway involving membrane-bound water transporters, such as aquaporins. Low-level passive diffusion of water through the plasma membranes of surface cells almost certainly also occurs. The exact water absorption mechanisms involved have yet to be fully determined, but there are various lines of circumstantial evidence that suggest all three pathways may operate.

When seawater teleost fish drink, the imbibed fluid is initially desalinated in the oesophagus, and then possibly further in the anterior intestine. Fluid eventually reaches a iso-osmotic concentration and both ions and water are further absorbed. Studies have shown that much of this water absorption is linked to solute uptake and for example in the eel, solute-linked water uptake increases 3- to 3.4-fold following acclimation of the fish from FW to SW (Utida *et al.*, 1972; Ando, 1975). Passive osmotic water permeability has also been shown to increase 2- to 6-fold (Skadhauge, 1969; Ando, 1975), although other studies suggest variation in passive osmotic water permeability is not related to the acclimation status of the fish or associated water up-take in seawater (Skadhauge, 1974). One interesting finding is that water could be absorbed by European eel intestine against an osmotic gradient of up to 200 mOsm (Skadhauge, 1974). This was suggested to be due to the presence of standing gradients in the paracellular spaces between cells (see Diamond and Bosert, 1967; see also above). Essentially Na^+,K^+-ATPase on the lateral side membranes of columnar epithelial cells would produce a locally elevated Na^+ ion concentration, which would be continuously diluted by influx of water (from the intestinal lumen) into the paracellular space by osmosis. Fluid would then be exuded to the basal side of the surface epithelial cell layer. However, the concentration of sodium in the lateral space would be continuously maintained at an elevated level (i.e., the standing gradient) by Na^+,K^+-ATPase, generating the hyperosmotic fluid in the lateral paracellular space. There are several features that are necessary or implied by this mechanism:

(i)   The Na^+ ion permeability of the tight junctions of the surface cell layer should be very low.

(ii)   The maximum luminal osmotic concentration against which water could be absorbed should be approximately equivalent to the osmotic concentration generated in the paracellular space.

(iii)   The standing gradient generated in the paracellular space would correlate with Na^+,K^+-ATPase activity of surface epithelial cells and this itself should be correlated with Na^+,K^+-ATPase enzyme abundance.

(iv)   As pointed out by Skadhauge (1974), the osmotic water flow could come directly from the lumen via the tight junctions, if these had significant water permeability, but equally osmotic water flow could occur through a transcellular route, i.e., through aquaporins on the apical and lateral surfaces of cells. One requirement for a transcellular pathway would be that the intracellular osmotic concentration would need to be intermediate between that of the intestinal lumen and that of the paracellular space. It's much easier to believe this could occur, if the fluid in the intestinal lumen was iso-osmotic (rather than significantly hyper-osmotic) compared to the interstitial fluid and/or plasma.

(v)   The K^+ ion concentration in the paracellular space would need to be maintained at a level sufficient to allow continued Na^+,K^+-ATPase activity. This would probably occur due to laterally located potassium channels, although a K^+ ion permeability of tight junctions might also make a contribution.

(vi)   Anions (presumably Cl^- ions) may be transported into the paracellular space, as otherwise a significant positive charge would develop.

One of the reasons why a standing gradient mechanism would work well in the particular instance of the seawater teleost intestine, is that a continuous supply of intracellular Na^+ ions are needed to supply Na^+,K^+-ATPase to create and maintain the standing gradient. As noted above, the intestine of seawater teleostean fish also continuously absorbs Na^+ ions from the lumen, providing a ready supply for Na^+,K^+-ATPase, although Na^+ ions may also be recycled back into the cell basally through other transporters. Some of the features of the paracellular standing gradient listed above have also been demonstrated. The level of the osmotic gradient against which the intestine could transport water, was shown to be proportional to the salinity to which the fish were acclimated (Skadhauge, 1974). The expression of Na^+,K^+-ATPase is also elevated when fish are acclimated to higher salinities (i.e., SW; see Figure 5).

The presence and role of aquaporins in teleost intestinal water absorption has been investigated in recent years. European eel AQP3 was shown to be unlikely to be involved in intestinal water absorption, as it was expressed in macrophage-like cells in intestine and mucus/goblet cells in the rectum (Lignot et al., 2002a). On the other hand, AQP1 likely plays a major role in water uptake particularly in the more posterior regions of the intestine or rectum. Eel AQP1 was localized to the apical surface of tall columnar epithelial cells in these regions, and its mRNA and protein abundance were also upregulated following acclimation from FW to SW, or following the infusion of the 'SW acclimating' hormone, cortisol, into FW eels (Aoki et al., 2003; Martinez et al., 2005a). Essentially similar results were also obtained from sea bass, where acclimation from SW to FW, reduced AQP1 mRNA expression in all intestinal segments (Giffard-Mena et al., 2007). There is also sporadic expression of European eel AQP1dup in the intestine. Most European eels show only barely detectable levels of intestinal AQP1dup mRNA expression, although the occasional eel (around 5% of those tested) showed high levels of intestinal expression (data not shown). In sea bream, AQP1 (saAQP1/saAQP1a) protein expression was also down-regulated in all intestinal segments following SW to FW acclimation (Raldua et al., 2008). However, illustrating species differences, saAQP1a had lower levels of mRNA expression in the rectum compared to other intestinal segments. Furthermore, sea bream expresses an orthologue of AQP1dup (saAQP1o/saAQP1b) that showed significantly higher levels of mRNA in the rectum than other intestinal regions in SW fish. Following acclimation from SW to FW levels of saAQP1b protein were significantly reduced (Raldua et al., 2008). Sea bream saAQP1a was localized apically and laterally in surface intestinal epithelial cells with only faint apical expression of saAQP1b. Whereas in the rectum, saAQP1a had an intracellular location, but saAQP1b was located apically (Raldua et al., 2008). Another aquaporin, AQPe in European eel (sbAQP in sea bream), is expressed in the fish intestine (Santos et al., 2004; Martinez et al., 2005). In eel, AQPe mRNA was expressed in all intestinal segments at similar levels but its level was not upregulated by acclimation of the FW fish to SW (Martinez et al., 2005). Sea bream sbAQP mRNA was also expressed in all intestinal regions but had highest levels in hind gut (Santos et al., 2004). Expression of sbAQP was localized to the lamina propria, at the interface between the two muscle layers of the intestinal muscle wall (Santos et al., 2004). In a study using microarrays, AQP4 was shown to be possibly upregulated in SW acclimated eel intestine, particularly in long-term acclimated fish (Kalujnaia et al., 2007). Eel AQP8 and 8b are both expressed equally in all segments of the intestine, mRNA expression of both genes is upregulated following SW-acclimation, but in pilot studies, neither increase was mimicked by cortisol infusion of FW fish (data not shown). Aquaporins 7, 9 and 9b are also expressed in European eel intestine at relatively low levels, the localization of these proteins has not been performed and so the likelihood that they play a role in intestinal water uptake cannot be assessed and their role is consequently unknown. Taken together the recent research on aquaporins suggests that they may well be involved in intestinal water absorption, particularly in the rectal or posterior region, but the number of transporters expressed in intestine suggests their role may be complex.

3.4.4 Posterior intestine/rectum

A number of lines of evidence have recently been produced that have begun to suggest that the transport mechanism operating in the rectal or posterior regions of teleostean fish intestine may be significantly different from anterior regions, particularly in eels. Expression of the NCC cotransporter, the eKir potassium channel and surface epithelial expression of AQP1 are all localized either exclusively or predominantly to the rectal/posterior region (Suzuki et al., 1999; Aoki et al., 2003; Martinez et al., 2005a; Cutler and Cramb, 2008).

3.5 Oesophagus

When marine fish drink the imbibed fluid is de-salinated in the oesophagus. Salts are absorbed without concomitant net uptake of water. (Hirano and Mayer-Gostan, 1976; Parmalee and Renfro, 1983) The overall water permeability of the oesophagus is thought to be low, but this may mask larger influxes and effluxes that cancel each other (Parmalee and Renfro, 1983). Not many studies have investigated the transporters involved in ion uptake, although this process is thought to involve passive ion exchangers such as NHEs rather than cotransporters (Parmalee and Renfro, 1983). Several aquaporin water channels have been shown to be expressed in the European eel oesophagus, including AQP1, 1dup and 3, although given the overall low level of water permeability their role is currently unclear (Martinez et al., 2005c; Cutler et al., 2007a). RT-PCR experiments suggest that European eel AQP4, 4b, 7, 9, 9b are all also expressed in the oesophagus at relatively low levels (data not shown).

3.6 Kidney

In FW fish, teleosts take up a net amount of water across permeable body surfaces and eradicate this by producing copious quantities of dilute urine (around 3 ml kg^{-1} hr^{-1}; Marshall and Grosell, 2006). Seawater fish have dramatically lower levels of urine production (around 0.3 ml kg^{-1} h^{-1}; Marshall and Grosell,

2006), the main ionregulatory function of which concerns the excretion of excess divalent ions. In Marine fish, the kidney cannot produce urine of a concentration significantly above that of extracellular fluids (Marshall and Grosell, 2006). In the marine environment, the main problem for fish is dehydration due to water loss, fish eradicate NaCl (coming from the drinking response and gastrointestinal uptake) through the gills instead of through a renal route (Marshall and Grosell, 2006). Teleostean fish kidneys may be glomerular or aglomerular (lacking a glomerulus/ glomerular filtration of blood plasma), depending on species. In glomerular teleost fish species, one of the main ways fish reduce water loss from urine production, is to have a low glomerular filtration rate (0.3 ml kg^{-1} hr^{-1} compared to 4 ml kg^{-1} hr^{-1} in FW fish; Marshall and Grosell, 2006). The early proximal segments of renal tubules of both glomerular and aglomerular fish have the capacity to secrete fluid containing Na$^+$, Cl$^-$, Mg^{2+} and SO$_4^{2-}$ ions (Beyenbach and Baustien, 1989; Beyenbach and Liu, 1996; Beyenbach, 2004). This occurs principally to enhance Mg^{2+} and SO$_4^{2-}$ ion excretion (Marshall and Grosell, 2006). NaCl is probably secreted to enhance water reabsorption in more distal segments of the nephron (late proximal or possibly distal segments in seawater acclimated euryhaline teleosts) and in the urinary bladder, but it also allows iso-osmotic fluid secretion to occur in the early proximal tubule. In general in marine teleosts, Na$^+$ ions are reabsorbed in the late proximal tubule due to cotransport with other solutes or through NHE. Chloride ion reabsorption occurs in the late proximal tubule via AE ion exchangers (Marshall and Grosell, 2006).

In FW teleosts the main osmoregulatory problem is the continuous uptake of water across permeable body surfaces by osmosis. Renal output in FW teleosts consequently produces large quantities of dilute urine in order to eliminate excess water while conserving salts. Kidney glomerular filtration rates are higher in FW than in SW teleosts. Proximal tubule fluid secretion is still thought to occur in FW teleosts and probably contributes to water excretion (Beyenbach, 2004). Most of the filtered and secreted NaCl is reabsorbed, in conjunction with other solutes in the late proximal tubule or otherwise in the distal tubule or urinary bladder (Marshall and Grosell, 2006). Consequently the NaCl concentration in the urine is low (5-10 mM) to prevent loss of salt by this route (Hickman and Trump, 1969). NaCl reabsorption in the distal tubule of FW fish is thought to occur via an NKCC2 cotransporter located in the apical membrane of tubule cells (Nishimura *et al.*, 1982; Braun and Danzler, 1997; Danzler, 2003).

Various data suggest that the eel kidney operates somewhat differently to the general situation outlined above for teleosts. Although urine flow rate is lower (one third) in SW eels compared to FW eels, glomerular filtration rates have been shown to be similar (Schmidt-Nielsen and Renfro, 1975). Also unlike in the killifish, eel renal fluid secretion was lower in SW- than in FW- acclimated animals (Schmidt-Nielsen and Renfro, 1975; Bayenbach, 2004). The postulated components of the proximal fluid (NaCl) secretion mechanism, namely the secretory NKCC1a cotransporter and CFTR are expressed in European eel kidney (Cutler and Cramb, 2002a; data not shown). Renal NKCC1a mRNA expression was also decreased in SW-acclimated fish compared to FW eels (depending on developmental status of the fish; Cutler and Cramb, 2002a), in keeping with the lower levels of fluid secretion in SW-acclimated eels (than FW eels; Schmidt-Nielsen and Renfro, 1975). NKCC2α and NCCα were both expressed in European eel kidney, suggesting a potential ability to absorb NaCl in the distal segments of the nephron (Cutler and Cramb, 2008). Only NCC mRNA expression decreased following SW acclimation of eels (depending on developmental status of the fish, i.e., in silver but not yellow adult eels; Cutler and Cramb, 2008), suggesting that the eel can absorb NaCl via at least NKCC cotransporters even in seawater unlike the currently suggested mechanism for sodium chloride reabsorption in marine teleost kidney (Marshall and Grosell, 2006). Furosemide, a NKCC inhibitor has been shown to inhibit Na^+ ion reabsorption in the kidney of both FW and SW eels, although NaCl urinary excretion was only increased in SW eels, probably due to a subsequent increase in reabsorption in the urinary bladder of FW eels (Schmidt-Nielsen and Renfro, 1975).

Mammalian kidney expresses AQP1 in the proximal segments of the nephron (Nejsum, 2005). Eel kidney also expresses AQP1, AQP1dup and AQPe, all of which are down regulated following SW acclimation (depending on developmental status of the fish; Martinez *et al.*, 2005b), suggesting a role in fluid secretion in the proximal tubule (which decreases in SW), rather than fluid reabsorption in the distal tubule. However, the role of these aquaporins remains unknown, and their expression may be associated with reabsorption of solutes and sodium chloride in the late proximal renal tubule segment. Although, the fact that glomerular filtration rates were the same in FW and SW eels suggests there would be no need to down-regulate this mechanism in SW eels, as solutes such as glucose etc would still need to be absorbed (Schmidt-Nielsen and Renfro, 1975; Martinez *et al.*, 2005b). The down-regulation of kidney AQP1 and AQP1dup (but not AQPe) mRNA levels was also mimicked by infusions of FW eels with the 'SW-acclimating' hormone, cortisol (Martinez, *et al.*, 2005b). AQP3 is also expressed in eel kidney and as in mammals, it may be located in the distal tubule nephron segment and be involved in water reabsorption, although its current tubular localization is unknown (Nejsum, 2005; Cutler *et al.*, 2007a). Additionally, AQP 4, 4b, 7, 9, 9b mRNAs are all expressed at low level in European eel kidney, although their roles are currently unknown (data not shown).

Acknowledgements

Dr Christopher P. Cutler has been the recipient of four New Investigator Award Research Fellowships from the Mount Desert Island Biological Laboratory (MDIBL).

References

Agre, P. (2006). The aquaporin water channels. Proc Am Thorac Soc. 3: 5–13.

Aleksandrov, A. A., Aleksandrov, L. A. and Riordan J. R. (2007). CFTR (AB-CC7) is a hydrolysable-ligand-gated channel. Pflugers Arch 453: 693–702.

Alpers, S. L. (2006). Molecular physiology of SLC4 anion exchangers. Exp Physiol 91: 153–161.

Alvarez, B. V., Vilas, G. L. and Casey, J. R. (2005). Metabolon disruption: A mechanism that regulates bicarbonate transport. EMBO J 24: 2499–2511.

Ando, M. (1975). Intestinal water transport and chloride pump in relation to seawater adaptation of the eel, *Anguilla japonica*. Comp Physiol Biochem 52A: 229–233.

Ando, M. (1985). Relationship between coupled Na^+-K^+-Cl^- transport and water absorption across the seawater eel intestine. J Comp Physiol 155: 311–317.

Ando, M. and Subramanyam, M. V. V. (1990). Bicarbonate transport systems in the eel intestine of the seawater eel. J Exp Biol 150: 381–394.

Ando, M., Mukuda, T. and Kozaka, T. (2003). Water metabolism in the eel acclimated to sea water: from mouth to intestine. Comp Biochem Physiol 136: 621–633.

Aoki, M., Kanekato, T., Katoh, F., Hasegawa, S., Tsutsui, N. and Aida, K. (2003). Intestinal water absorption through aquaporin 1 expressed in the apical membrane of mucosal epithelial cells in seawater-acclimated Japanese eel. J Exp Biol 206: 3495–3505.

Appel, C., Gloor, S., Schmalzing, G., Schachner, M. and Bernhardt, R. R. (1996). Expression of a Na^+,K^+-ATPase beta3 subunit during development of the zebrafish central nervous system. J Neurosci Res 46: 551–564.

Beyenbach, K. (2004). Kidneys sans glomeruli. Am J Physiol 286: F811–F827.

Beyenbach, K. W. and Baustian, M. D. (1989). Comparative physiology of the proximal tubule. From the perspective of aglomerular urine formation. In: Kinne, R. H. K. and Stolte, H. (eds) Structure and Function of the Kidney. Comparative Physiology, Vol. 1 Karger, Basel: 103–142.

Beyenbach, K. and Liu, P. L-F. (1996). Mechanism of fluid secretion common to aglomerular and glomerular kidneys. Kidney Int 49: 1543–1548.

Beyenbach, K. and Wieczorek, H. (2006). The V-type H^+ ATPase: Molecular structure and function, physiological roles and regulation. J Exp Biol 209: 577–589.

Blasiole, B., Canfield, V., Degrave, A., Thisse, C., Thisse, B., Rajarao, J. and Levenson, R. (2002). Cloning, mapping and developmental expression of a sixth Na^+,K^+-ATPase a1 subunit gene (atp1a1a.5). Mech Dev 119S: S211–S214.

Bobe, J., Montfort, J., Nguyen, T. and Fostier, A. (2006). Identification of new participants in the rainbow trout (*Oncorhynchus mykiss*) oocyte maturation and ovulation processes using cDNA microarrays. Reprod Biol Endocrinol 4: 39.

Borgese, F., Sardet, C., Cappadoro, M., Pouyssegur, J. and Motais, R. (1992). Cloning and expression of a cAMP-activated Na$^+$/H+ exchanger - evidence that the cytoplasmic domain mediates hormonal-regulation. Proc Natl Acad Sci USA 89: 6765–6769.

Braun, E. J. and Danzler, W. H. (1997). Vetebrate renal system. In: Danzler, W. H. (ed) Handbook of Physiology Vol 1, Section 13 Comparative Physiology, Oxford University Press, New York: 481–576.

Brett, C. L. Donowitz, M. and Rao, R. (2005). Evolutionary origins of eukaryotic sodium/proton exchangers. Am J Physiol 288: C223–C239.

Burnett, K. G., Bain, L. J., Baldwin, W. S., Callard, G. V., Cohen, S., Giulio, R. T., Evans, D. H., Gomez-Chiarri, M., Hahn, M. E., Hoover, C. A., Karchner, S. I., Katoh, F., MacLatchy, D. L., Marshall, W. S., Meyer, J. N., Nacci, D. E., Oleksiak, M. F., Rees, B. B., Singer, T. D., Stegeman, J. J., Towle, D. W., Van Veld, P. A., Vogelbein, W. K., Whitehead, A., Winn, R. N. and Crawford, D. L. (2007). Fundulus as the premier teleost model in environmental biology. Opportunities for new insights using genomics. Comp Biochem Physiol 2D: 257–286.

Bystriansky, J. S., Frick, N. T., Richards, J. G., Schulte, P. M. and Ballantyne, J. S. (2007). Failure to up-regulate Na$^+$,K$^+$-ATPase a-subunit isoform a1b may limit seawater tolerance of land-locked Artic char (Salvelinus alpinus). Comp Biochem Physiol 148A: 332–338.

Bystriansky, J. S. and Kaplan, J. H. (2007). Sodium pump localization in epithelia. J Bioenerg Biomembr 39: 373–378.

Bystriansky, J. S. Richards, J. G., Schulte, P. M. and Ballantyne, J. S. (2006). Reciprocal expression of gill Na$^+$/K$^+$-ATPase a-subunit isoforms a1a and a1b during seawater acclimation of three salmonid fishes that vary in their salinity tolerance. J Exp Biol 209: 1848–1858.

Canfield, V. A., Loppin, B., Thisse, C., Thisse, B., Postlethwait, J. H., Mohideen, M-A. P. K., Rajarao, J. R. and Levenson, R. (2002). Na$^+$,K$^+$-ATPase a and bsubunit genes exhibit unique expression patterns during zebrafish embryogenesis. Mech Dev 116: 51–59.

Chen, J. M., Cutler, C. P., Jacques, C., Denamur, E., Lecointre, G., Boeuf, G., Mercier, B., Cramb, G. and Ferec, C. (2001). A combined analysis of the cystic fibrosis transmembrane conductance regulator. Implications for structure and disease models. Mol Biol Evol 18: 1771–1778.

Cheung, J. C. and Deber, C. M. (2008). Misfolding of the cystic fibrosis transmembrane conductance regulator and disease. Biochemistry 47: 1465–1473.

Claiborne, J. B., Blackston, C. R., Choe, K. P., Dawson, D. C., Harris, S. P., Mackensie, L. A., Morrison-Shetlar, A. I. (1999). A mechanism for branchial acid excretion in marine fish: Identification of multiple Na$^+$/H+ antiporter (NHE) isoforms in gills of two seawater teleosts. J Exp Biol 202: 315–324.

Claiborne, J. B., Edwards, S. L. and Morrison-Shetler, A. I. (2002). Acid-base regulation in fishes: Cellular and molecular mechanisms. J Exp Zool 293: 302–319.

Comrie, M., Cutler, C. P. and Cramb, G. (2001a). Cloning and expression of guanylin from the European eel (*Anguilla anguilla*). Biochem Biophys Res Commun 281: 1078–1085.

Comrie, M., Cutler, C. P. and Cramb, G. (2001b). Cloning and Expression of two isoforms of guanylate cyclase C (GC-C) in the European Eel (Anguilla anguilla). Comp Biochem Physiol 129: 575–586.

Cramb, G., Martinez, A-S., McWilliam, I. and Wilson, G. D. (2005). Cloning and expression of guanylin-like peptides in teleost fish. Ann NY Acad Sci 1040: 277–280.

Crambert, G., Beguin, P., Pestov, N. B., Modyanov, N. N. and Geering, K. (2002). bm, a structural member of the X,K-ATPase b subunit family, resides in the ER and does not associate with any known X,K-ATPase a subunit. Biochemistry 41: 6723–6733.

Cutler, C. P. and Cramb, G. (2000). Water transport and aquaporin expression in fish. In: Hohmann, S.and Nielsen, S. (eds) Molecular Biology and Physiology of Water and Solute Transport, Kluwer academic press, London, UK: 431–441.

Cutler, C. P. and Cramb, G. (2001). Molecular physiology of osmoregulation in eels and other teleosts: The role of transporter isoforms and gene duplication. Comp Biochem Physiol 130: 551–564.

Cutler, C. P. and Cramb, G. (2002a). Two isoforms of the $Na^+/K^+/2Cl^-$ cotransporter (NKCC1) are expressed in the European eel (*Anguilla anguilla*). Biochim Biophys Acta 1566: 92–103.

Cutler, C. P. and Cramb, G. (2002b). Branchial expression of an aquaporin 3 (AQP-3) homologue is downregulated in the European eel (*Anguilla anguilla*) following seawater acclimation. J Exp Biol 205: 2643–2651.

Cutler, C. P. and Cramb, G. (2008). Differential expression of absorptive cation-chloride cotransporters in the intestinal and renal tissues of the European eel (*Anguilla anguilla*). Comp Biochem Physiol 149: 63–73.

Cutler, C. P., Brezillon, S., Bekir, S., Sanders, I. L., Hazon, N. and Cramb, G. (2000). Expression of a duplicate Na^+,K^+-ATPase b1-isoform in the European eel (*Anguilla anguilla*). Am J Physiol 279: R222–229.

Cutler, C. P., Martinez, A-S. and Cramb, G. (2007a). The role of aquaporin 3 in teleost fish. Comp Biochem Physiol 148A: 82–91.

Cutler, C. P., Phillips, C., Hazon, N., and Cramb, G. (2007b). Cortisol regulates eel (*Anguilla anguilla*) aquaporin 3 (AQP3) mRNA expression levels in gill. Gen Comp Endo 152: 310–313.

Cutler, C. P., Sanders, I. L. and Cramb, G. (1997a). Expression of a Na^+,K^+-ATPase b subunit isoforms in the European eel (*Anguilla anguilla*). Fish Physiol Biochem 17: 371–376.

Cutler, C. P., Sanders, I. L. and Cramb, G. (1997b). Isolation of six putative P-type ATPase b subunit PCR fragments from the brain of the European eel (*Anguilla anguilla*). Annals N Y Acad Sci 834: 123–125.

Cutler, C. P., Sanders, I. L., Hazon, N. and Cramb, G. (1995a). Primary sequence, tissue specificity and expression of the Na$^+$,K$^+$-ATPase a1 subunit in the European eel (*Anguilla anguilla*). Comp Biochem Physiol 111B: 567–573.

Cutler, C. P., Sanders, I. L., Hazon, N. and Cramb, G. (1995b). Primary sequence, tissue specificity and expression of the Na$^+$,K$^+$-ATPase b1 subunit in the European eel (*Anguilla anguilla*). Fish Physiol Biochem 14: 423–429.

Cutler, C. P., Sanders, I. L., Luke, G., Hazon, N. and Cramb, G. (1996). Ion transport in teleosts: identification and expression of ion transporting proteins in the branchial and intestinal epithelia of the European eel (*Anguilla anguilla*). In: Ennion, S.J. and Goldspink, G. (eds) Gene Expression and Manipulation in Aquatic Organisms. Society for Experimental Biology Seminar Series Vol. 58, Cambridge University Press, Cambridge: pp 43–74.

Danzler, W. H. (2003). Regulation of renal proximal tubule transport: Sodium, chloride and organic anions. Comp Biochem Physiol 136A: 453–478.

D'Cotta, H. C., Gallais, C., Saulier, B. and Prunet, P. (1996). Comparison between parr and smolt Atlantic salmon (*Salmo salar*) a subunit gene expression of Na$^+$/K$^+$ ATPase in gill tissue. Fish Physiol Biochem 15: 29–39.

D'Cotta, H. C., Valotaire, C., Le Gac, F. and Prunet, P. (2000). Synthesis of Na$^+$,K$^+$-ATPase in Atlantic salmon smolts: differences in a-mRNA and a-protein levels. Am J Physiol 278: R101–R110.

Deane, E. E. and Woo, N. Y. S. (2004). Differential gene expression associated with euryhalinity in sea bream (*Sparus sarba*). Am J Physiol 287: R1054–R1063.

Diamond, J. M. and Bossert, W. H. (1967). Standing-gradient osmotic flow. A mechanism for coupling of water and solute transport in epithelia. J Gen Physiol 50: 2061–2083.

Drummond, H. A., Jernigan, N. L. and Grifoni, S. C. (2008). Sensing tension. Epithelial sodium channel/acid-sensing ion channel proteins in cardiovascular homeostasis. Hypertension 51: 1265–1271.

Echevarria, M., Windhager, E. E. and Frindt, G. (1996). Selectivity of the renal collecting duct water channel Aquaporin-3. J Biol Chem 271: 25079–25082.

Evans, D. H., Piermarini, P. M. and Choe, K. P. (2005). The multifunctional fish gill: Dominant site of gas exchange, osmoregulation, acid-base regulation, and excretion of nitrogenous waste. Physiol Rev 85: 97–177.

Fabra, M., Raldua, D., Power, D. M., Deen M. T. and Cerda J. (2005). Marine fish egg hydration is aquaporin-mediated. Science 307: 545.

Feng, S-H., Leu, J-H., Yang, C-H., Fang, M-J., Huang, C-J. and Hwang, P-P. (2002). Gene expression of Na$^+$-K$^+$-ATPase a1 and a3 subunits in gills of the teleost *Oreochromis mossambicus*, adapted to different environmental salinities. Mar Biotechnol 4: 379–391.

Field, M., Smith, P. L. and Bolton, J. E. (1980). Ion transport across isolated mucosa of the winter flounder, *Pseudopleuronectes americanus*. II. Effects of cAMP. J Membr Biol 55: 157–163.

Fishman, M. C. (2001). Zebrafish-the canonical vertebrate. Science 294:

1290–1291.

Franzin, C. M., Gong, X-M., Teriete, P. and Marassi, F. M. (2007). Structures of the FXYD proteins in lipid micelles and membranes. J Bioenerg Biomembr 39: 379–383.

Frizell, R. A., Smith, P. L., Field, M. and Vosburgh, E. (1979). Coupled sodium-chloride influx across brush border of flounder intestine. J Membr Biol 46: 27–39.

Gamba, G. (2005). Molecular physiology and pathophysiology of electroneutral cation-chloride cotransporters. Physiol Rev 85: 423–493.

Gamba, G., Saltzberg, S. N., Lombardi, M., Miyanoshita, A., Lytton, J., Hediger, M. A., Brenner, B. M. and Hebert, S. C. (1993). Primary structure and functional expression of a cDNA encoding the thiazide-sensitive, electroneutral sodium-chloride cotransporter. Proc Natl Acad Sci USA 90: 2749–2753.

Garty, H. and Karlish, S. J. D. (2006). Role of FXYD proteins in ion transport. Ann Rev Physiol 68: 431–459.

Geering, K. (2005). Function of FXYD proteins, regulators of Na^+,K^+-ATPase. J Bioenerg Biomembr 37: 387–392.

Geering, K. (2006). FXYD proteins: New regulators of Na^+,K^+-ATPase. Am J Physiol 290: F241–F250.

Getman, H. C. (1950). Adaptive changes in the chloride cells of Anguilla rostrata. Biol Bull 99: 439–445.

Gharbi, K., Ferguson, M. M. and Danzmann, R. G. (2005). Characterization of Na^+,K^+-ATPase genes in Atlantic salmon (*Salmo salar*) and comparative genomic organization with rainbow trout (*Oncorhynchus mykiss*). Mol Genet Genomics 273: 474–483.

Giffard-Mena, I., Buolo, V., Aujoulat, F., Fowden, H., Castille, R., Charmantier, G. and Cramb, G. (2007). Aquaporin molecular characterization in the sea-bass (*Dicentrarchus labrax*). The effect of salinity on AQP1 and AQP3 expression. Comp Biochem Physiol 148A: 430–444.

Gimenez, I. (2006). Molecular mechanisms and regulation of furosemide-sensitive Na^+-K^+-Cl^- cotransporters. Curr Opin Nephrol Hypertens 15: 517–523.

Gorin, N. B., Yancey, S. B., Cline, J., Revel, J. P. and Horwitz, J. (1984). The major intrinsic protein (MIP) of the bovine lens fiber membrane. Cell 39: 49–59.

Grosell, M. (2006). Intestinal anion exchange in marine fish osmoregulation. J Exp Biol 209: 2813–2827.

Grosell, M. and Jensen, F. B. (1999). NO2- uptake and HCO_3^- excretion in the intestine of the European flounder (Platichthys flesus). J Exp Biol 202: 2103–2110.

Grosell, M., DeBoeck, G., Johannsson, O. and Wood, C. M. (1999). The effects of silver on intestinal ion and acid-base regulation in the marine teleost fish, Papophrys vetulus. Comp Biochem Physiol 124C: 259–270.

Grosell, M., Laliberte, C. N., Wood, S., Jensen, F. B. and Wood C. M. (2001).

Intestinal HCO3⁻ secretion in marine teleost fish: Evidence for an apical rather than a basolateral Cl⁻/ HCO3⁻ exchanger. Fish Physiol Biochem 24: 81–95.

Grosell, M., Wood, C. M., Wilson, R. W., Bury, N. R., Hogstrand, C., Rankin, C. and Jensen, F. B. (2005). Bicarbonate secretion plays a role in chloride and water absorption in the European flounder intestine. Am J Physiol 288: R936–R946.

Guynn, S. R., Scofield, M. A. and Petzel, D. H. (2002). Identification of mRNA and protein expression of the Na⁺/K⁺-ATPase a1- a2- a3- isoforms in Antarctic and New Zealand Nototheniid fishes. J Exp Mar Biol Ecol 273: 15–32.

Halm, D. R., Krasny, E. J. Jr. and Frizzell, R. A. (1985). Electrophysiology of flounder intestinal mucosa. II. Relation of the electrical potential profile to coupled NaCl absorption. J Gen Physiol 85: 865–883.

Hickman, C. P. Jr. (1968). Ingestion, intestinal absorption, and elimination of seawater and salts in the southern flounder, Paralichthys lethostigma. Can J Zool 46: 457–466.

Hickman, C. P. and Trump, B. F. (1969). The Kidney. In Hoar, W.S. and Randall, D.J. (eds) Fish physiology, Academic press, New York: 91–239.

Hirano, T. (1974). Some factors regulating water intake by the eel, Anguilla japonica. J Exp Biol 61: 737–747.

Hirano, T. and Mayer-Gostan, N. (1976). Eel esophagus as an osmoregulatory organ. Proc Natl Acad Sci USA 73: 1348–1350.

Hirata, T., Kaneko, T., Ono, T., Nakazato, T., Furukawa, N., Hasegawa, S., Wakabayashi, S., Shigekawa, M., Chang, M. H., Romero, M. and Hirose, S. (2003). Mechanism of acid adaptation of a fish living in a pH 3.5 lake. Am J Physiol 284: R1199–R1212.

Hiroi, J. and McCormick, S. D. (2007). Variation in salinity tolerance, gill Na⁺/ K⁺- ATPase, Na⁺/K⁺/2Cl⁻ cotransporter and mitochondria-rich cell distribution in three salmonids Salvelinus namaycush, Salvelinus fontinalis and Salmo salar. J Exp Biol 210: 1015–1024.

Hirose, S., Kaneko, T., Naito, N. and Takei, Y. (2003). Molecular biology of major components of chloride cells. Comp Biochem Physiol 136: 593–620.

Hoegg, S., Brinkmann, H., Taylor, J. S. and Meyer, A. (2004). Phylogenetic timing of the fish-specific genome duplication correlates with the diversification of teleost fish. J Mol Evol 59: 190–203.

Hoegg, S. and Meyer, A. (2007). Phylogenomic analyses of KCNA gene clusters in vertebrates: why do gene clusters stay intact? BMC Evol Biol 7: 139.

Hoffmann, E. K., Hoffmann, E., Lang, F. and Zadunaisky, J. A. (2002). Control of Cl⁻ transport in the operculum epithelium of Fundulus heteroclitus: long- and short-term salinity adaptation. Biochim Biophys Acta 1566: 129–139.

Hoffmann, E. K., Schettino, T. and Marshall W. S. (2007). The role of volume-sensitive ion transport systems in regulation of epithelial transport. Comp Biochem Physiol 148A: 29–43.

Hubner, S., Michel, F., Rudloff, V. and Appelhans, H. (1992). Amino acid sequence of band-3 protein from rainbow trout erythrocytes derived from cDNA. Biochem J 285: 17–23.

Hwang, P-P. and Lee, T-H. (2007). New insights into fish ion regulation and mitochondrial-rich cells. Comp Biochem Physiol 148A: 479–497.

Isaia, J. (1984). Water and Nonelectrolyte permeation. In Hoar, W.S. and Randall, D.J. (eds) Fish Physiology, vol. X, Gills; Part B, Ion and Water Transfer, London, Academic Press: 1–38.

Ishibashi, K., Kuwahara, M., Gu, Y., Tanaka, Y., Marumo, F. and Sasaki, S. (1998). Cloning and functional expression of a new aquaporin (AQP 9) abundantly expressed in the peripheral leukocytes permeable to water and urea, but not glycerol. Biochem Biophys Res Commun 244: 268–274.

Ishibashi, K., Kuwahara M., Kageyama, Y., Sasaki, S., Suzuki, F. and Imai, M. (2000). Molecular cloning of a new aquaporin superfamily in mammals. In: Hohmann, S. and Neilsen, S. (eds) Molecular Biology and Physiology of Water and Solute Transport, Kluwer Academic/Plenum Publishers, New York: 123–125.

Ishibashi, K., Sasaki, S., Fushimi, K., Yamamoto, T., Kuwahara, M. and Marumo, F. (1997). Immunolocalisation and effect of dehydration on AQP3, a basolateral water channel of kidney collecting ducts. Am J Physiol 272: F235–F241.

Kalujnaia, S., McWilliam, I. S., Zaguinaiko, V. A., Feilen, A., Nicholson, J., Hazon, N., Cutler, C. P., Cramb, G. (2007). A transcriptomic approach to the study of osmoregulation in European eel Anguilla anguilla. Phys Genomics 31: 385–401.

Karnaky, K. J. (1998). Osmotic and ionic regulation. In: Evans, D.H. (ed), The Physiology of Fishes, 2nd edition. CRC Press, Boca Raton, Florida: 157–176.

Katoh, F., Hyodo, S. and Kaneko, T. (2003). Vacuolar-type proton pump in the basolateral plasma membrane energizes uptake in branchial mitochondria-rich cells of killifish Fundulus heteroclitus adapted to a low ion environment. J Exp Biol 206: 793–803.

Kirsch, R. (1978). Role of the oesophagus in osmoregulation. In: Jorgenson, and C. B. and Skadhauge, E. (eds), Osmotic and Volume Regulation. Alfred Benzon Symposium XI, Munksgaard. Academic Press, New York: 138–154.

Kirsch, R. and Meister, M. F. (1982). Progressive processing of of ingested seawater in the gut of seawater teleosts. J Exp Biol 98: 67–81.

Krane, C. M. and Goldstein D. L. (2007). Comparative functional analysis of aquaporins/aquaglyceroporins in mammals and anurans. Mamm Genome 18: 452–462.

Kumar, S. and Hedges, B. (1998). A molecular timescale for vetebrate evolution. Nature 392: 917–920.

Kurita, Y., Nakada, T., Kato, A., Doi, H., Mistry, A. C., Chang, M-H., Romero, M. F. and Hirose, S. (2008). Identification of intestinal bicarbonate transporters involved in formation of carbonate precipitates to stimulate water absorption in marine teleost fish. Am J Physiol 294: R1402–R1412.

Lanier, C. and Claiborne, J. B. (2004). Analysis of branchial longhorn sculpin (Myoxocephalus octodecimspinosus) Na^+/H^+ exchanger isoform 3 using Northern hybridization. Bull Mt Desert Isl Biol Lab 43: 107.

Lee, T. H., Hwang, P. P., Shieh, Y. E. and Lin, C. H. (2000). The relationship between 'deep-hole' mitochondria-rich cells and salinity adaptation in the euryhaline teleost, Oreochromis mossambicus. Fish Physiol Biochem 23: 133–140.

Li, X., Alvarez, B., Casey, J. R., Reithmeier, R. A. and Fliegel, L. (2002). Carbonic anhydrase II binds to and enhances activity of the Na^+/H^+ exchanger. J Biol Chem 277: 36085–36091.

Li, X., Liu, Y., Alvarez, B. V., Casey, J. R. and Fliegel, L. (2006). A novel carbonic anhydrase II binding site regulates NHE1 activity. Biochemistry 45: 2414–2424.

Lignot, J-H., Cutler, C. P., Hazon, N. and Cramb, G. (2002a). Immunolocalisation of aquaporin 3 in the gill and the gastrointestinal tract of the European eel (*Anguilla anguilla L.*). J Exp Biol 205: 2653–2663.

Lignot, J-H., Cutler, C. P., Hazon, N. and Cramb, G. (2002b) Water transport and aquaporins in the gill and gastrointestinal tract of the European eel *Angullia anguilla L.* In Flik, G. and Hazon, N. (eds), Osmoregulation and Drinking in Vertebrates, Society for Experimental Biology Seminar Series Vol. 54, BIOS Scientific Publishers Ltd, Oxford: 49–60.

Lin, Y. M., Chen, C. N. and Lee, T. H. (2003). The expression of gill Na^+,K^+-ATPase in milkfish, *Chanos chanos*, acclimated to seawater, brackish water and fresh water. Comp Biochem Physiol 135A: 489–497.

Lin, Y. M., Chen, C. N., Yoshinaga, T., Tsai, S. C., Shen, I. D. and Lee, T. H. (2006). Short-term effects of hyposmotic shock on Na^+/K^+-ATPase expression in gills of the euryhaline milkfish, *Chanos chanos*. Comp Biochem Physiol 143A: 406–415.

Lin, C. H., Huang, C. L., Yang, C. H., Lee, T. H. and Hwang, P. P. (2004). Time-course changes in the expression of Na^+,K^+-ATPase and the morphometry of mitochondrion-rich cells in gills of euryhaline tilapia (*Oreochromis mossambicus*) during freshwater acclimation. J Exp Zool 301A: 85–96.

Lingrel, J. B., Williams, M. T., Vorhees, C. V. and Moseley, A. E. (2007). Na^+,K^+-ATPase and the role of a isoforms in behavior. J Bioenerg Biomembr 39: 385–389.

Loretz, C. A. (1995). Electrophysiology of ion transport in teleost intestinal cells. In: Wood, C. M. and Shuttleworth, T. (eds), Fish Physiology, Vol. 14, Cellular and Molecular Approaches to Fish Ionic Regulation, Academic Press, London: 25–56.

Lorin-Nebel, C., Boulo, V., Bodinier, C. and Charmantier, G. (2006). The $Na^+/K^+/2Cl^-$ cotransporter in the sea bass *Dicentrarchus labrax* during ontogeny: involvement in osmoregulation. J Exp Biol 209: 4908–4922.

Madsen, S. S., Jensen, L. N., Tipsmark, C. K., Kiilerich, P. and Borski, R. J. (2007). Differential regulation of cystic fibrosis transmembrane conductance regulator and Na$^+$,K$^+$,-ATPase in gills of striped bass, *Morone saxatilis*: effect of salinity and hormones. J Endocrinol 192: 249–260.

Marshall, W. S. and Bryson, S. E. (1998). Transport mechanisms of seawater teleost chloride cells: An inclusive model of a multifunctional cell. Comp Biochem Physiol 119A: 97–106.

Marshall, W. S. and Grosell, M. (2006). Ion transport, osmoregulation and acid-base balance. In: Evans, D.H. and Claiborne, J.B. (eds), The physiology of fishes, 3rd edition. CRC Press, Boca Raton, Florida: 177–230.

Marshall, W. S., Bryson, S. E., Midelfart, A. and Hamilton, W. F. (1995). Low-conductance anion channel activated by cAMP in teleost Cl$^-$-secreting cells. Am J Physiol 268: R963–R969.

Marshall, W. S., Howard, J. A., Cozzi, R. R. F. and Lynch, E. M. (2002). NaCl and fluid secretion by the intestine of the teleost *Fundulus heteroclitus*: involvement of CFTR. J Exp Biol 205: 745–758.

Martinez, A.-S., Cutler, C. P., Wilson, G., Phillips, C., Hazon, N. and Cramb, G. (2005a). Regulation of expression of two aquaporin homologues in the intestine of the European eel: Effects of seawater acclimation and cortisol treatment. Am J Physiol 288: R1733–43.

Martinez, A.-S., Cutler, C. P., Wilson, G., Phillips, C., Hazon, N. and Cramb, G. (2005b). Cloning and expression of three aquaporin homologues from the European eel (*Anguilla anguilla*): effects of seawater acclimation and cortisol treatment on renal expression. Biol Cell 97: 615–627.

Martinez, A.-S., Wilson, G., Phillips, C., Cutler, C. P., Hazon, N. and Cramb, G. (2005c). Cortisol and aquaporin expression in the eel oesophagus. Effect of cortisol on aquaporin expression in the oesophagus of the European eel, *Anguilla anguilla*. Ann NY Acad Sci 1040: 395–8.

Meyer, A. and Van de Peer, Y. (2005). From 2R to 3R: Evidence for fish-specific genome duplication (FSGD). Bioessays 27: 937–945.

Morishita, Y., Sakube, Y., Sasaki, S. and Ishibashi, K. (2004). Molecular mechanisms and drug development in aquaporin water channel diseases: aquaporin superfamily (superaquaporins): expansion of aquaporins restricted to multicellular organisms. J Pharmacol Sci 96: 276–9.

Musch, M. W., Orellana, S. A., Kimberg, L. S., Field, M., Halm, D. R., Krasny, E. J. Jr. and Frizzell, R. A. (1982). Na$^+$-K$^+$-Cl$^-$ co-transport in the intestine of a marine teleost. Nature 300: 351–353.

Nagashima, K. and Ando, M. (1993). Characterization of esopageal desalination in the seawater eel, *Anguilla japonica*. J Comp Physiol 164B: 47–54.

Nejsum, L. N. (2005). The renal plumbing system: aquaporin water channels. Cell Mol Life Sci 62: 1692–1706.

Niederstatter, H. and Pelster, B. (2000). Expression of two vacuolar-type AT-Pase B subunit isoforms in swimbladder gas gland cells of the European eel: nucleotide sequences and deduced amino acid sequences. Biochim Biophys Acta 1491: 133–142.

Nilsen, T. O., Ebbesson, L. O., Madsen, S. S., McCormick, S. D., Andersson,

E., Bjornsson, B. T., Prunet, P., Stefansson, S. O. (2007). Differential expression of gill Na⁺,K⁺-ATPase alpha- and beta-subunits, Na⁺,K⁺,2Cl⁻ cotransporter and CFTR anion channel in juvenile anandromous and landlocked Atlantic salmon *Salmo salar*. J Exp Biol 210: 2885–2896.

Nishimura, M., Imai, M. and Ogawa, M. (1982). Sodium chloride and water transport in renal distal tubule of the rainbow trout. Am J Physiol 244: F247–F254.

Noel, J. and Pouyssegur, J. (1995). Hormonal regulation, pharmacology, and membrane sorting of vertebrate Na⁺/H⁺ exchanger isoforms. Am. J. Physiol. 268: C283–C296.

Orlowski, J. and Grinstein, S. (2004). Diversity of the mammalian sodium/proton exchanger SLC9 gene family. Pflugers Arch 447: 549–565.

Okiyoneda, T. and Lukacs, G. L. (2007). Cell surface dynamics of CFTR: The ins and outs. Biochim Biophys Acta 1773: 476–479.

Parks, S. K., Tresguerres, M. and Goss, G. G. (2007). Interactions between Na⁺ channels and Na⁺-HCO3⁻ cotransporters in the freshwater fish gill MR cell: a model for transepithelial Na⁺ uptake. Am J Physiol. 292: C935–C944.

Parmelee, J. T. and Renfro, J. L. (1983). Esophageal desalination of seawater in flounder: role of active sodium transport. Am J Physiol. 245: R888–R893.

Paukert, M., Sidi, S., Russell, C., Siba, M., Wilson, S. W., Nicolson, T. and Grunder, S. (2004). A family of acid-sensing ion channels from zebrafish. J Biol Chem 279: 18788–18791.

Paw, B. H., Davidson, A. J., Zhou, Y., Li, R., Pratt, S. J., Lee, C., Trede, N. S., Brownlie, A., Donovan, A., Liao, E. C., Ziai, J. M., Drejer, A. H., Guo, W., Kim, C. H., Gwynn, B., Peters, L. L., Chernova, M. N., Alper, S. L., Zapata, A., Wickramasinghe, S. N., Lee, M. J., Lux, S. E., Fritz, A., Postlethwait, J. H. and Zon, L. I. (2003). Cell-specific mitotic defect and dyserythropoiesis associated with erythroid band 3 deficiency. Nature Genet 34: 59–64.

Pedersen, S. F., King, S. A., Rigor, R. R., Zhuang, Z., Warren, J. M., Cala, P. M. (2003). Molecular cloning of NHE1 from winter flounder RBCs: Activation by osmotic shrinkage, camp, and calyculin A. Am J Physiol 284: C1561–1576.

Pelis R. M and Renfro J. L. (2003). Active sulfate secretion by the intestine of winter flounder is through exchange for luminal chloride. Am J Physiol 284: 380–388.

Perry, S. F., Beyers, M. L. and Johnson, D. A. (2000). Cloning and molecular characterization of the trout (*Oncorhynchus mykiss*) vacuolar H+-ATPase B subunit. J Exp Biol 203: 459–470.

Perry, S. F., Furimsky, M., Bayaa, M., Georgalis, T., Shahsavarani, A., Nickerson, J. G. and Moon, T. W. (2003a). Integrated responses of Na⁺/HCO₃⁻ cotransporters and V-type H⁺-ATPase in the fish gill and kidney during respiratory acidocis. Biochim Biophys Acta 1618: 175–184.

Perry, S. F., Shahsavarani, A., Georgalis, T., Bayaa, M., Furimsky, M. and Thomas S. L. Y. (2003b). Channels, pumps, and exchangers in the gill and kidney of freshwater fishes: Their role in ionic and acid-base regulation. . J Exp Zool 300A: 53–62.

Preston, G. M. and Agre, P. (1991). Molecular cloning of the red cell integral protein of Mr 28,000: a member of an ancient channel family. Proc Natl Acad Sci USA 88: 11110–11114.

Rajarao, J. R, Canfield, V. A., Loppin, B., Thisse, C., Thisse, B., Yan, Y-L., Postlethwait, J. H. and Levenson, R. (2002). Two Na$^+$,K$^+$-ATPase b2 subunit isoforms are differentially expressed within the central nervous system and sensory organs during zebrafish embryogenesis. Dev Dynamics 223: 254–261.

Rajarao, S. J. R., Canfield, V. A., Mohideen, M-A. P. K., Yan, Y-L., Postlethwait, J. H., Cheng, K. C. and Levenson, R. (2001).The repertoire of Na$^+$,K$^+$-ATPase a and b subunit genes in the zebrafish, *Danio rerio*. Genome Res 11: 1211–1220.

Raldua, D., Otero, D., Fabra, M. and Cerda, J. (2008). Differential localization and regulation of two aquaporin-1 homologs in the intestinal epithelia of the marine teleost *Sparus aurata*. Am J Physiol 294: R993–R1003.

Reid, S. D., Hawkings, G. S., Galvez, F. and Goss, G. G. (2003). Localization and characterization of phenamil-sensitive Na$^+$ influx in isolated rainbow trout gill epithelial cells. J Exp Biol 206: 551–559.

Richards, J. G., Semple, J. W., Bystriansky, J. S. and Schulte, P. M. (2003). Na$^+$/K$^+$-ATPase a-isoform switching the gills of rainbow trout (*Oncorhynchus mykiss*) during salinity transfer. J Exp Biol 206: 4475–4486.

Romero, M. F. and Boron, W. F. (1999). Electrogenic Na$^+$/HCO$_3^-$ cotransporters: Cloning and physiology. Annu Rev Physiol 61: 699–723.

Rojek, A., Praetorius, J., Frokiaer, J., Nielsen S. and Fenton, R. A. (2008). A current view of the mammalian aquaglyceroporins. Ann Rev Physiol 70: 301–327.

Romero, M. F., Hediger, M. A., Boulpaep, E. L. and Boron, W. F. (1997). Expression cloning and characterization of a renal electrogenic Na$^+$/HCO$_3^-$ cotransporter. Nature 387: 409–413.

Santos, C. R. A., Estevao, M. D., Fuentes, J., Cardoso, J. C. R., Fabra, M., Passos, A. L., Detmers, F. J., Deen, P. M. T., Cerda, J. and Power, D. M. (2004). Isolation of a novel aquaglyceroporin from a marine teleost (*Sparus auratus*): function and tissue distribution. J Exp Biol 207: 1217–1227.

Saparov, S. M., Liu, K., Agre, P. and Pohl, P. (2007). Fast and selective ammonia transport by aquaporin 8. J Biol Chem 282: 5296–5301.

Schoenrock, C., Morley, S. D., Okawara, Y., Lederis, K. and Richter, D. (1991). Sodium and potassium ATPase of the teleost fish *Catostomus commersoni*: sequence, protein structure and evolutionary conservation of the alpha-subunit. Biol Chem Hoppe-Seyler 372: 16895–16903.

Scott, G. R., Richards, J. G., Forbush, B., Isenring, P. and Schulte, P. M. (2004). Changes in gene expression of the euryhaline killifish *Fundulus heteroclitus* after abrupt salinity transfer. Am J Physiol 287: C300–C309.

Seidelin, M., Madsen, S. S., Cutler, C. P. and Cramb, G. (2001). Expression of Gill Na⁺,K⁺-ATPase a- and b-subunits,and the Vacuolar-type H+-ATPase B-subunit in Atlantic Salmon (*Salmo salar, L.*) during smoltification. Zool Sci 18: 315–324.

Semple, J. W., Green, H. J. and Schulte, P. M. (2002). Molecular cloning and characterization of two Na⁺/K⁺ATPase in *Fundulus heteroclitus*. Mar Biotechnol 4: 512–519.

Shehadeh, Z. H. and Gordon, M. S. (1969). The role of the intestine in salinity adaptation of the rainbow trout, *Salmo gairdneri*. Comp Biochem Physiol 30: 397–418.

Singer, T. D., Clements, K. M., Semple, J. W., Schulte, P. M., Bystriansky, J. S., Finstad, B., Fleming, I. A. and McKinley, S. R. (2002). Seawater tolerance and gene expression in two strains of Atlantic salmon smolts. Can J Fish Aquat Sci 59: 125–135.

Singer, T. D., Tucker, S. J., Marshall, W. S. and Higgins, C. F. (1998). A divergent CFTR homologue: highly regulated salt transport in the euryhaline teleost *F. heteroclitus*. Am J Physiol 274: C715–723.

Skadhauge, E. (1969). The mechanism of salt and water absorption in the intestine of the eel (*Anguilla anguilla*) adapted to waters of various salinities. J Physiol 204: 135–158.

Skadhauge, E. (1974). Coupling of transmural flows of NaCl and water in the intestine of the eel (*Anguilla anguilla*). J Exp Biol 60: 535–546.

Schmidt-Nielsen, B. and Renfro, L. J. (1975). Kidney function of the American eel *Anguilla rostrata*. Am J Physiol 228: 420–431.

Smuckler, B. E., Clark, J. S., Hsu, A., Vandrope, D. H., Stewart, A. K., Kurschat, C. E., Choe, S-K., Zhou, Y., Amigo, J., Paw, B. H. and Alper, S. L. (2008). Zebrafish ae2.2 encodes a second slc4a2 anion exchanger. Am J Physiol 294: R1081–R1091.

Smuckler, B. E., Kurschat, C. E., Ackermann, G. E., Jiang, L., Zhou, Y., Barut, B., Stuart-Tilley, A. K., Zhao, J., Zon, L. I., Drummond, I. A., Vandrope, D. H., Paw, B. H. and Alper, S. L. (2005). Zebrafish slc4a2/ae2 anion exchanger: cDNA cloning mapping, functional characterization, and localization. Am J Physiol 289: F835–F849.

Sterling, D. and Casey, J.R. (2002). Bicarbonate transport proteins. Biochem Cell Biol 80: 483–497.

Suzuki, Y., Itakura, M., Kashiwagi, M., Nakamura, N., Matsuki, T., Sakuta, H., Naito, N., Takano, K., Fujita, T. and Hirose, S. (1999). Identification by differential display of a hypertonicity-inducible inward rectifier potassium channel highly expressed in chloride cells. J Biol Chem 274: 11376–11382.

Sweadner, K. J. and Rael, E. (2000). The FXYD gene family of small ion transport regulators or channels: cDNA sequence, protein signature sequence, and expression. Genomics 68: 41–56.

Takei, Y. and Yuge, S. (2007). The intestinal guanylin system and seawater adaptation in eels. Gen Comp Endo 152: 339–351.

Tang, C. H. and Lee, T. H. (2007). The effect of environmental salinity on the protein expression of Na^+/K^+-ATPase, $Na^+/K^+/2Cl^-$ cotransporter, cystic fibrosis transmembrane conductance regulator, anion exchanger 1, and chloride channel 3 in gills of a euryhaline teleost, Tetraodon nigroviridis. Comp Biochem Physiol 147A: 521–528.

Tenckhoff, S., Hollborn, M., Kohen, L., Wolf, S., Wiedemann, P. and Bringmann, A. (2005). Diversity of aquaporin mRNA expressed by rat and human retinas. Neuroreport 16: 53–6.

Tipsmark, C. K. (2008). Identification of FXYD protein genes in a teleost: tissue-specific expression and response to salinity change. Am J Physiol 294: R1367–R1368.

Tipsmark, C. K., Madsen, S. S. and Borski, R. J. (2004). Effect of salinity on expression of branchial ion transporters in striped bass (*Morone saxatilis*). J Exp Zool 301A: 979–991.

Tipsmark, C. K., Madsen, S. S., Seidelin, M., Christensen, A. S., Cutler, C. P. and Cramb, G. (2002). Dynamics of $Na^+,K^+,2Cl^-$ cotransporter and Na^+,K^+-ATPase expression in the branchial epithelium of brown trout (*Salmo trutta*) and Atlantic salmon (*Salmo salar*). J Exp Zool 293: 106–118.

Tresguerres, M., Katoh, F., Orr, E., Parks, S. K. and Goss, S. S. (2006). Chloride uptake and base secretion in freshwater fish: A transepithelial ion-transport metabolon? Physiol Biochem Zool 79: 981–996.

Tse, W. K. F., Au, D. W. T., Wong, C. K. C. (2006). Characterization of ion channel and transporter mRNA expressions in isolated gill chloride and pavement cells of seawater acclimating eels. Biochem Biophys Res Commun 346: 1181–1190.

Utida, S., Hirano, T., Oide, H., Ando, M., Johnson, D. W. and Bern, H. A. (1972). Hormonal control of the intestine and urinary bladder in teleost osmoregulation. Gen Comp Endo S3:317–327.

Vagin, O., Sachs, G. and Tokhtaeva, E. (2007). The roles of Na^+,K^+-ATPase beta 1 subunit in pump sorting and epithelial integrity. J Bioenerg Biomembr 39: 367–372.

Virkki, L. V., Cooper, G. J. and Boron, W. F. (2001). Cloning and functional expression of an MIP (AQP0) homolog from killifish (*Fundulus heteroclitus*) lens. Am J Physiol 281: R1994–R2003.

Walsh, P. J., Blackwelder, P., Gill, K. A., Danulet, E. and Mommsen, T. P. (1991). Carbonate deposits in marine fish intestines: A new source of biomineralization. Limnol Oceanography 36: 1227–1232.

Watanabe, S., Kaneko, T., and Aida, K. (2005). Aquaporin-3 expressed in the basolateral membrane of gill chloride cells in Mozambique tilapia *Oreochromis mossambicus* adapted to freshwater and seawater. J Exp Biol 208: 2673–2682.

Wilson, J. M., Laurent, P., Tufts, B. L., Benos, D. J., Donowitz, M., Vogl, A. W. and Randall, D. J. (2000a). NaCl uptake by the branchial epithelium in freshwater teleost fish: an immunological approach to ion-transport protein localization. J Exp Biol 203: 2279–2296.

Wilson, J. M., Whiteley, N. M. and Randall, D. J. (2002a). Ionoregulatory changes in the gill epithelia of coho salmon during seawater acclimation. Physiol Biochem Zool 75: 237–249.

Wilson, R. W. (1997). A novel role for the gut of seawater teleosts in acid-base balance. In: Taylor, E. W., Raven, J. A., and Eggiton, S. (eds), Acid-Base Status in Animals and Plants, Cambridge University Press, Cambridge: 257–274.

Wilson, R. W., Gilmour, K., Henry, R. and Wood, C. (1996). Intestinal base excretion in the seawater-adapted rainbow trout: a role in acid-base balance? J Exp Biol 199: 2331–2343.

Wilson, R. W., Wilson, J. M. and Grosell, M. (2002b). Intestinal bicarbonate secretion by marine teleost fish—why and how? Biochim Biophys Acta 1566: 182–193.

Wu,Y. C., Lin, L. Y. and Lee, T. H. (2003). $Na^+,K^+,2Cl^-$ cotransporter: a novel marker for identifying freshwater- and seawater-type mitochondria-rich cells in gills of the euryhaline tilapia, *Oreochromis mossambicus*. Zool Stud 42: 186–192.

Yan, J-J., Chou, M-Y., Kaneko, T. and Hwang, P-P. (2007). Gene expression of Na^+/H^+ exchanger in zebrafish H^+-ATPase-rich cells during acclimation to low-Na^+ and acidic environments. Am J Physiol 293: C1814–C1823.

Yang, B. and Verkman, A. S. (1997). Water and glycerol permeabilities of aquaporins 1-5 and MIP determined quantitatively by expression of epitope-tagged constructs in Xenopus oocytes. J Biol Chem 272: 16140–16146.

Yang, B., Zhao, D., Solenov, E. and Verkman, A. S. (2006). Evidence from knockout mice against physiologically significant aquaporin 8-facilitated ammonia transport. Am J Physiol 291: C417–C423.

Yuge, S. and Takei, Y. (2007). Regulation of ion transport in eel intestine by the homologous guanylin family of peptides. Zool. Sci. 24: 1222–1230.

Yuge, S., Inoue, K., Hyodo, S. and Takei, Y. (2003) A novel guanylin family (guanylin, uroguanylin and renoguanylin) in eels. J Biol Chem 278: 22726–22733.

Yuge, S., Yamagami, S., Inoue, K., Suzuki, N. and Takei, Y. (2006). Indentification of two functional guanylin receptors in eel: Multiple hormone-receptor system for osmoregulation in fish intestine and kidney. Gen Comp Endo 149: 10–20.

Zadunaisky, J. A. (1996). Chloride cells and osmoregulation. Kidney Int 49: 1563–1567.

Zadunaisky, J. A. (1997). Gill chloride cells activation by plasma osmolality. In: Hazon, N., Eddy, F. B. and Flik, G. (eds), Ionic Regulation in Animals, Springer verlag, Berlin Heidelberg: 87–105.

Zadunaisky, J. A., Cardona, S., Au, L., Roberts, D. M., Fisher, E., Lowenstein B., Cragoe, E. J. Jr. and Spring K. R. (1995). Chloride transport activation by plasma osmolarity during rapid adaptation to high salinity of *Fundulus heteroclitus*. J Membr Biol 143: 207–217.

Chapter 4

Effect of dietary salt on feeding, digestion, growth and osmoregulation in teleost fish

Nadir A. Salman

Keywords: Dietary salt, NaCl homeostasis, food intake, drinking, osmoregulation

Abstract

Diets supplemented with certain levels of salt (NaCl) have been widely used in fish farming industry especially those of euryhaline species where transfer between freshwater and salt water is necessary. The use of dietary salt in fish feeding is an extra-ordinary practice which aims at activating the osmoregulatory mechanisms in fish prior to seawater transfer. In addition dietary salt has many nutritional effects on growth and feeding efficiency in fish. Nutritional effects are not fully understood, with different assessments resulting from differences in diet preparation methods, salt contents, nutrients balance, feeding levels and other practices. Accordingly, results of research remain controversial, especially regarding the nutritional responses, but all agree upon the positive effect of dietary salt on seawater adaptation of fish. More work is still needed to clarify the real osmoregulatory role of internal salt load. The following review aims at evaluating the salt feeding hypothesis from the nutritional and physiological point of view. Papers published on this subject are few, but have covered most of the critical questions related to the way fish can handle internal salt load in freshwater and seawater. Since the pioneering paper of Zaugg and McLain (1969) on Chinook salmon, researchers in many parts of the world continued examining the possible effects of such practice. It can be seen that subjects such as the effect of dietary salt on sea water adaptation, osmoregulatory mechanisms, growth and feeding efficiency have been thoroughly investigated. Despite all that, many aspects still need more inspection. These include determination of dietary NaCl levels which can satisfy the sea water adaptation trials without affecting feeding efficiency and growth adversely. Secondly, responses of digestive enzymes and feed evacuation processes are of special interest to clarify causes of nutritional impacts. Research for quantifying the role of gills, kidney and gut in dealing with the internal salt load is also essential to understand ionic absorption and excretion (influx/efflux). Interactions of salty diets with hormonal action and responses towards toxicants are new fields for further investigations. This chapter critically debates previous work on all these subjects and outline the gaps that need further investigation.

4.1 Dietary salt requirements

The quantitative dietary requirements for sodium and chloride in freshwater fish can be determined according to the amount needed for growth, reproduction and that lost through the gut, kidney, as well as passive diffusion across the gills and body surface. Infact, mineral requirements in fish have not received the attention paid to other nutrients. This view was pointed out earlier (30 years ago) by Cowey and Sargent (1979) and Mackay (1979). Feeds for fish farming are usually supplied with 1–2% of mineral premix without accurate understanding of the real need for specific elements. These might differ according to many factors, including rearing and seasonal conditions in addition to feeding practices. A large percentage of dietary salt in commercial feeds for carnivorous fish originates from the fish meal component of the diet (Murray and Andrews, 1979). Fish meal is one of the major contributors of salt to the diet. It is therefore important to take this into account when replacing fish meal with various plant-derived meals, which are not as rich in salt. Total salt content in the diet should also be adjusted to the optimum levels when using a plant protein substitution.

In FW-adapted teleosts, passive outward flux of ions from fish must be overcome by active uptake of ions (e.g. Na^+, Cl^-, K^+, Mg^+ and Ca^{2+}) from the water and/ or through the diet (Karnaky, 1998). Smith et al. (1989) showed that the dietary sodium intake of salmonids kept in freshwater increased by about eight-fold from winter to summer (equalling the branchial sodium influx). Diets correspond to the increase in feeding and shows that almost all the sodium required can be derived from dietary salt. Diet can therefore be used as a source of salts for the fish kept in freshwater, providing ions which the fish cannot obtain from the hypotonic environment.

The question of how much salt is necessary as an optimum requirement for the wellbeing, growth and reproduction of cultured fish is still under debate. Some studies have revealed the beneficial advantage of feeding fish more than 2% dietary salt. Such as that of Murray and Andrew (1979) who stated that utilizing a diet enhanced with up to 4% salt has an advantage of leading to better feed utilization under intensive production conditions. In freshwater hybrid tilapia (Oreochromis niloticus x O. aureus) fed diet supplemented with 2 g kg^{-1} had a significantly greater weight gain than the fish fed the diets supplemented with 3 and 5 g Na^+ kg^{-1} diet (Shi Yen and Li Shan, 2004). Other studies, however, found no such benefit for more salt in the diet on growth of rainbow trout (Salman and Eddy, 1988), coho salmon (Zaugg and McLain, 1969) or Atlantic salmon (Basulto, 1976) as they interfere with other nutrients leading to some dilution (e.g. of protein content). Higher supplements of salt had adversely affected growth and feed efficiency of coho salmon and rainbow trout (Zaugg and McLain, 1969; Salman and Eddy, 1988).

As seen above, inclusion of salt to commercial pellets could result in nutrient (mainly protein) dilution (Table 1). Isonitrogenous and isocaloric diets can be formulated (Table 2) to reduce such effect (Salman, 1987). Harpaz et al. (2005) reached similar conclusions and postulated that, if the impact on growth is negligible, the addition of salt to the commercial rations can be considered advantageous from the economic point of view since the diet containing additional salt had a reduction in the level of other ingredients (nutrient dilution) corresponding to the level of added salt. This simple method can be applied by farmers as it can reduce the cost of feed by diluting expensive components with a cheap mineral and does not require special means.

Table 1. *Percentage composition of a commercial diet fed to rainbow trout after enrichment.*

Diet type	N	LS	HS	MS
Moisture	8.2	10.9	11.2	10.6
Protein	47.5	43.5	41.7	40.8
Energy (kcal g^{-1})	4.9	4.6	4.4	4.3
Ash	9.1	12.3	15.1	19.2
NaCl	1.3	4.5	9.2	11.6
Sodium	0.51	1.79	3.64	4.60
Chloride	1.04	2.49	5.61	8.10
Potassium	0.94	0.96	0.97	0.95
Calcium	2.17	1.81	1.98	1.95

low salt (LS) 4 % NaCl, medium salt (MS) 9 % NaCl and high salt (HS) 11 % NaCl compared to normal (N) commercial feed.

4.2 Levels of salt in aquaculture diets

Dietary NaCl levels of 1–4% are commonly used in salmon and trout diets. Tacon and De Silva (1983) while investigating the mineral composition of various fish feeds found that the content of salt in these feeds was on the average 1.5%, but could be as high as 6%, especially in the feeds used for early stage fingerling salmon. Nandeesha *et al.* (2000) found that fish fed 1.5% NaCl showed best growth and this level of salt increased digestive enzyme activity in *Cyprinus carpio* and *Cirrhinus mrigala* juveniles. In rainbow trout, levels of dietary NaCl up to 4.5%, when formulated without nutrients dilution, were reported to have a beneficial effect on growth of freshwater fish (Salman and Eddy, 1988). Nile tilapia fed on 6% dietary NaCl had consistently higher weight gain than those fed the normal diet (Lim, *et al.*, 2007). Such an effect has previously been reported by Ogino and Kamizono (1975) to promote growth in carp and trout. Kim *et al.* (2001) have also reported a beneficial effect of low level of salt.

Over 50 days of feeding European sea bass (initial weight of 4.9 g) five different levels of supplemental salt (0, 1%, 3%, 5% and 9% of diet) in fresh water, the final weight of fish fed the dietary salt up to the level of 5% was found to be 19% higher than the control group (Eroldoğan, *et al.*, 2005). In order to obtain maximum specific growth rate (SGR), the sea bass needed to obtain 3.4% supplementary salt in their diet. Moderate levels of salt (around 4% or 5%) have also been reported to have beneficial effects on growth and feed utilization by many authors (Ogino and Kamizono, 1975; Tacon and De Silva, 1983) for trout or carp respectively.

The supplementation of high levels (9.6–11.6%) of NaCl, resulted in lower feed efficiency and inhibited growth in trout (Salman and Eddy, 1988). Excess supplementary salt inclusion (9%) also decreased the feed conversion efficiency compared with moderate salt levels (1% and 3%) as reported by Eroldoğan, et al. (2005). In view of the previous findings, it can be established that dietary salt at moderate levels (1–4%) might be beneficial when fed, within balanced rations, to euryhaline and freshwater fish.

Calculations of dietary sodium intake based on feeding rainbow trout on low-salt diets at 0.6% body weight per day was done by D'Cruz and Wood (1998). It showed that trout consumed about 0.6–1.1% (258–468 μmol Na^+. Kg^{-1}) of their Na^+ pool per day, an amount that was insufficient to maintain internal Na^+ levels. Fish on the regular-salt diets consumed about 3.4–3.9% (1,462–1,694 μmol Na^+ kg^{-1}) of their Na^+ per pool per day, which was sufficient to correct for any ionoregulatory imbalances. This is substantially lower than the 10% of the Na^+ pool per day that trout voluntarily consume when they are allowed to feed to satiation under chronic acid stress (Dockray et al., 1996). Sodium intake in rainbow trout fed on high salt diet (11.6% NaCl) increased to 0.8 mmol kg^{-1} h^{-1} compared with the normally fed fish (0.09 mmol kg^{-1} h^{-1}) (Salman, 1987).

4.3 Growth responses to supplemented dietary salt

Controversial results have been published regarding the effect of dietary salt on fish growth. Part of the confusion is related to the differences in osmoregulatory responses of different fish species which have various degree of euryhalinity. The other part is related to the lack of experimental standardization for feeding trials conducted by various researchers. Feeding factors such as rations, salt levels and ionic intake in addition to differences in fish size and sexual status have resulted in controversial findings. Results of some reports on euryhaline species have indicated that growth and food efficiency can be improved by using salt-enriched diets. In two separate studies with juvenile red drum (*Sciaenops ocellatus*), reared in freshwater, growth and feed efficiency were improved when fish were fed a diet supplemented with NaCl (Getalin et al., 1992). The explanation of such growth enhancement potential for salt supplementation in euryhaline species might be related to the osmoregulatory advantages. Ion losses at low salinity can significantly impair growth if not compensated by supplemented dietary ions. The supplementation of diet with moderate levels of salt might also spare energy that has to be used in osmoregulation, thereby leaving more energy available for growth (Zaugg et al., 1983; Gatlin et al., 1992). Furthermore, Smith (1995) observed that redirection of the Na^+ to the tissue may reflect enhanced uptake and distribution of nutrients (e.g. amino acids, glucose) for growth of salt-loaded fish after feeding. Apart from the metabolic cost of osmoregulation, growth differences may also be the result of

Table 2. *Composition and proximate analysis of isonitrogenous-isocaloric formulated diet fed to rainbow trout*

Ingredients (% of total)	Diet types			
	Control	LS	MS	HS
Herring meal	52	52	52	52
Cod liver oil	5	5	5	5
Corn oil	2	2	2	2
Dextrin	8	8	8	8
Corn starch	10	10	10	10
Cellulose	15	11	7	3
Sodium chloride	0	4	8	12
Mineral mixture	4	4	4	4
Vitamin premix	2	2	2	2
CMC	2	2	2	2
Proximate analysis (% dry matter)				
Moisture	7.8	9.4	10.6	9.7
Crude protein	40.9	41.0	40.8	40.8
Total lipids	11.1	11.5	11.2	11.8
Energy kcal/g	4.4	4.2	4.2	4.2
Ash	12.6	14.9	19.0	23.8
Sodium	1.0	2.3	3.3	4.3
Chloride	1.3	3.3	6.1	6.8
Sodium chloride	2.3	5.6	9.2	11.1

Low salt (LS) enriched with 4%, medium salt (MS) with 8 % and high salt (HS) with 12 % levels of NaCl. Adapted from Salman (1987)

(a)

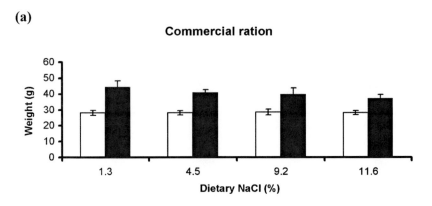

(b)

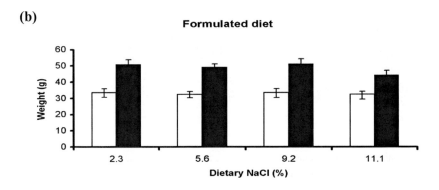

Figure 1.
Growth of rainbow trout fed on different levels of dietary NaCl salt-supplemented to a commercial ration for 7 weeks **(a)** *and formulated isonitrogenous-isocaloric diet for 8 weeks* **(b)** *(redrawn from Salman, 1987). Light bars, initial weights; dark bars, final weights.*

changes in hormonal status, digestion, absorption feed efficiency and metabolism.

In contrast, other studies on euryhaline species have indicated that feeding fish extra salt has negligible, or even negative effects, on growth and feed efficiency (Shaw *et al.*, 1975; Murray and Andrews, 1979). Growth would inversely be affected by the addition of high levels of salt (9–12%) in the diet, if nutrient dilution occurred in the ration (Salman and Eddy, 1990). Dietary NaCl appears only to affect growth rate inversely when the level of supplemented salt interferes with the balance of other essential dietary components, and hence affect feed utilization efficiency. Impairment to growth was controlled when isonitrogenous-isocaloric salty diets were used (Salman, 1987) as compared with diluted commercial diet (Figure 1).

Factors such as fish size and sexual status may also affect growth responses. Little information is available about the different response of males and females toward salt feeding. Results from Fontaínhas-Fernandes *et al.* (2000) indicated beneficial effects on females during salinity acclimation, when reared in 10‰ brackish water, extended over the entire sampling period but disappeared after 30 days in males. Size of fish is another factor which needs more investigation in terms of growth responses towards salt-enriched diet. Results from Salman and Eddy (1990) showed different growth responses between small-sized (10–20 g) and large-sized (> 40 g) fish to salt feeding.

4.3.1   Growth in freshwater

It is generally agreed that growth responses in freshwater-adapted fish is different from that in brackish and seawater. Results of certain experiments on red drum indicated that dietary supplementation with NaCl improved the growth of the fish in dilute (fresh and brackish) waters, but not in full-strength seawater. Low levels of NaCl ranging from 1–4% may have a positive effect on growth of freshwater fish rather than seawater ones. In an experiment conducted in freshwater with juvenile red drum, it was clearly shown that the addition of 2% NaCl to the diet resulted, in greater feed efficiency and greater weight gain (Gatlin *et al.*, 1992).

In India, the addition of salt to the diet of freshwater carp at a level of 1.5% resulted in significantly better growth and is in widespread use in India (Nandeesha *et al.*, 2000). In European sea bass, Eroldoğan, *et al.* (2005) found that the final weight, specific growth rate and feed efficiency were greatest at the moderate level (1–5%) of salt supplementation. Optimum level of dietary salt inclusion was calculated as 3% and feed efficiency was significantly enhanced with increasing salt level up to 5%. Higher levels of salt have resulted in lower growth rate in many fish species (Shaw *et al.*, 1975; Murray and Andrews, 1979; Salman and Eddy, 1988; D'Cruz and Wood, 1999).

Few explanations can be recorded for the growth response in freshwater fish toward salt feeding. Dietary salts in dilute waters may increase the absorption of amino acids and/or satisfy other metabolic requirements by providing ions that the fish cannot sufficiently extract from hypotonic environments for whole-body Na^+ and Cl^- homeostasis (Gatlin *et al.*, 1992), and thus save energy expenditure. Fish reared in freshwater might spend more energy than those in seawater for ionic and acid-base regulation (Eroldogan *et al.*, 2004). The lost ions via the gill, kidney and guts in fresh water are regained by the fish through the salt included in their diets. It was also reported earlier that adding salt to the diet of fish has the advantages of increasing appetite and also acts as a humectant by reducing water activity (Zaugg and McLain, 1969). Smith *et al.* (1995) reported an enhanced uptake and distribution of nutrients for growth in freshwater-adapted rainbow trout, *Oncorhynchus mykiss*, after feeding with salt-enriched diets. In the end, growth differences are definitely affected by changes in the hormonal status, digestion, absorption and metabolism activities.

4.3.2   Growth in seawater

It has been shown that the salinity of the rearing water has an influence on feeding activities of fish. Feed intake in rainbow trout adapted to (up to

28‰) salinity increased but the growth rate decreased, negatively affecting feed conversion ratio (MacLeod, 1978; Jurss et al., 1985). This confirms the previously noted negative relationship between salinity as a masking factor and growth (MacLeod, 1977; Nahhas, 1982; McKay and Gjerde, 1985). Yet, in euryhaline species, salinity affects growth in a different way and maximal growth is not always obtained under isosmotic conditions (Brett, 1979).

Dietary salt treatments seemed to be ineffective in terms of improving the growth rate of fish reared in sea water. A depressed growth rate of small-sized rainbow trout (10–20 g) fed on salt-enriched diet was observed by Salman and Eddy (1990) after transfer to sea water due to reduced feed conversion efficiency (Table 3). The same authors reported that a compensatory feed intake occurred in seawater-transferred rainbow trout to overcome nutrient dilution in the salt-enriched diet, but this was not sustained over a long term rearing period as fish receiving undiluted normal diet grew better. Protein requirement should be considered while using salt-enriched diet in seawater, as it is reported to be increased in seawater adapted fish (Jurss et al., 1985).

Table 3. Comparison of growth rates in non-smolting rainbow trout after feeding on salty diets in half and full strength seawater (SW)

	Normal feeding		Salt feeding	
	50% SW	100% SW	50% SW	100% SW
Experimental period (days)	33	45	33	45
Average Initial weight (g)	24.6	19.0	14.9	27.7
Average final weight (g)	25.8	24.4	15.6	32.6
Initial Growth rate, IGR (% per day)	0.15	0.55	0.15	0.36
Relative weight gain (%)	5.1	28.2	5.1	17.6

Adapted from Salman (1987)

No influence has been noted for dietary salt on growth of some other fish species reared in sea water. Tests conducted on red drum kept in seawater showed no advantage to the addition of NaCl at a level of 2% over the basal diet (Gatlin et al., 1992). In full-strength artificial seawater (35‰), juvenile red drum fed diets supplemented with NaCl at 2 and 10% had weight gains not significantly different from those of fish fed the basal diet, and those fed the diet supplemented with NaCl at 10% had significantly reduced feed efficiency (Gatlin, et al.,1992). Groups of one-year-old smolts of Arctic charr (Salvelinus alpinus) reared under a simulated natural photoperiod and fed pelleted feed with a NaCl content of either 1.5% or 9.5% for 6 weeks showed no differences in growth from fish fed the two normal diets (Staurnes and Finstad, 2000). Surprisingly, one of the two groups that had been fed the 9.5% NaCl diet, however, had both a significantly higher recapture rate and growth in seawater than the two groups fed the 1.5% NaCl diet. The authors had no explanation for that result and further investigation is needed.

The results of Harpaz *et al*. (2005) showed that fish reared in saltwater and fed feed containing additional salt exhibited a slightly lower, but not significantly different, growth rate trend compared with the control group that had no added salt to their feed. The digestive enzymatic activity in these fish was different from that observed in freshwater. Thus, even if the addition of salt did have a slight impact on growth, this effect is reduced due to better utilization of the food, which is manifested by the increase in the enzymatic activity. It should be mentioned that although the addition of salt did not result in better growth, it did not hamper the growth of the fish reared in saltwater. In conclusion, the up-to-date information about the role of salt-enriched diet in seawater adapted fish confirmed the need for further detailed research regarding digestive enzyme activity, ionic absorption and nutrient requirements to enable better understanding.

4.3.3   Growth in brackish water

Data of several salt feeding trials confirmed that growth of salt fed fish in brackish water was as good as normally fed fish, if not better. As seen from the data (Table 3) adopted from Salman (1987), rainbow trout fed the salt diet in ½ seawater reached a similar growth rate to that of the normally fed fish and gain better survival as well. This is comparable to the findings of Fontaínhas-Fernandes *et al.* (2000) on tilapia Oreochromis niloticus which emphasized the beneficial effect of this acclimation method in females reared in 10‰ brackish water extended over the entire sampling period. Al-Amoudi (1987) suggested that gradual acclimation regimes of a salt diet did stimulate the osmoregulatory organs of different tilapia species (*O. mossambicus, O. spilurus and O. aureus* × *O. niloticus*) in brackish water and that the fish were able to regulate the osmotic concentration of the plasma. Common carp (*Cyprinus carpio*) fed on a salty diet and then transferred to brackish water exhibited satisfactory rates of growth compared with fish fed on normal commercial pellets (Salman *et al.*, 1997). In Juvenile bluegill, *Lepomis macrochirus*, collected from Mississippi coastal drainages and held at 0, 5, and 10‰, growth rates did not differ in fish fed ad libitum diets containing 0.2 and 4% dietary NaCl (Musselman *et al.*, 1995). Juvenile red drum kept in brackish water of 6‰ and fed a salt-enhanced diet (2%) showed an increase in weight gain over the basal diet, but this increase was not significant (Gatlin *et al.*, 1992). It seems that a salt-enriched diet has an advantage in salinity adaptation trials at intermediate salinities. The use of dietary salt in combination with a gradual transfer to higher salinities appeared to aid the activation of osmoregulatory mechanisms, which in turn, reduced the cost of osmotic shock and help early resumption of feeding activities. The subject needs further physiological and nutritional studies.

4.4 Dietary salt and feeding activities

4.4.1 Impact of dietary salt on feed intake

Most of the reviewed papers on salt diet in fish revealed that dietary salt has no adverse effect on fish appetite and food intake. This has been previously reported by the early papers of Zaugg and McLain (1969) and MacLeod (1978) in coho salmon and rainbow trout respectively. Nutrient dilution caused by the supplemented salt to the diet may be expected to impose a compensatory increase in feed intake similar to that reported in fish fed increased amounts of indigestible fibres (Hilton *et al.*, 1983). Such nutrient-dependent compensatory mechanisms are considered to be only partly effective. This may raise the question whether fish feed for bulk or for caloric value, therefore, depressed growth rate in fish fed the 'salty diet' can not entirely be a function of feed intake or appetite changes. Factors like digestibility and evacuation rate might play a decisive role, as noted by Salman (1987) who pointed out a reduced total and nutrient digestibility, and faster evacuation rates, for salt-enriched diets.

According to Salman and Eddy (1988), feed intake and appetite were not affected adversely by dietary salt, and feeding to satiation enhanced growth in all feeding treatments in fresh water, but this feeding regime did not alter the differences in growth rate between normally fed fish and those fed on salty diets in freshwater. In a similar observation, Fontaínhas-Fernandes *et al.* (2000) found no differences in feed efficiency or feed intake between tilapia, Oreochromis niloticus, feeding on normal or high-salt diets. In seawater adaptation trials, feed intake in salt fed rainbow trout was higher than fish fed the normal diet as a possible compensatory mechanism connected with nutrient dilution and subsequent influence on the chemical energy or specific nutrient intake (Salman and Eddy, 1990). The same authors recorded an early resumption of feeding activities in non-smolting rainbow trout fed the salt-enriched diet compared with the normally fed fish after the osmotic shock of transfer to full strength sea water.

4.4.2 Impact of dietary salt on feed conversion efficiency

Early work of MacLeod (1978) revealed that the addition of up to 8.5% sodium chloride to the diet of rainbow trout *Salmo gairdneri* had no significant effect on either food intake or food conversion efficiency. Salman and Eddy (1988) demonstrated that food conversion efficiency of fish fed the isonitrogeous diets was not affected by the added salt, but both conversion efficiency and growth rate were adversely influenced by the salt-supplemented commercial food (Figure 2). Any extra salt incorporated in commercial diets could, of course, be compensated by increasing the feeding level (ration), so that the weight of NaCl ingested is additional to the normal ration of the basic food. Nile tilapia showed better conversion efficiency when fed 6% dietary NaCl in freshwater (Lim *et al.*, 2006).

According to Salman (1987), the absence of any significant differences in protein efficiency ratio (PER) values between fish fed normal and salt-enriched diets support the idea that poor conversion efficiency associated with dietary salt is mainly due to sub-optimal protein intake. The decisive role of protein content of food in the growth of fish is well established (Jurss *et al.*, 1983). In addition, low digestibility and faster evacuation of food has been associated with the diets diluted with high levels of NaCl (9–11%) (Salman, 1987) which in turn, may affect assimilation and conversion efficiency. The dilution effect of indigestible dietary components is

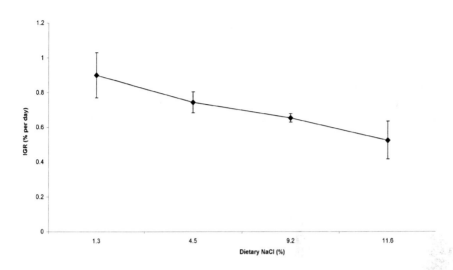

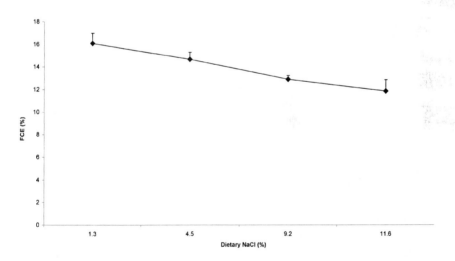

Figure 2.
Negative relationships between dietary salt and both cumulative instantaneous growth rate (IGR) and feed conversion efficiency (FCE) in rainbow trout reared in freshwater (20 fish per treatment). Regression equations are y = 16.5-0.4x (r² = 0.8344) for FCE and y = 0.86-0.02x (r² = 0.8783) for IGR (redrawn from Salman, 1987).

well documented (Hilton *et al.*, 1983: Jobling, 1986; Tekinay and Davies, 2002).

Low feed efficiency values in fish receiving high salt load (9–12%) may also be attributed to the energy expenditure for ionic regulation (Gatlin *et al.*, 1992; Fontainhas-Fernandes *et al.*, 2000). The energy demands for salt excretion might be increased by dietary salt loading. The assumption that such demands would be reflected in decreased growth can be accepted only if the salt load is actively excreted. According to Salman and Eddy (1987), most of the dietary salt absorbed into the blood is excreted via the gills, supported by the elevated number of chloride cells and activity of Na^+/K^+-ATPase. The osmoregulatory cost expressed as energy expenditure, may be saved by the use of dietary salt (energy sparing effect), through the role of the ingested salt in activation osmoregulatory mechanisms.

In some more recent papers, positive relationship has been established between salt-enriched diet and feed conversion efficiency. Eroldogan *et al.* (2005) reported a positive link between feed utilization and dietary salt in sea bass, as feed conversion efficiency and feed intake were positively influenced by the dietary salt at 1–5% levels. The data of Harpaz *et al.* (2005) suggests that the addition of salt to the diet of the fish reared in freshwater resulted in a better food conversion ratio (FCR). Enhanced feed efficiency might have been the result of stimulated digestive enzymes by the introduction of salt into the diet. In acid exposure, fish fed low-salt diets had better food conversion efficiencies than the low-energy/regular-salt fed fish, which were in a catabolic state (D'Cruz and Wood, 1999).

Nandeesha *et al.* (2000) found an increase in protease, amylase and lipase activity and digestibility in *C. carpio* and *C. mrigala* fed salt-loaded diets. Hapraz *et al.* (2005) reported an enhanced activity of the brush border enzymes alkaline phosphatase, lactase and leucine amino peptidase in Asian sea bass (*Lates calcarifer*) reared in freshwater and fed dietary salt, with the most pronounced effect exhibited in the pyloric caeca. Fish reared in saltwater exhibited significant higher enzymatic activity of maltase, sucrase, and γ-glutamyl transpeptidase when fed a diet with added salt compared to the control treatment. The marked increase in the activity of the brush border enzymes might explain the improved feed efficiency. The better enzymatic activity in the fish fed a diet containing added salt can be explained by the absorption mechanism of the end products, glucose and amino acids (Harpaz *et al.*, 2005). Since the glucose and most of the amino acid absorption is depended on the Na^+/K^+-ATPase pump (Klein *et al.*, 1998), a higher concentration of Na^+ in the lumen might lead to a better absorption of carbohydrates and amino acids. Since the enzyme activity might be inhibited by its end product (carbohydrates or amino acids) (De La Fuente *et al.*, 1997), reduction of the end product concentration can lead to better enzymatic activity in the lumen of fish fed feed enriched with NaCl. Salt feeding may act like seawater transfer and result in enhancement of intestinal and branchial Na^+/K^+-ATPase activity (Salman and Eddy, 1987; De La Fuentes *et al.*, 1997).

4.5 Impacts on digestibility, absorption and evacuation

4.5.1 Effect of dietary salt on nutrient digestibility

The apparent digestibility coefficients of nutrients and energy were found to be affected by increasing the level of salt in the diet. It has a beneficial effect when added at moderate levels (1–4%), as it increased the apparent digestibility coefficients for protein, lipids and energy (Salman, 1987) leading to better growth and satisfying nutrient requirements (Tacon et al., 1984). Improvement of digestibility under such moderate salt levels may have resulted from the increased acid secretion which was reported to be stimulated by increased gastric levels of the chloride ion (Hille, 1984). Higher levels of salt (more than 4%) caused lower nutrient and energy digestibility (Figure 3), as they interfere with the acid secretion. Ingestion of more dietary chloride ions is apparently correlated with acid secretion in a kind of feedback relationship as suggested by Salman (1987). The other possible reason is the dilution of nutrients in the salt-enriched diets. According to Pfeffer (1982), low protein digestibility was associated with lower protein levels in the diet.

Interaction between digestibility and evacuation of salt-enriched diet may also explain the low digestibility of a high salt diet. It is possible to relate the reduction in apparent digestibility of salty diets to their faster evacuation. High salt levels increased the rate of passage of digesta (see section 5.2) and therefore reduced the time available for the digestive enzymes to attack their substrate with subsequent reductions in digestibility. Rapid emptying of stomach could also overload the digestive and absorptive capacities of the intestine leading to a decrease in the digestibility of the diet as shown by Jobling (1986) using high energy diets. In contrast, slower passage of the diet through the gut would allow more digestion and better conversion efficiency.

The adverse effect of high salt levels on digestibility is comparable to that of increased levels of indigestible carbohydrates such as fibers which was shown to reduce digestibility at levels of more than 10% in trout diet (Hilton at al., 1983). Lower digestibility of carbohydrate in the diet of rainbow trout was apparently affected by the acceleration passage of food in the salt-fed fish. A positive relationship was also found between mineral contents and ash digestibility. The excess salt was apparently absorbed, as ash contents of faeces collected from fish fed the normal and salt diet were nearly similar. Fish adapted to seawater revealed lower digestibility (Jurss et al., 1983), possibly due to the increased imbibed seawater and ion fluxes that accompany the osmoregulation process. Feeding on salty diet in seawater might further interfere with the ingested seawater and enzyme activities leading to lower digestibility of most nutrients.

As seen from the above review, little is known about the absolute effect of dietary salt on the digestibility of nutrients and energy in fish ration. Detailed investigations are needed to explore various causes of the decreased digestibility associated with elevated NaCl levels in freshwater and seawater adapted fish. These might include production and activity of certain digestive enzymes and HCl secretions. The digestion-evacuation relationship in respect

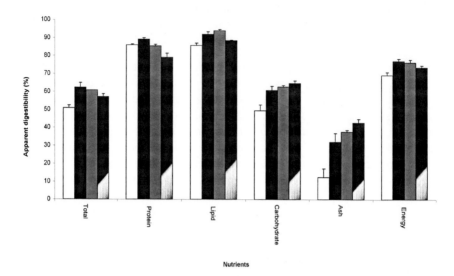

Figure 3. *Effect of elevated levels of dietary NaCl on apparent digestibility coefficients (ADC) of various dietary components (protein, lipids, carbohydrates, ash) and energy.*

Control □, low salt ■, medium salt ▨, high salt ▢. Data represent average of six samples per each dietary salt treatment ± SE. Total digestibility = 100 - 100 (marker in food / marker in faeces), (redrawn from Salman, 1987).

to salt feeding is also another aspect to be investigated. Such information is vital before suggesting the use of salt diet in aquaculture practices.

4.5.2 Effects of dietary salt on ionic absorption

Dietary ionic load has been found to be readily absorbed by several freshwater fish species. It is usually accompanied by a sudden rise of plasma ions within 24 hour of feeding high levels of dietary salt, and also by a minimum ionic excretion via faeces (Shaw *et al.*, 1975; Basulto, 1976; Wilson *et al.*, 1985). The absorbed ions into the blood seemed to be retained and slowly excreted via the gills (within 48 h) as found by Salman (1987). Two indications may lead to the conclusion that fish could efficiently absorb high levels of dietary salt: 1) The progressive increase in plasma ions during 24 h of feeding, and the drop to normal levels after 48h. 2) Similarity in the amount of salt excreted via the faeces in fish fed the normal and salt-enriched diets.

According to Salman (1987), absorption of Na^+ and Cl^- in fish fed on 11.6% NaCl averaged 83.8% and 94.3% respectively. Such efficient absorption of salt was also reported in rainbow trout fed on 63.8 meq Na^+ per 100g food (Wilson *et al.*, 1985) and in Atlantic salmon fed on 2 and 12% NaCl (Shaw *et al.*, 1975). Several mechanisms are suggested for the acceleration of ionic absorption by dietary salt which include changes in digestive and absorptive enzymes, passive permeability and pumping efficiency of ion transporters. In contrast, oral salt load might reduce ionic absorption across the gut wall of rainbow trout by affecting the composition of the specialized intestinal membrane and altering their functional properties.

In seawater adapted fish, dietary salt provides an extra salt load to the imbibed sea water and inversely affects ionic absorption (Salman, 1987). It would appear that a compensatory mechanism by which intestine reduces salt absorption in the presence of high ion influxes exists. An increase in the relative ionic absorption of seawater adapted rainbow trout with increasing salinity was previously reported by Shehadeh and Gordon (1969) and was attributed to an increase in blood perfusion, accumulation of divalent ions and hormonal control. Mainoya (1982) reported a reduction in NaCl absorption rates in seawater adapted tilapia due to high transintegumentary ion influx and low permeability of the skin to water. Increased levels of ionic absorption in seawater-adapted fish could be explained in terms of increased gastric capacity and digestive and absorptive enzymes.

4.5.3 Effect of dietary salt on drinking rate

Dietary salt caused a slight, but insignificant, increase in drinking rate of freshwater fish from 0.68 ml kg^{-1} h^{-1} in normally fed fish to 0.74 ml kg^{-1} h^{-1} in fish fed on diet containing 11.6% NaCl (Salman, 1987). This might be attributed to a reduction of intracellular volume, compensated by an increase in extracellular volume in the form of water incorporation. The increase in salt excretion exhibited by fish facing the internal dietary salt load could also be a stimulus for such increase in drinking rate as suggested earlier by Shehadeh and Gordon (1969). Such explanation can also be used for the interpretation of the significantly elevated drinking rate of seawater-adapted fish as an osmoregulatory response to the dehydrating effect of hypertonic medium (Bath and Eddy, 1979).

4.5.4 Impact of dietary salt on food evacuation

Typical effects of dietary NaCl on feed evacuation in rainbow trout were discussed by Salman (1987) and are illustrated (Figure 4). Data on gastric evacuation can be collected by using iron powder as a marker in the food, and taking X-ray photographs of the fish at intervals after feeding. The radiographic method outlined by Talbot and Higgins (1983) was used to estimate the stomach and gut contents and then calculate feed evacuation rates from the slopes of the plots against time according to Jobling (1981), as seen in Figure 4. The results demonstrated that supplemented NaCl when added to commercial diet of rainbow trout could cause a slight increase in the food evacuation rate. This might be due to its dilution effect as the salt was increased at the expense of other dietary components leading to an alteration of the nutritive and caloric value of the meal and affect gastric handling. Such effect has also been mentioned in rainbow trout fed on high levels of dietary carbohydrates (Hilton et al., 1983; Jobling, 1986; Tekinay and Davies, 2002).

The mechanism responsible for the increase in gastric motility in response to food dilution is not fully understood. Physiologically, decreases of enterogastrone

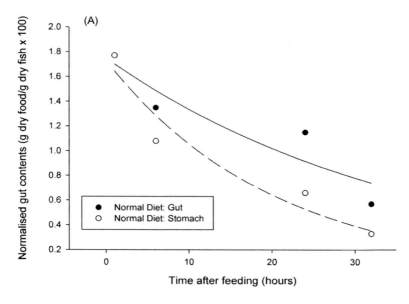

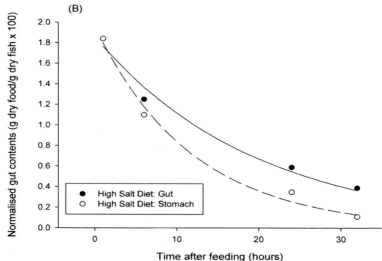

Figure 4.
Curve fits of gastric (dashed lines) and gut (solid lines) evacuation rates for **(a)** *normal and* **(b)** *high salt diets. Curves are fitted to the median data using Sigma plot. Redrawn from original data in Salman (1987). Regression equations are as follows:*

Normal diet: stomach, $y=1.729(-0.0494x)$, $r^2=0.93$; gut, $y=1.7497(-0.0269x)$, $r^2=0.85$
High salt: stomach, $y=1.9589(-0.0846x)$, $r^2=0.99$, gut, $y=1.858(-0.0509x)$, $r^2=0.98$

production by the intestine and changes in the activity of extrinsic nerves which supply the gut were suggested earlier to play a role (Fange and Grove, 1979). From a nutritional point of view, two possible mechanisms may occur in fish when fed a diet diluted with salt: 1) Fish might adapt to the increase in dietary salt and nutrient dilution by increasing food consumption or meal size. 2) Fish might increase their feeding frequency by more rapid gastric emptying rate if the food is available continuously bringing about an earlier return of appetite.

Several other factors may explain the absolute effect of dietary salt on accelerating food evacuation. Dietary salt might increase food motility as it was accompanied with more water absorption especially in sea water adapted fish. Fish fed 11.6% salt drank slightly more (0.74 ml kg^{-1} h^{-1}) than fish fed the normal diet (0.68 ml kg^{-1} h^{-1}) in fresh water, and 4.4 and 3.5 ml kg^{-1} h^{-1} respectively in sea water (Salman, 1987). Moisture levels of gut contents in salt fed fish increased as the level of salt increased in the diet. Greater evacuation of moist diets was previously reported in yellow Perch Perca fluvescens (Garber, 1983). Dietary salt might also affect evacuation through increasing the osmolality of the chime, which in turn could affect gastric motility through the release of polypeptide hormones. Salt in the diet may affect gastric distention and secretion of gastric acid and certain enzymes which induce peristaltic action, and therefore alter the rate of digestion and evacuation of the stomach (Mills et al., 1984; Talbot et al., 1984). Reduction in the time a meal remains in the gastrointestinal tract caused by dietary salt seemed to reduce the assimilation efficiency.

The above review of the influence of dietary salt on food evacuation illustrates a big knowledge gap regarding physiological and nutritional explanations of the accelerating effect of dietary NaCl. Despite the pioneer study of Salman (1987) no serious trials have been attempted to explore this subject using new techniques. Most of the explanations stated above are still within comparable expectations with other inert materials such as indigestible carbohydrates. Food evacuation is considered as an essential parameter to be determined prior to the use of any new dietary component in aquaculture practices.

4.6 Use of dietary salt for seawater adaptation

It has been agreed upon by nearly all published research that dietary salt addition is a useful practice for seawater acclimation trials (Salman, 1993). Many researchers have addressed the issue of using dietary salt to help alleviate the problems associated with transferring fish to seawater or saltwater growing conditions. Increased survival rates of salt-fed fish upon transfer to sea water have been reported by many authors (Zaugg and McLain, 1969; Basulto, 1976; Zaugg et al., 1983 in Chinook salmon Oncorhynchus tshawytscha; Salman and Eddy, 1990 in rainbow trout; and Pellertier and Besner, 1992 in brook charr, Salvelinus fontinalis). The results of these studies show a marked advantage in the use of dietary salt resulting in better survival. Zaugg et al. (1983) reported that the addition of NaCl to the diet of juvenile fall chinook salmon for 6 weeks prior to release, resulted in 65% better adult recovery in the fishery and return to the hatchery than obtained with controls fed an unsupplemented diet. Later, Salman and Eddy (1990) showed that freshwater rainbow trout fed for a month on a high-salt diet showed reduced mortality (compared with those fed normal diets), when transferred immediately or gradually to full strength sea water.

Even the transfer of tilapia, a freshwater (non-anadromous) species, to saltwater (15–20‰) conditions was easier for fish that were pre-acclimatized by adding salt to their diet (Fontainhas-Fernandes et al., 2001). Feeding of dietary sodium chloride considerably enhanced the survival rates of tilapia O. mossambicus up to 84%, and the O. aureus/O. niloticus hybrids and O. spilurus up to 62 % and 50%, respectively, in sea water. Best survival rates were recorded after 2 weeks of feeding the salty diet for O. mossambicus and O. aureus/O. niloticus hybrids, whereas in O. spilurus best survival was not achieved until 3 weeks (Al-Amoudi, 1987). The same author suggested that gradual acclimation regimes of a salt diet did stimulate the osmoregulatory organs of different tilapia species and that the fish were able to regulate the osmotic concentration of the plasma throughout the experimental period. Dietary salt was also tried for the acclimation of common carp (Cyprinus carpio), another freshwater fish, to salt water and proved successful (Salman et al., 1997).

Both salty diets and exposure to brackish water during 6 days help brook charr face osmotic stress and improved their survival rate when introduced into full-strength sea water. The combined use of these preconditioning strategies might facilitate rearing this species in sea cages or silos (Pelletier and Besnor, 1992). One-year-old smolts of Arctic charr (Salvelinus alpinus L.) fed 9.5% NaCl diet had better hypo-osmoregulatory ability than those fed the 1.5% diet, and a level of gill Na^+/K^+-ATPase activity that was several times higher (Staurnes and Finstad, 2000). These results on Arctic charr indicate that a NaCl-enriched diet could be used to ensure sufficient hypo-osmoregulatory ability of charr's smolts that would otherwise have insufficient regulatory ability. The study of Gatlin et al. (1992) was the only trial in which unimproved survivability was reported of juvenile red drums transferred to full-strength seawater after 4 weeks of feeding while maintained in brackish or fresh water. Salt supplementation has not affected blood osmolality or total thyroid hormone levels.

The influence of fish size on survival during seawater adaptation has been investigated in rainbow trout by Salman and Eddy (1990). As seen in Figure 5, fish of 40 g and more survive the seawater challenge better than smaller ones. Nearly 90% survival was recorded in large-sized fish with normal feeding, but with salt feeding, even small-sized fish (20–40 g) had better survival. Similar observations were recorded by Bendezu-Lopez et al. (2004) in triploid brook charr (Salvelinus fontinalis) who stated that mortality was significantly lower on the basis of size. Fish of 100 g weight displayed less than 5% of mortality compared to 32% and 23% in non-supplemented and supplemented salty diet fish respectively.

Failure to survive in sea water could be attributed partly to reduced feeding activity and also failure to activate and induce ionoregulatory mechanism to remove excess ions from the body (Eddy, 1982). The above SW survival findings apparently

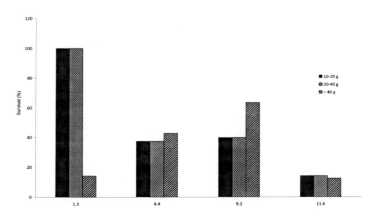

Figure 5.
Percentage survival of rainbow trout of different sizes gradually transferred to sew water and fed normal (N 1.3 %) and salt-enriched diets (LS 4.5 %, MS 9.2 % and HS 11.6 %). There was no previous salt feeding in fresh water. Results represent 25 fish per tank, no SE bars due to tank effect being n = 1, (redrawn from raw data in Salman, 1987).

confirmed the beneficial role of salt diet during the adjustment phase of adaptation which is characterized by increased plasma osmotic concentration. Contrary to the sudden increase in plasma osmotic concentration recorded in the fish transferred directly from freshwater to 60% seawater (Bath and Eddy, 1979), high salt diet feeding prior to the transfer resulted in only a slight increase in the plasma osmotic concentration in tilapia adapted to seawater (Al-Amoudi, 1987). Based on the results of the study of Perry *et al.* (2006), the mechanism underlying the increased survivability is salt-induced structural and molecular re-modelling of the gill to partial seawater phenotype. Salt-enriched diets therefore could have a practical effect on the activation of some physiological mechanisms involved in salt secretion.

After the osmotic shock of sea-water transfer, salt-fed rainbow trout seemed to resume feeding earlier than those fed on normal food (Salman and Eddy, 1990), which could be related to intestinal ion absorption during the adjustment phase of adaptation (Shehadeh and Gordon, 1969; Potts, 1970). Changes in gastric acid and enzyme secretion could also be significant (see more details in the role of gut section). Diet is an important source of salts that could satisfy the osmoregulatory requirements of the fish in brackish and freshwater. It might spare energy used for osmoregulation, and leaving more energy for growth (Zaugg, *et al.*, 1983; Gatlin *et al.*, 1992; Fontainhas-Fernandes *et al.*, 2001). The effect of dietary salt during the regulative phase of sea-water adaptation, when control is established over changes in blood plasma electrolytes, may be associated with activation of the branchial ion excretion mechanisms. This conclusion is supported by the reported elevation in chloride cell numbers and activation of gill Na^+/K^+-ATPase (Salman and Eddy, 1987; Perry et al., 2006).

4.7 Effect of dietary salt on blood parameters

4.7.1 Impact on blood osmolality and plasma ions

The sudden increase in plasma osmotic concentration of fish transferred directly from fresh water to sea water is a well known phenomena in fish subjected to an external salt load. Feeding on a high salt diet prior to the transfer often results in only a slight increase in the plasma osmotic concentration in many fish species adapted to seawater (Al-Amoudi, 1987; Gatlin et al., 1992; Fontainhas-Fernandes et al., 2001). More recently, Lim et al. (2006) found that feeding dietary salt to Nile tilapia had no effect on blood glucose and haematocrit levels, but serum osmolality reduced in fish fed the dietary salt.

Analysis of sodium: chloride ratio in fish maintained on salt-enriched diets indicated that elevated dietary NaCl exposure increased plasma Cl^- to a greater extent than that of plasma Na^+, which is generally indicative of the condition of metabolic acidosis reflected in a decrease in plasma HCO_3^- concentration (Wood, 2001). Interestingly, metabolic acidosis associated with a decrease in the strong ion difference (SID) between plasma Na^+ and Cl^- concentrations is a well-known effect of exposure to high waterborne NaCl levels (reviewed by Walker et al., 1989). The mechanism of this differential effect of elevated dietary NaCl exposure on the relative plasma concentrations of Na^+ and Cl^- is at present unknown but we speculate a greater inhibition of Na^+ influx and (or) greater stimulation of Na^+ efflux relative to Cl^-. Indeed, some mechanisms of red blood cell volume regulation can cause differential transport of Na^+ and Cl^- between the plasma and red blood cells compartments.

Results of Fontainhas-Fernandes et al. (2000) on tilapia, revealed that the normally-fed group showed a more rapid increase in plasma osmolality and Cl^- concentration than fish fed dietary salt, especially when tilapia are transferred to 20‰ seawater. The timing of the decrease in plasma Cl^- and osmolality and the increase in gill Na^+/K^+-ATPase activity observed in this study are consistent with the known role of this enzyme in salt secretion to maintain ionic balance in seawater-adapted fish (Zadunaisky, 1984).

4.7.2 Impact on blood pressure and hypertension

Recent experiments conducted by Chen et al. (2007) on rainbow trout to investigate impact of dietary salt on arterial blood pressure proved that fish fed on salt-enriched diet exhibited a 37% elevation of dorsal aortic pressure (from 23.8 to 32.6 mmHg) and an 18% increase in ventral aortic pressure (from 33.0 to 38.9 mmHg). The hypertension presumably reflected the increase in cardiac output (from 31.0 to 36.4 ml $min^{-1}kg^{-1}$) because systemic and branchial resistances were statistically unaltered by salt feeding. The chronic hypertension was associated with a decrease in the pressor responses of the systemic vasculature to catecholamines and hypercapnia in the salt-fed fish.

Quite recently Olson and Ogland (2008) investigated the effect of dietary salt of freshwater fish on fluid compartments, blood pressure and venous capacitance. They found that vascular capacitance in seawater fish appeared to be continuous with the capacitance curve of freshwater fish and reflect a passive volume-dependent unloading of the venous system of freshwater fish. Vascular capacitance curves for freshwater fish fed on high salt diet were displaced upward and parallel to those of freshwater fish, and indicative of an active increase in unstressed blood volume without any change in vascular compliance. These studies are the first in any vertebrate to measure the relationship between fluid compartments and cardiovascular function during independent manipulation of volume and salt balance and they show that volume, but not salt balance, is the primary determinant of blood pressure in trout. They also present a new paradigm with which to investigate the relative contributions of water and salt balance in cardiovascular homeostasis.

4.8 Dietary salt and the role of the gut

In addition to the routine digestive and absorptive functions of the gastrointestinal tract, it plays an important role in ionic and osmoregulation (Evans 1979; Smith *et al.* 1989). It has a hypo-osmoregulatory role in marine fish which drink seawater to replace water lost diffusively to their environment. Ingested seawater passes through the gastrointestinal tract and ions must be differentially absorbed across the intestinal epithelium to facilitate water absorption. A large portion of Cl^- and water absorption in the intestine is accomplished via apical Cl^-/HCO_3^- exchange (Grosell et al., 2005), making intestinal anion exchange an important addition to long-recognized co-transporters Na^+-Cl^- and Na^+-K^+-$2Cl^-$ in the marine teleosts intestine. It is now being recognized that intestinal anion exchange is responsible for high luminal HCO_3^- and CO_3^{2-} concentrations while at the same time contributing substantially to intestinal Cl^- and thereby water absorption, which is vital for marine fish osmoregulation.

In species examined to date as reviewed by Grosell (2006), the majority of $HCO3^-$ secreted by the apical anion exchange process is derived from hydration of metabolic CO_2 with the resulting H^+ being extruded via a Na^+/H^+ exchange mechanism in the basolateral membrane. The basolateral H^+ extrusion is critical for the apical anion exchange and relies on the Na^+ gradient established by the Na^+-K^+-ATPase. This enzyme thereby ultimately fuels the secondary active transport of HCO_3^- and Cl^- by the apical anion exchanger. High cellular HCO_3^- concentrations (> 10 mmol l^{-1}) are required for the anion exchange process and could be the result of both a high metabolic activity of the intestinal epithelium and a close association of the anion exchange protein and the enzyme carbonic anhydrase. The anion exchange activity *in vivo* is likely most pronounced in the anterior segment and results in net intestinal acid absorption. In contrast to other water absorbing vertebrate epithelia, the marine teleost intestine absorbs what appears to be a hypertonic fluid to displace diffusive fluid loss to the marine environment.

Increased influx of dietary salts may cause changes in fluid absorption and/or secretion, and could also stimulate intestinal HCO_3^- secretion. The mechanisms of these intestinal transport properties (and changes therein) may be unique to digestive physiology or may be identical to mechanisms utilized to osmoregulate in a marine environment (Taylor and Grosell, 2006). Dabrowski *et al.* (1986) found that feeding in seawater and freshwater drastically changes the ionic balance in the euryhaline fish intestine, even though the salt intake that accompanies drinking in seawater fish largely surpassed dietary intake (Shehadeh and Gordon, 1969). Accordingly dietary salt intake may increase the osmoregulatory function of the gastrointestinal tract.

Little Na^+ is lost through faecal material even in fish fed high Na^+ diets (Salman and Eddy, 1988a), suggesting that reduction of gastrointestinal Na^+ uptake may not be important in Na^+ homeostasis in freshwater fish. However, during simultaneous exposure of rainbow trout to elevated dietary NaCl and waterborne Cu, the gut appears to play a role in conserving Na^+ (Kamunde *et al.*, 2005). Apparently, compensatory gut Na^+ absorption occurs in the face of branchial loss when Na^+ availability via the diet is maintained. The amount of Na^+ absorbed from food is likely dependent on the fish's Na^+ balance.

4.9 Dietary salt and gill function

4.9.1 Impact on branchial ion fluxes

Fluxes of ions through the gills are mainly a function of the salt load imposed upon the fish (Eddy, 1982). In an attempt to calculate the internal salt load imposed by dietary salt in freshwater fish and drinking seawater, Salman (1987) found that the dietary ionic intake in fish fed a normal diet (1.3% NaCl) was 2.11 and 2.78 mmol $kg^{-1}day^{-1}$ for Na^+ and Cl^- respectively. In fish fed a high salt diet (11.6% NaCl), dietary Na^+ and Cl^- intake increased rapidly to an average of 19.2 and 21.9 mmol $kg^{-1}day^{-1}$ for Na^+ and Cl^- respectively. The increase in dietary ionic intake was not reflected in an increase of ionic excretion via the faeces, but through an increase in plasma ions due to an efficient gut absorption mechanism. Such a salt load (0.8 mmol kg^{-1} h^{-1}) was recorded as a result of feeding rainbow trout 10 g food containing 11.6% salt kg^{-1} day^{-1} and represents one third of the salt load imposed by drinking 5 mmol kg^{-1} h^{-1} of water in the seawater-adapted fish. Figure 6 summarizes the branchial ionic movement in response to the internal dietary salt load. Two mechanisms were acting:

1. Reduction in the ionic uptake mechanism from 0.249 mmol kg^{-1} h^{-1} in normally fed fish to 0.072 mmol kg^{-1} h^{-1} in salt-fed fish. This may indicate that freshwater fish have not activated the ionic uptake mechanism to compensate the passive losses of ions because of the availability of sufficient dietary ions.

2. Increase in branchial ion efflux from 0.257 mmol kg^{-1} h^{-1} in normally fed fish to a three-fold increase of 0.733 mmol kg^{-1} h^{-1} in salt-fed fish. The partition of total efflux into passive and active components needs more investigation.

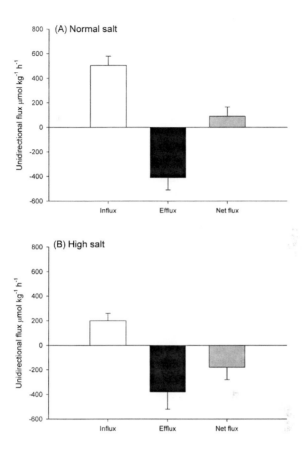

Figure 6.
Unidirectional Na⁺ fluxes in the gill of rainbow trout fed on **(a)** *normal and* **(b)** *salt-enriched diet (0.8 mmol kg⁻¹ h⁻¹) for 2 months. Data represents the average ± SE of six fish per sample for a typical 24 hour period (adapted from Salman, 1987).*

Smith *et al.* (1989) also calculated and compared dietary sodium intake for freshwater salmonids feeding in the wild (invertebrate diet), and in captivity (pellet diet), with published branchial sodium influx values. Dietary sodium intake (mmol kg⁻¹ per month) increases from winter minimum values of 5 and 30–40 to reach maximum values in summer of 175 and 240 for invertebrate and pellet diet, respectively. In summer, dietary sodium intake for fish feeding in the wild was of the same magnitude as branchial sodium influx. Smith *et al.* (1995) confirmed the previously noticed observation by Salman (1987) by stating that dietary Na⁺ loads were almost completely absorbed in rainbow trout within 7 h, and branchial Na⁺ excretion commenced within 1 h. Almost all the dietary salt is lost via the gills, suggesting an active role of the gills in salt excretion in the freshwater fish. The Na^+ balance also confirmed the similarity in action between internal (dietary) and external (seawater medium) salt loads in activating the gill osmoregulatory mechanisms such as increase chloride cell number and $Na^+/K^+ATPase$ (Salman and Eddy, 1987). Benefits of dietary salt may be twofold, replacing branchial ion loss and stimulating branchial uptake.

Smith *et al.* (1995) explained the control mechanism of branchial ion fluxes in salt-fed fish depending on the amount of salt load. They found that Na^+ loads of less than 1 mmol kg^{-1} in salt-fed fish were lost through the gills by a significant decrease in Na^+ influx and with an unaltered Na^+ efflux rate (compared with Na^+ fluxes in unfed fish). At higher salt loads (> 18 mmol kg^{-1}), Na^+ loss increased as a result of significantly higher Na^+ efflux rates, with no further decrease in Na^+ influx rate. Similar findings of branchial net Na^+ efflux were previously reported by Salman (1987) in rainbow trout fed high salt diet. The same author reported a reduction in Na^+ influx and nearly three times as much Na^+ was excreted via the gills by salt-fed fish than normally fed controls (Figure 6). The exposure of freshwater fish to elevated dietary NaCl was found to suppress branchial uptake and increase the diffusive efflux of Na^+ via the gills by Kamunde *et al.* (2003), and Pyle *et al.* (2003). These results show that branchial Na^+ fluxes may be rapidly adjusted in response to prevailing conditions with possible control mechanisms.

4.9.2 Impact on chloride cells and Na^+/K^+-ATPase

Activation of ion fluxes through the gills in response to dietary salt has led to more detailed investigations of the role of gills. Activation of a sodium pump (Na^+/K^+-ATPase) was previously reported by Zaugg *et al.* (1983). Salman and Eddy (1987) demonstrated that rainbow trout fed a diet enriched in NaCl exhibited a significant increase in the number of branchial chloride cells (10% of total branchial cells) and an increase in Na^+/K^+-ATPase activity (50% or more), compared with a 12% increase in chloride cells contribution and an 8-fold increase in seawater adapted fish (Langdon and Thorpe, 1984). Trombetti *et al.* (1996) also showed higher gill Na^+/K^+-ATPase activity and chloride cells number in trout receiving dietary NaCl in fresh water. The dietary salt treatment changed the enzyme activation kinetics by ATP and Na^+. There was also a higher gill Na^+/K^+-ATPase activity and higher plasma levels of cortisol in tilapia fed on a salty diet than in the control group (Fontanhas-Fernandes *et al.*, 2000). All these results confirmed the similarity between the responses elicited by salt ingestion and those occurring when freshwater fish are transferred to sea water. Both processes result in transient increases in internal salt levels.

Building on these observations, Perry *et al.* (2006) demonstrated that internal salt loading alone is able to induce various elements of the seawater gill phenotype. These include up-regulation of three ion transport genes, cystic fibrosis transmembrane conductance regulator (CFTR), $Na^+/K^+/2Cl^-$ co-transporters (NKCC1) and Na^+/K^+-ATPase, which are essential for ionic regulation in seawater, and the appearance of chloride cell-accessory cell complexes of fish inhabiting seawater. These data provide compelling evidence that gill remodelling during migration from freshwater to seawater may involve sensing of elevated levels of internal salt. The idea that internal salt sensing may promote physiological responses accompanying migration of fish into sea water was also proposed by Nearing *et al.* (2002).

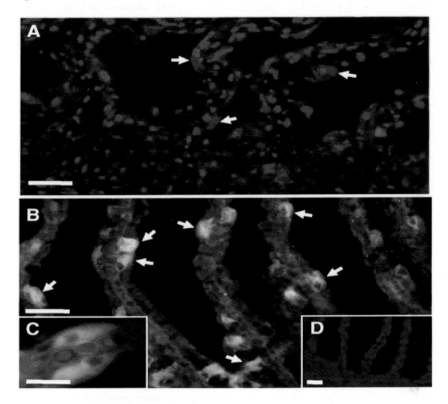

Figure 7.
  Elevated dietary salt intake increases the expression of NKCC1 in branchial mitochondria-rich cells. Localisation of Na⁺/K⁺-ATPase (NKA; red), NKCC1 (green) and nuclei (blue) in gill sections from **(a)** *control or* **(b,c)** *salt-fed fish. Areas of co-localisation of NKA with NKCC1 appear as yellow/orange.* **(d)** *is a representative image depicting a gill section from which both primary antibodies were omitted. Arrows in* **(a)** *indicate cells exhibiting NKA immunofluorescence, and in* **(b)** *co-localisation of NKA and NKCC1. Scale bars, 10 μm. From Perry et al. (2006).*

Fish fed a salt enriched diet displayed obvious branchial expression of NKCC1 that was co-localized with NKA (Na^+/K^+-ATPase) and thus appeared to be uniquely confined to mitochondrial rich cells, MRCs (Figure 7b). Perry *et al.* (2006) postulated that, western blots clearly revealed the presence of NKCC1 protein (immunoreactive band at 160 kDa) in three of the four salt-fed fish that were examined. The levels of NKCC1 and CFTR mRNA were increased 6- and 15-fold, respectively, compared to control fish (Figure 7c). In control fish, NKCC1 was undetectable by immunofluorescence (Figure 7a). Structural alteration in gills was also noticed in response to salt feeding. Salman and Eddy (1987) reported an increase in microridges on the lamellar epithelial surface, a dotted appearance of chloride cells resulted from numerous short projections at the cell surface (Figure 8). Elevated dietary salt intake results in the appearance of seawater-like chloride cells (Perry *et al.*, 2006).

According to Fontanhas-Fernandes *et al.* (2000), tilapia fed dietary salt for 3 weeks showed some gill morphological features in freshwater similar to those previously described in seawater-adapted tilapia. Most of the mitochondrial rich cells (MRC) exhibited a deep apical crypt and a more developed tubular system than in the control group in addition to the organization of most MRC in multicellular complexes and the development of apical interdigitation and leaky junctions. These changes are similar to those described generally in the MRC of marine and seawater-adapted teleosts (Hwang, 1987; Cioni *et al.* 1991).

4.10 Dietary salt and the role of kidney

The gill is the main organ for regulating Na^+ in freshwater fish, while the kidney contributes 10–30% to whole-body Na^+ balance depending on the prevailing conditions (Wood, 1995). The role of the kidney becomes greater when branchial Na^+ regulating mechanisms are impaired in fish due to toxicants exposure, or when faced with higher dietary Na^+ loads (Kamunde *et al.*, 2005). Renal response to dietary Na^+ load was investigated in detail by Salman and Eddy (1988b) in non smolting rainbow trout. It showed an increase in Na^+ excretion compared with normally fed fish (Figure 9). This was accompanied by an increase in urinary flow rate and glomerular filtration rate, together with a slight reduction in ionic reabsorption capacity. The renal Na^+ excretion rate was doubled to about 100 $\mu mol\ kg^{-1}\ h^{-1}$, but was not entirely a consequence of a reduction in tubular ionic reabsorption, as increased glomerular filtration was also involved. A diuretic response to feeding or infusion of ions has previously been reported in rainbow trout (Hunn, 1982; Rankin *et al.*, 1984).

Such increases in renal Na^+ excretion could simply be related to the role of the kidney in freshwater teleosts which acts to prevent any disturbances in extracellular fluid created by an increase in plasma electrolytes in response to dramatic increase in gastric Na^+ and Cl^- (Wheatly *et al.*, 1984). The mechanism responsible for the renal elimination of extra salt load in freshwater fish remains unclear. Regulation of glomerular filtration and urinary flow rate, as well as distal salt reabsorption, in response to the state of salt balance might act under the control of renal and endocrine factors such as the renin-angiotensin system (Bailey and Randall, 1982). The possible stimulation of the atrial natriuretic factors (ANF) as suggested by Duff and Olson (1986) to increase diuresis and electrolytes excretion may also play a role, but the subject needs more investigation.

The relative roles of the kidney in ion regulation were also examined by Curtis and Wood (1992) in freshwater rainbow trout chronically infused with 140 mmol l^{-1} NaCl. Infusions of salt caused an increase of about 125% in glomerular filtration rate when expressed as a percentage of the infusion rate, but urine flow rate (UFR) increased by only 80%, reflecting increased tubular reabsorption of

(a)

(b)

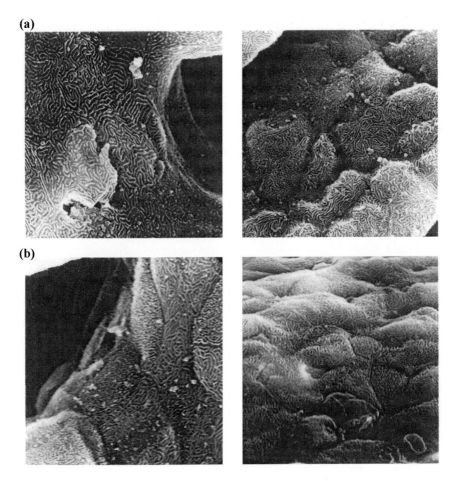

Figure 8.
Scanning electron micrographs of gill interlamellar surface of rainbow trout fed on normal (a) and salt-enriched diet (b) where frequent and large sized chloride cells are noted. Note the micro-ridged surface of the epithelial cells and chloride cells distinguished by the 'dotted' appearance of their surface. From Salman (1987).

H_2O. During NaCl infusion, virtually all of the extra Na^+ and Cl^- filtered were reabsorbed by the kidney tubules, resulting in an increased UFR with largely unchanged composition. It seems that the freshwater kidney functions to remove as much NaCl as possible from the urine, regardless of the NaCl load, and this role may also be supplemented by salt reabsorption in the bladder. In fish maintained on high salt diet, renal Na^+ concentrations recovered and surpassed values of the fish maintained on normal diet or high salt diet and Cu^{2+} exposure, suggesting that compensatory renal Na^+ retention occurs in animals faced with branchial Na^+ loss when Na^+ availability via the diet is maintained (Kamunde *et al.*, 2005).

4.11 Salt balance in fish fed salt-enriched diet

For fish to be in ionic balance, salt uptake should equal salt output. In fresh water, salt uptake by feeding fish includes branchial ion influx, oral ingestion of dietary and water ions, and on minor scale a possible ionic intake through the body surface. Salt output routes include branchial ionic efflux which represents the main route (Bath and Eddy, 1979) in addition to ionic excretion via urine (renal), faeces (faecal) and body surface. The influence of feeding status necessitates a reassessment of ionic efflux routes of the fasted fish. Although the gills of fed fish are still the main site of osmoregulation (Figure 9), their contribution is only 66% of the total Na^+-efflux, compared to more than 90% in fasted fish (Bath, 1979). The contribution of renal and faecal routes in total Na^+ excretion increased to 12% and 22% respectively in the fed fish compared with only 1% in the fasted fish.

Table 4. *Sodium balance in rainbow trout fed on normal (N) and high salt diets (HSD) in fresh water*

Source	N		HSD	
	mmol kg^{-1} h^{-1}	%	mmol kg^{-1} h^{-1}	%
Influx				
Branchial	0.249	73.88	0.072	8.26
Dietary	0.088	26.11	0.8	91.74
Drinking	0.00034	0.1	0.00035	0.04
Total	0.337		0.872	
Efflux				
Branchial	0.257	65.73	0.733	78.90
Renal	0.048	12.28	0.098	10.78
Faecal	0.086	21.99	0.078	8.58
Total	0.391		0.909	

N - 1.3 % NaCl, HSD - 11.6 % NaCl.

Salt balance data of rainbow trout fed normal (1.3% NaCl) and salt-enriched (11.6% NaCl) diets are shown in Table 4 and Figure 9 (Salman, 1987). The contribution of branchial efflux to the total Na^+ efflux increased to 79% in salt fed fish while those of renal and faecal excretion decreased to 11% and 8% respectively, compared with the values recorded for the normally-fed fish. This indicates that high levels of dietary salt stimulate the branchial efflux mechanism more than renal and faecal excretion. The contribution of branchial Na^+ efflux to the total efflux increased from 65.7% in fish fed the normal diet to 78.9% in the salt-fed fish, an increase corresponding with the increase in dietary salt load and reflecting the important role of branchial salt elimination. The contribution of renal and faecal efflux in normally-fed fish averaged 12.2% and 21.9% respectively. In contrast, renal and faecal salt excretions in the salt-fed fish represent only 10.7% and 8.5% respectively.

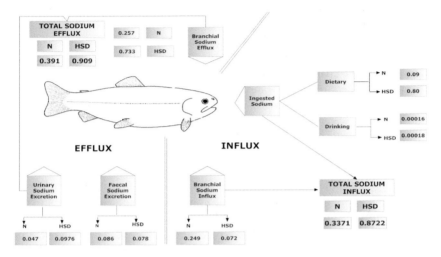

Figure 9.
   Schematic diagram of the salt balance (ionic influx and efflux) in rainbow trout fed on normal (N, 1.3 % NaCl) and high-salt (HSD, 11.6 % NaCl) diets. All values are in mmol kg^{-1} h^{-1} (Adapted from Salman, 1987).

4.12   Impact of dietary salt on tissue composition

4.12.1 Proximate composition

Few papers discuss the effect of dietary salt on proximate composition. Little effects have been reported for the salt diet on the proximate composition of the salt fed fish. The dry matter and ash contents were reported to be slightly increased with increasing salt supplementation by Tacon *et al.* (1984) and Nandeesha *et al.* (2000) in carp; and by Ogino and Kamizono (1975) in trout. The dry matter and ash content of muscle also rose slightly with increasing dietary salt in the diet of European sea bass (Eroldoğan *et al.*, 2005). This might be due to the higher mineral content in the salty diet. Duston (1993) found that muscle water content in trout reared in freshwater was not significantly affected by the experimental diets containing either control or 10% dietary salt.

An increase in protein and lipid content was noticed in rainbow trout (Orino and Kamizono, 1975) and common carp (Tacon *et al.*, 1984; Nandeesha *et al.*, 2000), but not in sea bass (Eroldoğan *et al.*, 2005). Viscera and hepatosomatic indices were not affected by salt inclusion. The body composition of the Asian sea bass was not significantly affected by salt feeding although, there was a trend showing less fat accumulation in the fish fed diets containing additional salt (Harpaz *et al.*, 2005).

4.12.2 Tissue ions and compartmental distribution

As a result of the efficient elimination of excess dietary salt load, tissue ionic retention was not seriously altered. According to Salman (1987) who studied the compartmental distribution of ions and water in rainbow trout fed different levels of salt, the ionic contents of many tissues showed a state of stability. Changes in the extracellular ions imposed by dietary salt have not affected the intracellular ionic content of the muscles and whole body. Significant ionic increase, however, was reported in organs such as gills, kidney and gut, being the sites of osmoregulation (Table 5). Slight changes in the distribution of water and ions between body compartments were reported in response to salt feeding as temporary regulating mechanisms to restore homeostasis. Slight gain in extracellular water and slight loss of cellular water was noticed in salt fed fish (Salman, 1987) leading to a slight increase in the ion spaces. Similar observations were noticed in tilapia upon transfer to seawater (Assem, 1981). Highly significant elevations in whole-body and tissue Na^+ levels in response to elevated dietary NaCl exposure has also been reported by Kamunde et al. (2005). Values of such elevations were: whole-body Na^+ concentrations significantly increased from 50–53 $\mu mol\ g^{-1}$ in control fish on a low salt diet, and 63–72 $\mu mol\ g^{-1}$ in fish maintained on high salt diet. Gill Na^+ concentration increased from 40–50 to 64–75 $\mu mol\ g^{-1}$ for the control and high salt diets respectively. Liver Na^+ concentrations increased dramatically in response to the high salt diet exposure, with values ranging from 42–50 $\mu mol\ g^{-1}$ in the controls to 70–88 $\mu mol\ g^{-1}$ in the group maintained on high salt diet. This is probably because tissue Na^+ concentration followed food Na^+ absorption from the gut which occurs relatively rapidly (Salman, 1987). However, Smith et al. (1995) did not find any difference in muscle Na^+ ion content of rainbow trout fed with diet containing salt levels between 0% (no added salt) and 12%. It seems that the regulatory mechanisms promptly control the attendant upsurge in tissue Na^+ concentrations.

Table 5. Ionic contents of selected tissues of rainbow trout fed on normal and salt-enriched diet for two months

Tissue	Normal diet (1.3% NaCl)		Salt diet (11.6% NaCl)	
	Sodium	Chloride	Sodium	Chloride
Gills	38.6 ± 4.8	43.8 ± 3.8	60.6 ± 6.3**	59.3 ± 6.7*
Liver	44.4 ± 0.8	55.2 ± 5.7	45.3 ± 4.4	55.4 ± 2.7
Gut	52.7 ± 5.1	65.2 ± 7.6	78.7 ± 2.7**	58.2 ± 7.3
Kidney	51.8 ± 3.1	55.0 ± 1.4	78.8 ± 2.1**	67.8 ± 5.6*
Muscles	17.7 ± 0.9	11.7 ± 3.0	20.2 ± 0.5*	12.7 ± 1.6
Whole body	40.9 ± 4.1	31.9 ± 1.4	42.1 ± 2.4	39.8 ± 4.3

Values are mmol kg^{-1} tissue water, average ± SE (n = 6). * and ** indicate significant differences at 0.05 and 0.01 in t-tests. (Adapted from Salman, 1987).

4.13   Dietary salt interactions

4.13.1   Interaction with hormones

It has been shown previously, that the transfer of fish from freshwater to sea water involves an increase in T4 and T3 metabolism, and a stimulation of deiodination of T4 to T3, suggesting an increased requirement for T3 in seawater (Leloup and Lebel, 1993). Several other studies have demonstrated that the administration of thyroid hormones increases the survival and growth of fish in seawater (Saunders *et al.*, 1985; Howerton *et al.*, 1992), a practice seems similar to that of salt feeding.

To understand the interaction between dietary salt and thyroid hormones regarding the osmoregulatory functions, the results of three studies are discussed. According to Gatlin *et al.* (1992), none of the salt supplementations to the red drum juveniles food had significantly affected blood osmolality or total thyroid hormone levels at 4 weeks, or the ability of fish maintained in brackish or freshwater to survive transfer to full strength seawater at 8 weeks. Results of Fontaínhas-Fernandes *et al.* (2000) showed that pre-acclimation with a salt-enriched diet increased growth rates of males and females tilapia (*Oreochromis niloticus*) reared in 10‰ brackish water and was accompanied by higher plasma thyroid hormones than in freshwater. In another experiment on rainbow trout, Trombetti *et al.* (1996) investigated the effects of oral T3 and NaCl administration on trout hypo-osmoregulatory mechanisms. During the freshwater phase T3-fed trout showed a two fold higher serum T3 level and unchanged gill Na^+/K^+-ATPase activity and chloride cells number, whereas salt fed trout showed higher gill Na^+/K^+-ATPase activity and chloride cells number. The authors concluded that T3 administration promotes the development of hypo-osmoregulatory mechanisms of trout but it leaves the Na^+/K^+-ATPase activity, while salt feeding promotes activity of Na^+/K^+-ATPase activity. It appears that a complimentary hypo-osmoregulatory mechanism could be achieved by the combination of T3 and NaCl supplements in the diet, but the subject needs more investigation.

Hormones like cortisol, prolactin and growth hormones are widely considered to be osmoregulatory hormones. McCormick (2001) suggested that growth hormone promotes acclimation to seawater, prolactin promotes acclimation to freshwater, and cortisol interacts with both of these hormones thus having a dual osmoregulatory function. Those hormones might well be related to salt feeding as an internal tool of seawater adaptation. Fontaínhas-Fernandes (2001) studied the relationship between salt feeding and cortisol levels upon transferring tilapia (*Oreochromis niloticus*) from fresh water to 15‰ and 20‰ sea water. Following transfer from fresh water to 15‰ seawater, fish fed normal or salt diets exhibited a small decrease in plasma cortisol levels, but this began to increase at 48 h. At all sampling periods, the salt fed fish group showed similar values of cortisol to those obtained with the control group. Salt-fed fish transferred to 20‰ sea water showed plasma cortisol levels higher than the normal-fed group, and the differences were statistically significant ($p < 0.05$) at 6 and 24 h. The seawater group showed higher plasma levels of cortisol than the control, which maintained its initial levels during the experiment.

The hormonal regulation of intestinal water transport has received special attention. Several hormones have been reported to stimulate or inhibit water fluxes across the intestine. Both cortisol and ACTH were shown to significantly increase the flux of water across the intestine in freshwater-acclimated eels, while prolactin acts antagonistically to cortisol and decreases water fluxes in seawater-acclimated eels (Utida et al., 1972). Ando et al. (1992) found that eel atrial natriuretic peptide (ANP) inhibited the serosa-negative transepithelial potential difference and short-circuit current, accompanied by a decrease in NaCl and water absorption across the seawater eel intestine. ANP can inhibit net salt absorption by 50–60% after approximately one hour exposure to the hormone. They also reported that serotonin and acetylcholine, both inhibited water fluxes by around one third. Salman (1987) suggested that ANP may have a role in sodium excretion via the kidney of salt-fed fish similar to a previously reported functional role of reducing tubular Na^+ reabsorption and increasing Na^+ excretion in dogs.

4.13.2   Interaction with environmental acidity

Osmoregulatory disturbances in response to low environmental pH have been reported by many authors (Wood, 1989; Reid, 1995; D'Cruz and Wood, 1998). Sodium influx at the gills is depressed due to a possible competition between Na^+ and H^+ on transport sites or access channels leading to an ionic lose. Apart from such phenomena high ambient H^+ concentration impairs the ability of fish to excrete H^+ via both Na^+/H^+ exchange (NHE) mechanisms and by H^+ pumps due to unfavourable gradients. This, in turn, impairs Na^+ uptake via NHE and via channels due to a lesser degree of hyper polarization caused by reduced pump activity. Regardless of the mode of proton extrusion, cellular acidification is an outcome which in turn limits the availability of cellular substrate ($HCO3^-$) for $Cl^-/HCO3^-$ exchange and Cl^- uptake. Dietary NaCl under such circumstances may become essential for maintaining homeostasis during acid stress. It may provide energy necessary to meet increased demands in a low-pH environment and it may compensate for branchial ion loss.

D'Cruz and Wood (1998) evaluated the role of dietary energy and salt in response to acid stress. Following the initial acid challenge, typical osmoregulatory disturbances were observed in juvenile rainbow trout, but these disappeared after 20 days of exposure. Fish fed the regular-salt diets maintained the restored ionic homeostasis, whereas those fed low-salt diets did not, regardless of the energy content of the diet. In another experiment, trout maintained on a limited dietary regime of commercial fish food and chronically exposed to low pH (5.2), lost Na^+ at a net rate of about 50 $\mu mol\ kg^{-1}\ h^{-1}$ (1200 $\mu mol\ kg^{-1}\ day^{-1}$) which was higher than Na^+ intake from the low-salt diet.

4.13.3 Interaction with toxicity

Supplementation of fish diets with NaCl has shown promise in preventing toxicity to waterborne cations, such as copper in rainbow trout, by elevating sodium levels in blood. Kamunde *et al.* (2005) stated that, dietary NaCl protected fish against waterborne Cu^{2+} toxicity. They summarize the beneficial effects of salt feeding in Cu^{2+}-exposed (55 µg l^{-1} waterborne Cu) juvenile rainbow trout (*Oncorhynchus mykiss*) as follows:

1. Mortality was reduced to (11%) in fish fed on high salt diet (11% NaCl) compared with 26% mortality in fish maintained on the lower salt diet (1.4 % NaCl).
2. Waterborne Cu^{2+} exposure inhibited growth by 56 % in fish maintained on the lower salt diet, and by 35% in those maintained on the high salt diet.
3. Exposure to elevated waterborne Cu^{2+} increased whole-body and tissue Cu^{2+} levels, whereas exposure to high salt diet decreased these levels.
4. The whole-body and tissue Cu^{2+} concentrations were consistently lower in Cu exposed fish maintained on high salt diet relative to those maintained on low salt diet.
5. Plasma Na^+ and Cl^- levels were elevated by high salt diet exposure and reduced by waterborne Cu^{2+} exposure, whereas plasma Cu^{2+} levels were decreased and increased by exposure to high salt diet and waterborne Cu, respectively.

These results demonstrate that elevated dietary NaCl modulates Na^+ and Cl^- homeostasis and reduces accumulation and toxicity of waterborne Cu. The hydrated aqua form of Cu^{2+} is large and can therefore compete with Na^+ for diffusion sites on membranes. Moreover, the affinity of Cu^{2+} for binding (uptake) sites on the gill surface is more than that of Na^+ by four-fold to compensate the lower concentration of Cu^{2+} in natural waters (Santore *et al.*, 2001). Early studies of the interactions between Na^+ and Cu^{2+} in freshwater fish have showed that acute exposure of fish to waterborne Cu^{2+} reduces plasma Na^+ and Cl^- concentrations (Stagg and Shuttleworth, 1982) as a consequence of inhibition of branchial Na^+ and $Cl-$ uptake processes (Laurén and Mc-Donald, 1986). Copper competitively and non-competitively inhibits the basolaterally located sodium pump, Na^+/K^+-ATPase (Li *et al.*, 1998), leading to the impairment of branchial ionoregulatory mechanisms. All these mechanisms of toxicity are directly or indirectly associated with Na^+ metabolism. Handy *et al.* (2006) reviewed the evidence for Na^+ and Cu^{2+} interactions, and put it into the fundamental models for Cu^{2+} or Na^+ transport pathways. If membrane potential is altered, then so is the electrochemical gradient for Cu^{2+} uptake from the medium. Thus, apparent "Na^+- sensitive copper uptake could also be related to changes in Na^+/K^+- ATPase activity.

4.14 Conclusions

The present findings on the nutritional and physiological impacts of dietary NaCl in fish nutrition and seawater adaptation are summarised in Tables 6 and 7. They also illustrate fields that need further investigation. Some represent controversial aspects, while others are new approaches to clarify causes of fish responses or interactions with hormonal actions and responses towards toxicants.

Table 6. *Summary of nutritional impact of dietary NaCl on fish nutrition in terms of the up to date findings and aspects which need further future investigation*

Parameter	Present findings	Future investigation
Dietary level	Levels at 1–4% are acceptable but higher levels caused nutrient dilution and growth impairment.	1. Testing the use of high salt level without causing nutrient dilution. 2. Studying salt contents of fish meal substituted rations.
Growth	Impairment at levels higher than 4%.	Studying nutrient balance at high salt levels.
Feed intake	1. No effect on appetite. 2. Presence of compensation mechanism 3. Earlier return to appetite after osmotic shock.	Testing *ad lib* feeding for salty diets.
Feed conversion	1. Negative correlation at high levels. 2. Beneficial with low levels and balanced ration.	Test high levels but in balanced ration.
Apparent Digestibility	Beneficial at low levels.	Examining the digestive enzymes activity under salt load.
Food evacuation	Accelerated by dietary salt leading to early return of appetite.	Causes of acceleration compared with indigestible carbohydrates. Relationship between digestibility and evacuation of salty diet.

Table 7. *Physiological impacts of dietary NaCl on fish in terms of present findings and future investigations*

Parameter	Present findings	Future investigation
Seawater adaptation	1. Beneficial for euryhaline and freshwater fish. 2. Better feeding and growth in sea water.	Quantifying levels of dietary salt and time period of feeding in fresh water before transfer.
Branchial ion fluxes	Represents the main route of ion excretion under internal salt load.	Quantifying unidirectional ion fluxes of salt fed fish in fresh and sea water.
Chloride Cells	1. Increase in number 2. Ultra-structural changes approved.	Gill phenotype; ion transport genes and remodelling.
Gut function	Efficient ion transport approved.	Intestinal ionic exchange transporters such as apical HCO_3^-/H^+, co-transporters Na^+-Cl^- and $Na^+-K^+-2Cl^-$.
Kidney function	Dietary salt increases urinary flow rate; glomerular filtration rate and urinary ionic excretion.	1. Role of the decreased tubular ionic reabsorption 2. Role of endocrine factors such as rennin and atrial natriuretic factors (ANF).
Tissue ionic distribution	1. Increase of ionic content of osmoregulatory tissues (gills, kidney and gut). 2. Gain in extracellular water loss, cellular water and increase in ion spaces.	Detailed investigation of compartmental distribution of extra- and intra cellular ions and water.
Ionic balance	Major rule of gills (66%) and minor role of urinary and faecal ionic excretion.	Quantifying the ionic excretion by various routes.
Interactions	Little is known about 1. Hormonal interaction 2. Low pH 3. copper and nitrite toxicity.	1. Na^+- sensitive copper uptake and Cl-methaemglobin in nitrite toxicity. 2. Effect of cellular acidification Cl^-/HCO_3^- and Na^+/H^+ exchange. 3. Interactions with osmoregulatory hormones

References

Al-Amoudi, M. M. (1987). The effect of high salt diet on the direct transfer of *Oreochromis mossambicus, O. spilurus/O. niloticus* hybrids to sea water. Aquaculture 64: 333–338.

Ando, M., Kondo K. and Takei Y. (1992). Effects of eel atrial natriuretic peptide on NaCl and water transport across the intestine of the seawater eel. J Comp Physiol B 162: 436–439.

Assem, H. (1981). Problems of osmomineral regulation in the euryhaline teleosts *Sarotherodon mossambicus.* Comp Biochem Physiol 74A: 531–536.

Bailey, J. R. and Randall, D. J. (1982). Renal perfusion pressure and rennin secretion in the rainbow trout *Salmo gairdneri.* Comp J Zool 59: 1220–1226.

Basulto, S. (1976). Induced saltwater tolerance in connection with inorganic salts in the feeding of Atlantic salmon (*Salmo salar* L.). Aquaculture 8: 45–55.

Bath, N. R. and Eddy, F. B. (1979). Salt and water balance in rainbow trout (*Salmo gairdneri*) rapidly transferred from freshwater to seawater. J Exp Biol 83: 193–202.

Bendezu-Lopez, R. M., Francois, N. R. and Lamarre, S. G. (2004). Effect of size and diet on seawater mortality of triploid brook charr (*Salvelinus fontinalis*). Special Publication, Aquaculture Association of Canada, No. 19: 17–19.

Brett, J. R. (1979). Environmental factors and growth. In: Hoar W.S., Randall, D. J. and Brett, J.R. (eds) Fish Physiology vol. VIII, Academic Press, New York: 599–675.

Chen, X., Moon, T. W., Olson, K. R., Dombkowski R. A. and Perry S. F. (2007). The effects of salt-induced hypertension on 1-adrenoreceptor expression and cardiovascular physiology in the rainbow trout (*Oncorhynchus mykiss*). Am J Physiol 293: R1384–R1392.

Cioni, C., De Merich, D., Cataldi, E. and Cataudella, S. (1991). Fine structure of chloride cells in freshwater and saltwater-adapted *Oreochromis niloticus* (Linnaeus) and *Oreochromis mossambicus* (Peters). J Fish Biol 39: 197–209.

Cowey, C. P. and Sargent, J. R. (1979). Nutrition. In: In: Hoar W.S., Randall, D. J. and Brett, J.R. (eds) Fish Physiology vol. VIII, Academic Press, New York: 1–69.

Curtis, J. M. and Wood, C. M. (1992) Kidney and urinary bladder response of freshwater rainbow trout to isosmotic NaCl and $NaHCO_3$ infusion. J Exp Biol 173: 181–203.

Dabrowski, K., Leray, C., Nonnotte, G. and Colin, D. A. (1986). Protein digestion and ion concentrations in rainbow trout (*Salmo gairdnerii* Rich.) digestive tract in sea- and fresh water. Comp Biochem Physiol 83A: 27–39.

D'Cruz, L. M. and Wood, C. M. (1998). The influence of dietary salt and energy on the response to low pH in juvenile rainbow trout. Phys Zool 71: 642–657.

De la Fuente, J. L., Rumbero, A., Martín J. F. and Liras, P. (1997). DELTA-1 -piperideine-6-carboxylate dehydrogenase, a new enzyme that forms alpha-aminoadipate in *Streptomyces clavuligerus* and other cephamycin C-producing actinomycetes. J Biochem 327: 59–64.

Dockray, J. J., Reid, S. D. and Wood, C. M. (1996). Effects of elevated summer temperatures and reduced pH on metabolism and growth of juvenile rainbow trout (*Oncorhynchus mykiss*) on unlimited ration. Can J Fish Aquat Sci 25: 2752–2763.

Duff, D. W. and Olson, K. R. (1986) Trout vascular and renal responses to atrial natriuretic factor and heart extracts. Am J Physiol 20: R639–R642.

Duston J. (1993). Effects of dietary betain and sodium chloride on seawater adaptation in atlantic salmon parr (*Salmo salar* L.). Comp Biochem Physiol 105: 673–677.

Eddy, F. B. (1982). Osmotic and ionic regulation in captive fish with particular reference to salmonids. Comp Biochem Physiol 73B:125–143.

Evans, D. H. (1979). Osmotic and ionic regulation by freshwater and seawater fish. In: Ali, M. A. (ed.) Environmental Physiology of fish. Academic Press, New York: 93–122.

Eroldoğan, O. T., Kumlu, M. and Aktaş, M. (2004). Optimum feeding rate for European sea bass *Dicentrarchus labrax* reared in seawater and freshwater. Aquaculture, 231: 501–515.

Eroldoğan, O. T., Kumlu, M., Kır, M. and Kiris, G. A. (2005). Enhancement of growth and feed utilization of the European sea bass (*Dicentrarchus labrax*) fed supplementary dietary salt in freshwater. Aquacult Res 36: 361–369.

Fange, R. and Grove, D. (1979). Digestion. In: Hoar W.S., Randall, D. J. and Brett, J.R. (eds) Fish Physiology vol. VII, Academic Press, New York: 162–260.

Fontainhas-Fernandes, A., Monteiro, M., Gomes, E., Reis-Henriques, M. A. and Coimbra, J. (2000). Effect of dietary sodium chloride acclimation on growth and plasma thyroid hormones in tilapia *Oreochromis niloticus* (L.) in relation to sex. Aquacult Res 31: 507– 517.

Fontainhas-Fernandes, A., Russell-Pinto, F., Gomes, E., Reis-Henriques M. A. and Coimbra, J. (2001). The effect of dietary sodium chloride on some osmoregulatory parameters of the teleost, *Oreochromis niloticus*, after transfer from freshwater to seawater. Fish Physiol Biochem 23: 307–316.

Garber, K. J. (1983). Effect of fish size, meal size and dietary moisture on gastric evacuation of pelleted diets by yellow perch (*Perca flavescens*). Aquaculture 34: 41–49.

Gatlin, D. M., Mackenzie, D. S., Craig, S. R. and Naill, W. H. (1992). Effects of dietary sodium chloride on red drum juveniles in waters of various salinities. Prog Fish Cult 54: 220–227.

Grosell, M. (2006). Intestinal anion exchange in marine fish osmoregulation. J Exp Biol 209: 2813–2827.

Grosell, M., Wood, C. M., Wilson, R. W., Bury, N. R., Hogstrand, C., Rankin, C. and Jensen, F. B. (2005). Bicarbonate secretion plays a role in chloride and water absorption of the European flounder intestine. Am J Physiol 288: 936–946.

Handy, R. D., Eddy, F. B. and Baines, H. (2006). Sodium-dependent copper uptake across epithelia: a review of rationale with experimental evidence from gill and intestine. Biochim Biophys Acta 1566 :104 –115.

Harpaz, S., Hakim Y., Slosman, T. and Eroldoğan, O. T. (2005). Effects of adding salt to the diet of Asian sea bass *Lates calcarifer* reared in fresh or salt water recirculating tanks, on growth and brush border enzyme activity. Aquaculture 248: 315–324.

Hilton, J. W., Atkinson, J. L. and Slinger, S. J. (1983). Effect of increased dietary fibers on the growth of rainbow trout (*Salmo gairdneri*). Can J Fish Aquat Sci 40: 81–85.

Howerton, R. D., Okimoto, D. K. and Grau, E. G. (1992). The effect of orally administered 17αmethyltestosterone and 3,3` triiodo L-thyronine on growth of seawater adapted tilapia, *Oreochromis mossambicus* (Peters). Aquacult Fish Manag 23:123–128.

Hunn, J. B. (1982). Urine flow rate in freshwater salmonids: a review. Prog Fish Cult 44: 119–125.

Hwang, P. P. (1987). Tolerance and ultrastructural responses of branchial chloride cells to salinity changes in the euryhaline teleost *Oreochromis mossambicus*. Mar Biol 94: 643–649.

Jobling, M. (1986). Gastrointestinal overload - a problem with formulated feeds. Aquaculture 51: 257–263.

Jurss, K., Bittorf, T. H. and Vokler, T. H. (1985). Influence of salinity and ratio of lipid to protein in diets on certain enzyme activities in rainbow trout (*Salmo gairdneri* Richardson). Comp Biochem Physiol 81B: 73–79.

Karnaky, K. J. Jr. (1998). Osmotic and ionic regulation. In: David, H. E. (ed) The Physiology of Fish, 2nd edition, CRC Press, Boca Raton: 159–176.

Kamunde, C. N., Niyoi, S. and Wood, C. M. (2005). Interaction of dietary sodium chloride and waterborne copper in rainbow trout (*Oncorhynchus mykiss*): copper toxicity and sodium chloride homeostasis. Can J Fish Aquat Sci 62: 390–399.

Kim, P. K., Kim Y. and Jeon, J. K. (2001). Enhancement of seawater by supplemented dietary salt in rainbow trout, *Oncorhynchus mykiss*. 6th Asian Fisheries Forum. The Asian Fisheries Society, Ksohsiung, Taiwan: 128.

Klein, S., Cohn, S. M. and Alpers, D. H. (1998). The alimentary tract in nutrition. In: Shils, M. E., Olson, A. J., Shike, M. and Ross, A. C. (eds) Modern Nutrition in Health and Disease, 9th edition, Williams and Wilkins, Baltimore, MD: 605–630.

Langdon, J. S. and Thorpe, J. E. (1984). Response of gill Na/K-ATPase activity, SDH activity and chloride cells to saltwater adaptation in Atlantic salmon, *Salmo salar* L., parr and smolt. J Fish Biol 24: 323–331.

Laurén, D. J. and McDonald, D.G. (1986). Influence of water hardness, pH, and alkalinity on the mechanisms of copper toxicity in juvenile rainbow trout, *Salmo gairdneri*. Can J Fish Aquat Sci 43: 1488–1496.

Leloup, J. and Lebel, J. M. (1993). Triiodothyronine is necessary for the action of growth hormone in acclimation to seawater of brown trout (*Salmo trutta*) and rainbow trout (*Oncorhynchus mykiss*). Fish Physiol Biochem 11: 165–173.

Li, J., Quabius, E. S., Wendelaar Bonga, S. E., Flik, G. and Lock, R. A. C. (1998). Effects of water-borne copper on branchial Na^+/K^+-ATPase activities in Mozambique tilapia (*Oreochromis mossambicus*). Aquat Toxicol 43: 1–11.

Lim, C., Yildirim-Aksoy, M., Welker, T. and Veverica, K. (2006). Effect of feeding duration of sodium chloride containing diets on growth performance and some osmoregulatory parameters of Nile tilapia (*Oreochromis niloticus*) after transfer to water of different salinities. J App Aquacult 18: 1–17.

MacKay, W. C. (1979). Electrolytes. Comp Anim Nutr 3: 80–99.

MacLeod, M. G. (1977). Effect of salinity on food intake, absorption and conversion in rainbow trout, *Salmo gairdneri*. Mar Biol 43: 93–102.

MacLeod, M. G. (1978). Relationships between dietary sodium chloride, food intake and food conversion in the rainbow trout. J Fish Biol 13: 73–78.

Mainoya, J. R. (1982). Water and NaCl absorption by the intestine of the tilapia (*Sarotherodon mossambicus*) adapted to freshwater or seawater and the possible role of prolactin and cortisol. J Comp Physiol 146: 1–7.

McCormick S. D. (2001). Endocrine control of osmoregulation in teleost fish. Am Zool 41: 781–794.

Mckay, I. R. and Gjerde, B. (1985). The effect of salinity on growth of rainbow trout. Aquaculture 49: 325–331.

Murray, M. W. and Andrews, J. W. (1979). Channel catfish: the absence of an effect of dietary salt on growth. Prog Fish Cult 4: 155 –156.

Musselman, N. J., Peterson, M. S. and Diehl, W. J. (1995). The influence of salinity and prey salt content on growth and intestinal Na^+/K^+-ATPase activity of juvenile bluegill, *Lepomis macrochirus*. Environ Biol Fish 42: 303–311.

Nahhas, R., Jones, N. V. and Goldspink, G. (1982). Growth, training and swimming ability of young trout (*Salmo gairdneri* Richardson) maintained under different salinity conditions. J Mar Biol Assoc U.K. 62: 699–708.

Nandeesha, M. C., Gangadhar, B., Keshavanath, P. and Varghes, T. J. (2000). Effect of dietary sodium chloride supplementation on growth, biochemical composition and digestive enzyme activity of young *Cyprinus carpio* (Linn.) and *Cirrhinus mrigala* (Ham). J Aquacult Tropic 1: 135–144.

Nearing, J., Betka, M., Quinn, S., Hentschel, H., Elger, M., Baum, M., Bai, M., Chattopadyhay, N., Brown, E. M. and Hebert, S. C. (2002). Polyvalent cation receptor proteins (CaRs) are salinity sensors in fish. Proc Natl Acad Sci USA 99: 9231–9236.

Olson K. R. and Hoagland T. M. (2008). Effects of freshwater/saltwater adaptation and dietary salt on fluid compartments, blood pressure and venous capacitance in trout. Am J Physiol 294: R1061–R1067.

Ogino, C. and Kamizono, M. (1975). Mineral requirements in fish. I. Effect of dietary salt mixture level on growth, mortality and body composition in rainbow trout and carp. Bull Jap Soc Sci Fish 41: 429–432.

Pellertier, D. and Besner, M. (1992). The effects of salty diets and gradual transfer to sea water on osmotic adaptation, gill Na⁺-K⁺-ATPase activation, and survival of brood charr, *Salvelinus fontinalis*, Mitchill. J Fish Biol 41: 791–803.

Perry, S. F., Rivero-Lopez, L., McNeill, B. and Wilson, J. (2006). Fooling a freshwater fish: how dietary salt transforms the rainbow trout gill into a seawater gill phenotype. J Exp Biol 209: 4591–4596.

Potts, W. T. W., Foster M. A. and Stather J. W. (1970). Salt and water balance in salmon smolts. J Exp Biol 52: 533–564.

Pyle, G. G., Kamunde, C. N., McDonald, D. G. and Wood, C. M. (2003). Dietary sodium inhibits aqueous copper uptake in rainbow trout, *Oncorhynchus mykiss*. J Exp Biol 206: 609–618.

Rankin, J. C., Henderson, I.W. and Brown, J.A. (1983). Osmoregulation and the control of kidney function. In: Rankin, J. C., Pitcher, T. J. and Duggan, R. (eds) Control Processes in Fish Physiology. Croom Helm, London: 66–88.

Reid S. D. (1995). Adaptation to and effects of acid water on the fish gill. In: Hochachka, P. W. and Mommsen, T. P. (eds) Biochemistry and Molecular Biology of Fishes. Elsevier, Amsterdam, 5: 213–227.

Salman, N. A. (1987). Nutritional and physiological effects of dietary NaCl on rainbow trout (*Salma gairdneri* Richardson) and its application in fish culture. PhD Thesis, University of Dundee, Scotland, UK. 467 pp.

Salman, N. A. and Eddy, F. B. (1987). Response of chloride cell numbers and gill Na⁺-K⁺-ATPase activity of freshwater rainbow trout (*Salmo gairdneri* Richardson). Aquaculture 61: 41–48.

Salman, N. A. and Eddy, F. B. (1988a). Effects of dietary sodium chloride, on growth, food intake and conversion efficiency in rainbow trout (*Salmo gairdneri*, Richardson). Aquaculture 70: 131–144.

Salman, N. A. and Eddy, F.B. (1988b). Kidney function in response to salt feeding in rainbow trout (*Salmo gaidneri* Richardson). Comp Physiol A 89: 535–539.

Salman, N. A. and Eddy, F. B. (1990). Increased sea-water adaptability of non-smolting rainbow trout by salt feeding. Aquaculture 86: 259–270.

Salman, N. A. (1993). The use of salt feeding for mariculture. J Fish Resources 13: 78–80.

Salman, N. A., Almahdawi, G. J. and Alrudainy, A. J. (1997). The use of dietary salt to increase adaptability of common carp (*Cyprinus carpio* L.) to salt water. Basrah J Agr Sci 10: 15–23.

Santore, R. C., Di Toro, D. M., Paquin, P. R., Allen, H. E. and Meyer, J. S. (2001). Biotic ligand model of the acute toxicity of metals. 2. Application to acute copper toxicity in freshwater fish and daphnia. Environ Toxicol Chem 20: 2397–2402.

Saunders, R. L., McCormick, S. D., Henderson, E. B., Eales, J. G. and Johnston, C. E. (1985). The effect of orally administered 3,5,3`-triiodo-L-thyronine on growth and salinity tolerance of Atlantic salmon (*Salmo salar*

L.). Aquaculture 45: 143–156.

Shaw, H. M., Saunders, R. L., Hall, M. C. and Henderson E. B. (1979). Effect of dietary sodium chloride on growth of Atlantic salmon (*Salmo salar*). J Fish Res Bd Can 32: 1813–1819.

Shehadeh Z. H. and Gordon, M. S. (1969). The role of the intestine in salinity adaptation of the rainbow trout (*Salmo gairdneri*). Comp Biochem Physiol 30: 397–418.

Shi Yen, S. and Li Shan, L. (2004). Dietary sodium chloride requirement determined for juvenile hybrid tilapia (*Oreochromis niloticus* x *O. aureus*) reared in fresh water and sea water. Brit J Nutr 91: 585–590.

Smith, N. F., Talbot, C. and Eddy, F. B. (1989). Dietary salt intake and its relevance to ionic regulation in freshwater salmonids. J Fish Biol 35: 749–753.

Smith, N. F. Eddy, F. B. and Talbot, C. (1995). Effect of dietary salt load on transepithelial Na^+ exchange in freshwater rainbow trout (*Oncorhynchus mykiss*). J Exp Biol, 198: 2359–2364.

Stagg, R. M. and Shuttleworth, T. J. (1982). The effects of copper on ionic regulation by the gills of the freshwater adapted flounder (*Platichthys flesus* L.). J Comp Physiol B 149: 83–90.

Staurnes, M. and Finstad, B. (2000) The effects of dietary NaCl supplement on hypo-osmoregulatory ability and sea water performance of Arctic charr (*Salvelinus alpinus* L.) smolts. Aquacult Res 31: 737–743.

Talbot, C. and Higgins, P. J. (1983). A radiographic method for feeding studies on fish using metallic iron powder as a marker. J Fish Biol 23: 211–220.

Tacon, A. G. J. and De-Silva, S. S. (1983). Mineral composition of some commercial fish feeds available in Europe. Aquaculture 31: 11–20.

Tacon, A. G. J., Knox, D. and Cowey, C. B. (1984). Effect of different dietary levels of salt mixture on growth and body composition in carp. Bull Jap Soc Sci Fish 50: 1217–1222.

Taylor, J. R. and Grosell, M. (2006). Feeding and osmoregulation: dual function of the marine teleost intestine. J Exp Biol 209: 2939–2951.

Tekinay, A. and Davies, S. J. (2002).Effect of dietary carbohydrate level on gastric evacuation and return of appetite in rainbow trout, *Oncorhynchus mykiss*. Turk J Biol 26: 25–31.

Trombetti, F., Ventrella, V., Pagliarani, A., Ballestrazzi, R., Galeotti, M., Trigari, G., Pirini, M. and Borgatti, A. (1996). Response of rainbow trout gill ($Na^{++}K^+$)-ATPase and chloride cells to T3 and NaCl administration. Fish Physiol Biochem 15: 264–275.

Utida S., Hirano T., Oide H., Ando M., Johnson D. W., and Bern H. A. (1972). Hormonal control of the intestine and urinary bladder in teleost osmoregulation. Gen Comp Endocrinol Suppl 3: 317–327.

Walker, R. L., Wilkes, P. R. H. and Wood, C. M. (1989). The effect of hypersaline exposure on the oxygen affinity of the blood of the freshwater teleost, *Catostamus commersoni*. J Exp Biol 142: 125–142.

Welker, T., Lim, C., Aksoy, M. and Klesius, P. (2007). Susceptibility of channel catfish (*Ictalurus punctatus*) fed dietary sodium chloride to nitrite toxicity. Aquaculture Conf Proc, 26 Feb.-2 Mar., 2007. San Antonio, Texas: 990.

Wheatly, M. G. Hobe, H. and Wood, C. M. (1984). The mechanisms of acid base and ionoregulation in the freshwater rainbow trout during environmental hyperoxia and subsequent normoxia. II. The role of the kidney. Respiration Physiology 55: 155–173.

Willson, R. P., Cowey, C. B. and Adron, J. W. (1985). Effect of dietary electrolyte balance on growth and acid-base balance in rainbow trout (*Salma gairdneri*). Comp Biochem Physiol 82A: 257–260.

Wood, C. M. (1989). The physiological problems of fish in acid waters. In: Morris, R., Taylor, E. W., Brown, D. J. A. and Brown, J. A. (eds) Acid Toxicity and Aquatic Animals. Cambridge University Press, Cambridge: 125–152.

Wood, C. M. (1995). Excretion. In: Groot, C., Margolis, C., and Clarke, W. C. Physiological Ecology of Pacific Salmon. University of British Columbia Press, Vancouver: 381–438.

Wood, C. M. (2001). Toxic responses of the gill. In: Schlenk, D. and Benson, W H. (eds) Target Organ Toxicity in Marine and Freshwater Teleosts Volume 1, Taylor and Francis, NewYork: 1–89.

Zadunaisky, J. A. (1984). The chloride cell: the active transport of chloride cell and the paracellular pathways. In: Hoar, W. S. and Randall, D. J. (eds) Fish Physiology, volume XB, Academic Press, New York: 129–176.

Zaugg, W. S. and McLain, L. R. (1969). Inorganic salt effects on growth, salt water adaptation and gill ATPase of Pacific salmon. In: Halver, J. E. and Neuhaus, O.W. (eds) Fish in Research, Academic Press, New York: 293–306.

Zaugg, W. S., Roley, D. D., Prentice, E. F., Gores, K. X. and Waknitz, F. W. (1983). Increased seawater survival and contribution to the fishery of chinook salmon (*Oncorhynchus tshawytscha*) by supplemental dietary salt. Aquaculture 32: 183–188.

Chapter 5

Regulation of calcium and magnesium handling in fishes

Gert Flik*, Gideon S. Bevelander and Peter H. M. Klaren

Keywords: Calcium, magnesium, homeostasis, prolactin, parathyroid hormone related protein, parathyroid hormone (PTH), and calcitriol, stanniocalcin, calcitonin

Abstract

Divalent ions, such as Ca^{2+} and Mg^{2+} are carefully regulated in cells and body fluids, but also have wide influence on other processes in osmoregulation. For example, Ca^{2+} alters membrane permeability and electrical properties of epithelia, as well as the control of some ion transporters. Intracellular free Ca^{2+} levels are submicromolar, and extracellular fluid Ca^{2+} concentrations in fish are around 1.25 mM. Calcium influx, and the large inward gradient for Ca^{2+} must be carefully controlled, while export of Ca^{2+} from cells is an up-hill, energy-requiring process. The control of Ca^{2+} homeostasis can be considered in terms of hypercalcemic regulation and hypocalcemic regulation, dealing with control above and below the normal set point. This chapter reviews the roles of the hormones involved in hypercalcemic regulation including, prolactin, parathyroid hormone related protein (PTHrP), parathyroid hormone (PTH), and calcitriol. The roles of stanniocalcin and calcitonin in hypocalcemic regulation are also described. Knowledge gaps are identified, and potential new feedback loops in the endocrine control of Ca^{2+} regulation are discussed.

5.1 Introduction

5.1.1 Fishes, general considerations on calcium and magnesium handling

In this paper the term fishes is used to address teleostean, bony fishes (Osteichthyes). Fishes come in a great number of species (up to 35,000, comprising around 60% of all vertebrate species on earth) and inhabit a great variety of water types. These habitats form a continuum from very soft and ion-poor water, such as the Amazonian black water and snow melt water running on highly insoluble granite substrates, to very ion-rich water such as seawater and concentrated sea water bodies (e.g. Salton Sea, California, USA; tidal rock pools etc.). We know stenohaline fishes, fishes that are adapted to water of narrowly defined ionic composition, and euryhaline fishes, fishes that are able to live in waters with variable ionic composition, typically fresh water and seawater which are hypo- and hyperionic, respectively, to the blood plasma. Euryhaline fishes are often migratory and we discriminate anadromous (from the Greek ανα, up the river) and catadromous (from κατα , down to sea) fishes; the former spend most of their life in seawater and return to freshwater spawning grounds to reproduce (e.g. many salmonids), the latter migrate from freshwaters to sea to reproduce (e.g. eels).

Fishes in fresh water realise and maintain a hyperosmotic blood plasma and extracellular fluid compartment relative to the ambient water and thus gain water by osmosis and lose monovalent ions; living in fresh water requires active ion uptake to compensate for diffusive losses as well as a limit to water influx. Freshwater fishes produce large volumes of dilute hypoosmotic urine, up to one third of the body volume per day. Ion uptake, in particular monovalent ion transport is coupled to nitrogenous metabolic waste (NH_4^+) excretion (NH_4^+ can replace the potassium ion on the sodium pump), and bicarbonate secretion which links ion uptake to acid base balance regulation.

Marine fishes regulate their plasma osmotic value at approximately one third of that of the seawater; their prime problem is to counteract the body water loss due to osmosis. To this end seawater fishes drink seawater that is deionised in the oesophagus and intestine under strict endocrine control (Fuentes and Eddy, 1997; Takei et al., 1998; Takei, 2008). The surplus of sodium and chloride ions is excreted via the chloride cells in the integument covering gills, and skin; these cells are also called ionocytes or mitochondria-rich cells; their original name 'chloride cell' derives from their active role in chloride secretion in seawater (Perry, 1997). In the following we will refer to chloride cells. Divalent ions in surplus are excreted via the kidneys, but fish lack a Henle's loop structure in their nephrons, and consequently, a urine-concentrating mechanism (only birds and mammals can produce hyperosmotic urine). The general picture of osmoregulatory organs in marine fishes thus is: gills are the site for secretion of monovalent ions, kidneys excrete divalent ions to cope with surplus as a result of drinking seawater and passive inward diffusion.

Relatively little is known about the general role of the intestinal tract in osmoregulatory processes in fishes. This relates on the one hand to the great variety of intestinal specialisations found among fishes. Moreover, the intestinal tissue is difficult to handle and object of study in only few laboratories worldwide. In reproductively active, nest-building male sticklebacks (in fresh water) the intestine takes over the role the kidneys, which are temporarily transformed to glue-producing organs to allow for nest building (de Ruiter and Mein, 1982). Small intestinal enterocytes are as polarised a cell type as branchial chloride cells are, with defined apical and basolateral membrane domains harboring specific arrays of transport proteins. Clearly, intestinal epithelia play a first and foremost role in nutrient and ion absorption, both for monovalent and divalent ionic species, and thus can contribute significantly to osmoregulation. The case of the freshwater stickleback is a very convincing extreme example of the plasticity of the intestinal tract in this respect. Also, it is not difficult to envisage an even more profound osmoregulatory role of the intestinal epithelium in marine fishes that imbibe large volumes of seawater, and thus face considerable salt loads and osmolyte gradients (Flik et al., 2002).

What about the divalent ions? The pathways for uptake and efflux of divalent ions are summarised in Figure 1. The summed activities of calcium and magnesium (and phosphate) ions in blood plasma, that roughly add up to several millimoles, constitute only a minor fraction of all osmotically active ionic species, compared to the summed monovalent ions activity of 240–300 millimolar. However, the divalent ions play other important roles that are indirectly relevant for osmoregulatory processes (Wendelaar Bonga and van der Meij, 1981). Calcium determines the permeabilities of membranes and epithelial junctional complexes, controls ion channel activities in ion transporting cells and membrane electrical properties and is thus deeply involved in active and secondary active ion transports (Wendelaar Bonga and van der Meij, 1981; Wendelaar Bonga et al., 1984a). The magnesium ion stabilizes many proteins, including important enzymes such as the sodium, potassium-activated, ouabain-sensitive ATPase (the sodium pump), is required as a cofactor in various enzymes including the sodium pump and determines the conformation of, for instance, ATP that directly drives ion-pumping ATPases. Here, a magnesium ion is chelated in the triphosphate moiety of the ATP molecule which leads to a conformation change in the phosphate tail, and enables binding to the substrate site of the ATPase. Another relevant notion in the discussion of the regulation of calcium and magnesium handling is that transport of calcium, magnesium and phosphate are linked to monovalent ion transport or gradients of monovalent ions. These secondarily active transport mediated by exchangers and symporters indicate that transport of divalent ion species cannot be treated or understood independent of an understanding of transport of monovalent ions (Beyenbach, 1990; Bijvelds et al., 1996a; Handy et al., 1996a; Handy et al., 1996b; Bijvelds et al., 1997; Bijvelds et al., 1998b).

Natural waters, whether soft and ion-poor or full-strength sea water, always contains unlimited amounts of calcium for a fish; a key issue is whether the fish is able to extract the calcium from the water. This does not appear to confront fishes with a problem, as we see that fishes in all those water qualities are healthy, grow normally and thus accumulate calcium in their bodies. The uptake of

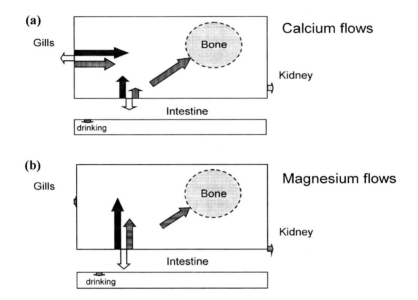

Figure 1. *Scheme of divalent ion flows in freshwater fish*

(a) ***Calcium flows.*** *Calcium from the ambient water and from the diet is taken up via gills and intestine, respectively. Unidirectional flows (black arrows for inflow, open arrows for efflow) indicate that the branchial epithelium is tighter (less unidirectional efflow) than the intestinal epithelium. Net flows of calcium (striped arrows) show that net inflow via the gills surpasses inflow via the intestine. All flows are presented relative to the unidirectional branchial inflow; data were first normalized to fish weight and corrected for estimated total gut surface. Little is known about specializations in the intestinal tract and net absorption or secretion of calcium; for the calculations presented here unidirectional flux data obtained for intestinal tissue of the first one third of the tract were normalized to total intestinal surface measured. Freshwater fish drink, but very little; the arrow size for drinking is based on the assumption that all calcium dissolved in the water drunk is absorbed (this may not be true). Renal calcium outflow is low in freshwater fish. In growing fish (many fishes continue to grow throughout their life) calcium flow to bone (for apatite/ whitlockite deposition) comes close to the summed net inflows of calcium via gills and intestine.*

(b) ***Magnesium flows.*** *Magnesium is mainly absorbed from food ingested. Although direct inflow from water appears possible, the relative contribution of this pathway is always small. Freshwater fish drink little, and therefore the contribution of magnesium absorption from water drunk is small; the arrow size for drinking is based on the assumption that all magnesium dissolved in the water drunk is absorbed. Arrow sizes are presented relative to the unidirectional intestinal influx (black arrow). A small proportion of magnesium is lost via renal and/ or intestinal routes, but the relative contribution of these pathways is not sure (indicated by arrow at shared position). A significant flow of magnesium to the growing bone occurs, where apatites are deposited; magnesium is an important component of the so–called 'defective' apatites such as whitlockite, which may represent the most abundant mineral in fish/vertebrate bone. Fish handle magnesium with great care and can retain close to 100% of the magnesium provided when availability of magnesium is restricted; on the other hand any surplus of magnesium above set point is easily lost via renal and or intestinal routes.*

Flow (moles per unit of time) refers to movement of ions when surface area is not exactly known; flux (moles per unit of time per surface area) is defined as flow per defined surface area. These schemes were compiled from a series of studies on tilapia and carp to which is referred extensively in the main text.

calcium from the water is for the larger part realised by the chloride cells in the gills (Perry and Flik, 1988; Perry *et al.*, 1992b; Perry, 1997). The chloride cells have their apical membrane directly exposed to the water. Calcium channels in this membrane domain can be opened to allow a passive influx of calcium (Perry, 1997; Shahsavarani *et al.*, 2006; Shahsavarani and Perry, 2006). Indeed, calcium can enter the cell easily, i.e. down its transmembrane electrochemical gradient, as the cytosolic calcium concentration is kept at submicromolar concentrations (high calcium is toxic to many cytosolic modalities). In addition, the cell interior is negatively charged relative to the outside world (typically about -70 mV, both in fresh water and in seawater) which further facilitates influx of the positively charged calcium ion. So, initial uptake, i.e. translocation into the cell, that will eventually secure the vectorial transcellular transport and uptake, is a matter of control over apical calcium channels. The low, submicromolar cytosolic free calcium concentration is maintained by a variety of mechanisms, including buffering of ionic calcium by calcium binding proteins and sequestering activities of cellular compartments such as the endoplasmic reticulum, calciosomes and mitochondria.

Calcium extrusion from the cytosol, in contrast, is an up-hill, energy-requiring process that is either mediated by basolateral plasma membrane calcium ATPase, a sodium-calcium exchanger activity, or both (Flik *et al.*, 1993; Flik *et al.*, 1994b). The energy provided by hydrolysis of ATP or that contained in the sodium gradient across the basolateral plasma membrane (maintained by the pumping activity of the sodium pump in this membrane) suffices to move calcium ions from the cytosol to the plasma compartment. The blood plasma calcium ion activity is in all vertebrates maintained at around 1.25 millimolar. Clearly, cellular transport is vectorial (i.e. it has a directional component) and allows for many modes of regulation at the level of the transporting cell proper (Flik *et al.*, 1993). An important notion in understanding the transport of calcium (and that of other ions) in fish gills or any calcium transporting epithelium is that the functioning of the calcium transporting cells is determined by the electrophysiology of the epithelium that harbors these cells (Flik *et al.*, 1990; Flik and Verbost, 1993). Of course the ion transporting cells for a larger degree determine the electrical conditions in the epithelium. Fish behave electrically as a calcium selectrode (McWilliams and Potts, 1978). At an essentially constant plasma calcium activity, variable water calcium concentrations result in specific disequilibria between plasma and water for the calcium ion. This disequilibrium (or calcium potential, perhaps) strongly determines the transepithelial electrical potential difference, which is several millivolts negative in hypocalcic (i.e. with lower concentration than in plasma) media, essentially zero in isocalcic (brackish) water and up to 30 millivolts positive in hypercalcic media such as seawater. The transepithelial electrochemical potential is a determining factor in how the epithelium as a whole handles ions: net uptake results when cell-mediated active transport overrides passive outward leakage. The passive loss of ions is determined by the specific leakiness of the epithelium, determined in turn by the properties of the junctional complexes that hold the epithelium together but may be more or less permeable for defined ionic species (Verbost *et al.*, 1997).

Here some comments should be added to complete our understanding of (net) ion transports. First, the waterborne calcium activity directly influences the properties of the junctional complexes connecting the cells in the epithelium. It is an important determinant of epithelial tightness, and this is reflected by the epithelial permeability to water and monovalent as well as divalent ions. The epithelium of freshwater fishes is considered to rank very high among the tight epithelia encountered in biology; the gills of seawater fishes are typically very leaky. This is a very counterintuitive situation, if we consider the low and high calcium concentrations in fresh water and seawater, respectively. It points to important endocrine control (e.g. by prolactin, see below) overruling direct chemical interactions between calcium and calcium-dependent proteins such as cadherins in the zonula adherens (Wendelaar Bonga and van der Meij, 1981; Wendelaar Bonga and Pang, 1991).

Second, soft fresh water, with a low calcium activity, activates directly or indirectly the pituitary prolactin cells (Wendelaar Bonga and van der Meij, 1981). This pleiotrope hormone of the type-I alpha helical cytokine family includes in its actions control over junctional tightness. Prolactin is generally considered as the hormone that allowed fish to adapt to fresh water, for which mechanisms securing ion retention and water exclusion *via* control over epithelial tightness were crucial. Third, the water calcium concentration will influence the plasma membrane composition and viscosity, directly by interaction with the phospholipids and *via* prolactin-regulated processes that determine membrane phospholipid composition (Molina *et al.*, 1997; Igal *et al.*, 1998). Changes in plasma membrane viscosity will in turn influence the functioning of the transport proteins therein, including the apical calcium channel and the energised transporters in the basolateral domain.

Consensus exists that the chloride cells in the gills secure active calcium transport. Numerous studies have established that the calcium transport capacity of an epithelium is directly and linearly related to the chloride cell density of the epithelium; extrapolation to an epithelium with no chloride cells yields a zero calcium influx (Perry *et al.*, 1992a). In chloride cells of both freshwater and seawater fishes a similar inwardly directed active transport of calcium ions occurs, which means that the basic mechanisms for transcellular calcium transport must be similar in hypo- and hypercalcic conditions.

Generally, we see higher densities of chloride cells in the integument (gills and skin) of seawater fishes compared to that of freshwater fishes, and it seems plausible to advance this notion to support the observation of higher calcium fluxes in seawater fish compared to freshwater fish (Flik and Verbost, 1993; Vonck *et al.*, 1998; Guerreiro *et al.*, 2001). For sure, the size of the chloride cell population is instrumental for that, but we should also consider that calcium balance is coupled to the handling of sodium and chloride as well. For instance, through the operation of symporter and antiporter entities that directly or indirectly couple calcium transport across the basolateral plasma membrane to that of sodium and or chloride (Flik *et al.*, 1997; Li *et al.*, 1997; Verbost *et al.*, 1997). It follows then that in water where sodium and chloride turnover is higher, i.e. in seawater or hypersaline water (Vonck *et al.*, 1998), the calcium turnover and unidirectional fluxes would also increase as a result of increased numbers of chloride cells. On the other hand, calcium fluxes will increase in fresh water when calcium concentrations are low or lowered (Flik *et al.*, 1986c; Vonck *et al.*, 1998), which relates to the changing endocrine status of the animal and inherent change in electrophysiology of the integument. This remains a difficult topic to discuss as few studies are available to support that sodium and calcium handling (analysed by unidirectional fluxes for the respective ions) are directly coupled such that stoichiometric relations can be revealed.

Apical calcium channels (Perry *et al.*, 2003) in the chloride cells thus determine cellular calcium influx, active transport mechanisms in the basolateral plasma membrane the extrusion to the blood compartment. Importantly, the fact that the TRP gene family calcium channel is not restricted to chloride cells in fish gills (Shahsavarani *et al.*, 2006), but also found in pavement cells, suggests that this channel in the earlier vertebrate may also serve to facilitate calcium influx in cells not involved in vectorial calcium transport. The high density of the channel in the apical membrane of the chloride cell must reflect then a specialization of this cell. The search for (endocrine) control mechanisms over the channel activity is indicated (see below) and studies on isolated chloride cells and sodium and calcium handling by these cells (Li *et al.*, 1997) may eventually substantiate such speculation.

The generalised picture that emerges then is that the chloride cell in the gills is a calcium ion influx securing entity. The epithelial electrophysiology and biochemistry (i.e. transporter make-up of the plasma membrane), dependent on ambient calcium levels and endocrine responses to the ambient calcium, eventually determine net movement of ions, including that of calcium across the branchial epithelium (Flik *et al.*, 1985; Flik and Verbost, 1993; Flik *et al.*, 1994a; Flik *et al.*, 1994b). The electrophysiological conditions of the gill epithelium and flux to internal stores (bone and scales) and renal excretion subsequently set the balance for calcium in the blood plasma.

There is also another important aspect of calcium homeostasis, and that is that calcium taken up by the fish is sequestered, stored internally in bone (Flik *et al.*, 1986a). Fishes continue to grow throughout their life, so bone as a sink for calcium is an important compartment that may allow for significant flux of calcium from the plasma. Fishes were the vertebrates that 'evolved' bone as we typically find in vertebrates. Bone is a special case of connective tissue with a mineralized matrix. The major form of calcium precipitates in vertebrate bone is apatite, a calcium phosphate with a molar calcium to phosphate ratio of 1.67, and among the hardest bio-minerals known. How do the fluxes from water to fish (plasma) and from plasma to bone compare? This is not such an easy question to answer.

From in-vivo radiotracer kinetics we calculated that in a freshwater tilapia 94% of the whole body calcium content is associated with bony structures, only 6% with soft tissues (Flik *et al.*, 1985; Flik *et al.*, 1986a). The accumulation of calcium in bone in a growing fish (around 15 g body weight) was calculated to occur at a pace of around 400 nmol per hour, and a very similar calcium net influx *via* the gills was observed in such fish (Flik *et al.*, 1985; Flik *et al.*, 1986a). Clearly, bone must be considered as a determining compartment to appreciate calcium movements in the fish: gill calcium transport may serve a major role to supply the growing bone with mineral.

One could wonder whether it is the calcium or the phosphate that really matters in fish physiology (of course the fish needs both). In contrast to calcium, phosphate is normally not present in the ambient water and it must be obtained from food ingested. No phosphate transport has been shown to occur in gills or skin, not even when fishes are maintained for significant times in phosphate-enriched water. Phosphate transport was demonstrated convincingly in intestinal and renal epithelia of fishes (Lu *et al.*, 1994a; Lu *et al.*, 1994b), and therefore there is no reason to believe that phosphate uptake in fishes is different from what we know in higher vertebrates. Considering the crucial role of phosphate in the (calcium) physiology of the fish/vertebrates (high-energy phosphate intermediates, bone mineralization, pH-buffering etc.), one would predict strong links in the regulation of calcium and phosphate as seen in vertebrates (Renkema *et al.*, 2008). Since the major chemical form of calcium in the vertebrate body is that of apatite, coupled uptake pathways of calcium and phosphate would appear plausible and efficient. But, a coupling of the intestinal uptake of calcium and phosphate has not yet been established. Interestingly, the quintessential calciotropic hormone stanniocalcin (see below) decreases calcium fluxes in mammalian intestine and renal tubular epithelium (Wagner *et al.*, 1997b), but increased that of phosphate (Madsen *et al.*, 1998). Apparently, phosphate and calcium are absorbed by separate mechanisms, and this reflects different if not opposed, phosphate and calcium requirements of the animal.

Fish obtain magnesium mostly from their diet. Food containing around 20 mmol kg^{-1} suffices for optimal growth (van der Velden *et al.*, 1992). Fish fed low magnesium diets grow less or not at all, and eventually will die (van der Velden *et al.*, 1991; Li *et al.*, 1997). However, magnesium accumulation in the body may surpass the amount provided in deficient diets, which suggests that magnesium is somehow obtained directly from the water (Bijvelds *et al.*, 1996a). This would indicate the gills as the site for direct magnesium uptake. So far nobody has been able to demonstrate an active mechanism for magnesium transport in gill epithelium. The electrochemical potential across the gill epithelium does not favor passive magnesium influx and thus transcellular active transport is indicated (Bijvelds *et al.*, 1998b).

In intestinal epithelium however, mechanisms for apical as well as basolateral membrane magnesium transport have been demonstrated (Bijvelds *et al.*, 1996b; Bijvelds *et al.*, 1998a; Bijvelds *et al.*, 2001). We have observed that tilapia handle magnesium extremely economically as evidenced by an efficient uptake, and undetectable excretion when magnesium availability is low. This suggests that strict endocrine control mechanisms over magnesium handling must exist. Unfortunately, so far we failed to demonstrate any such direct endocrine controls. The intestinal epithelium should be the target of choice to study regulation of magnesium transport.

Magnesium excretion proceeds almost exclusively *via* renal pathways (Beyenbach, 1990; Beyenbach *et al.*, 1993; Beyenbach, 2000; Beyenbach, 2004), although intestinal secretion and passive losses are other possible modes; the renal magnesium output is predominantly determined by secretory and reabsorptive actions of the tubular epithelia. In tubules of freshwater fish divalent ions including magnesium ions are reabsorbed. The magnesium content in the end urine of freshwater fish is lower than that in the initial glomerular ultrafiltrate, evidence for tubular reabsorption. In tubules of seawater fishes magnesium is secreted and urine magnesium concentrations may reach values up to 100 millimolar (Freire *et al.*, 1995; Freire *et al.*, 1996). This capacity may be particularly relevant in seawater fish that drink seawater with a magnesium content of around 55 millimolar (fresh water typically contains around 1 millimolar or less, and freshwater fish drink little water, if at all).

Magnesium transport is thus organised fundamentally different and mechanisms are far less clear compared to those described for calcium. At first glance many similarities seem to exist: magnesium channels in apical membranes, cytosolic binding proteins, sequestering in mitochondria and endoplasmic reticulum and energised co-transporters (sodium antiport, chloride symport) in basolateral plasma membranes of magnesium transporting epithelia have been described. None of the mechanisms for magnesium or calcium handling seem promiscuous for these ions, which in all likelihood relates to the fundamentally different chemistry of these elements (Bijvelds *et al.*, 2001). The ionic radius of magnesium is 66 pm, that of calcium 99 pm; the small size and relatively large charge make magnesium a hard metal ion, with great polarising ability and high hydration energy which makes most magnesium salts easily soluble. The large hydration size of magnesium (six water molecules surround the ion) makes magnesium pass with much greater difficulty through water-filled channels, and explains the low magnesium permeability of epithelia. Calcium ions are highly mobile and the ion is surrounded by a relatively small tetrahedral water mantle.

Yet, paracellular solute-linked transport may contribute significantly to the net movement of the magnesium ion, a situation reminiscent of passive calcium transport in renal tubules (Beyenbach *et al.*, 1993). Such passive paracellular transport depends on specific permeability of the junctional complexes for the magnesium ion (or calcium ion). The great variety of magnesium carriers compared to the two or three plasma membrane carriers (channel, ATPase, exchanger) known for calcium further illustrate fundamental differences between calcium and magnesium handling processes. Further, the much higher cytosolic magnesium activity, viz. 0.5 to 0.8 millimolar at rest (Grubbs and Walter, 1994), compared to the 100–200 nanomolar cytosolic calcium activity (Bijvelds *et al.*, 1998a) is another remarkable difference between the two metal ions in cell biology. In the following the focus will be on calcium, merely because so little is still known about regulation of magnesium handling, in particular in fishes.

5.1.2 Calcium sensing in and outside the cell

Cells in vertebrates, including fishes (Li *et al.*, 1997), control the cytosolic calcium concentration at sub-micromolar levels. The cell itself bathes in a medium with a calcium activity of roughly 1.25 millimolar, creating a very steep inwardly directed chemical gradient. Higher cytosolic concentrations of calcium are toxic and lead to cell death (Berridge, 1994; Kass and Orrenius, 1999; Pu *et al.*, 2002);

this statement is corroborated by direct inhibitory actions of calcium ions on a variety of cytosol-associated enzyme activities and high levels of calcium in cells doomed to undergo necrosis or apoptosis. Yet calcium plays a key role in intracellular signaling, which is realised by a very strict control over cytosolic calcium levels through calcium buffering proteins and pump-leak systems in intracellular compartments. Indeed, all mechanisms to sequester calcium from the cytosol, binding proteins and extrusion pumps in plasma membranes and endoplasmic reticular membranes, have affinities for nanomolar to micromolar concentrations of calcium (Verbost *et al.*, 1989; Verbost *et al.*, 1992; Zaccone *et al.*, 1992; Verbost *et al.*, 1994). We can consider calcium binding proteins such as calbindins, parvalbumin and calmodulin, but also the calcium binding sites of calcium ATPase and sodium-calcium exchangers, as sensitive intracellular calcium receptors. Their high affinity allows these proteins to respond to minute changes in total calcium activity thereby circumventing potential toxic actions of calcium. Many cells are equipped with calcium sensing receptors protruding from the plasma membrane and probing the extracellular medium. Theoretically they should have millimolar affinity, considering the extracellular calcium activity of around 1.25 millimolar. A calcium-sensing receptor was first described for the parathyroid hormone producing cells of the parathyroid gland in mammals. The cells producing parathyroid hormone become activated following minor drops in plasma calcium levels, and are inhibited by slight hypercalcemia (Motoyama and Friedman, 2002; Ba *et al.*, 2003; Toribio *et al.*, 2003). Calcium sensing receptors are found in many more tissues, including gill chloride cells, renal tubules and cells producing calciotropic hormones (Flanagan *et al.*, 2002). Variations in calcium are thus monitored anywhere inside and outside cells, which confers the strict calcium homeostasis seen in vertebrates. Calcium homeostasis is guaranteed by a large suite of hyper- and hyporegulating hormones, indicating the pressure on fine- tuning this homeostasis.

5.1.3 Regulation of calcium handling

From the above it follows that our understanding of the regulation of calcium handling should include regulatory systems that influence calcium handling indirectly, e.g. *via* actions on the sodium pump that secondarily affects sodium-calcium exchanger activity (Schoenmakers and Flik, 1992), as well as directly, e.g. *via* regulation of genes (Power *et al.*, 2002) that control expression of calciotropic hormones and calcium carriers. Where calciotropic hormones interact with others, synergism and antagonism should be considered. In the following, actions of hypercalcemic and hypocalcemic hormones (Figure 2) are addressed, and, where known, aspects of indirect and direct effects as well as synergism and antagonism will be discussed. A major division is hyper- versus hypocalcemic regulation. Importantly, the fact that fish rely primarily on gill calcium uptake (Verbost *et al.*, 1993c) – which by default (see above) only needs inhibitory control – requires that one should not confuse hypocalcemic control with antihypercalcemic control. Hypocalcemic control could involve sequestering of calcium ions into bone (Flik *et al*., 1994a), antihypercalcemic control refers to inhibition of branchial calcium influx that eventually may result in hypocalcemic effects.

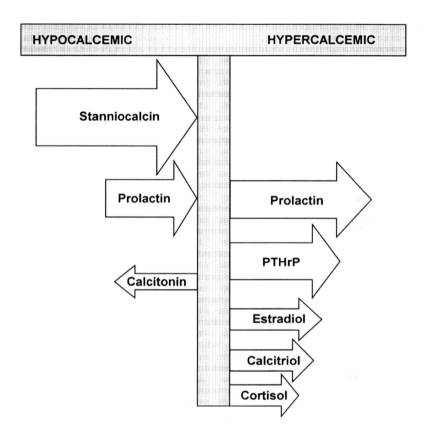

Figure 2. *Summary and hierarchy of endocrine factors that regulate calcium handling in freshwater fish*

    Calciotropic hormones exert either hypocalcemic or hypercalcemic effects. Stanniocalcin is the dominant calciotropic hormone in fish: it inhibits calcium inflow via the gills by control over apical calcium channels in the calcium transporting chloride cell of the gills. As its action is in fact antihypercalcemic, the arrow has been turned around. Prolactin exerts hypercalcemic effects through a decrease of integumental calcium loss (prolactin makes the integument tighter; therefore the arrow has been turned around) and increasing calcium inflow (prolactin enhances the calcium transport capacity of chloride cells). PTHrP has hypercalcemic effects through stimulation of calcium uptake from the water, and of calcium release from bone. Calcitonin is thought to exert mild hypocalcemic effects by inhibition of calcium influx via gills; exact mechanisms are unknown. The steroids estradiol, calcitriol and cortisol exert mild hypercalcemic actions in fish. The steroids exert their effects both via 'classical' transcription factors (estradiol receptors, VDRs and GRs and MRs) and via plasma membrane bound G–protein coupled receptors. A concerted action with PTHrP may be instrumental in hypercalcemic actions of steroids.

5.2 Hypercalcemic regulation

5.2.1 Prolactin

Prolactin is well known as the 'freshwater-adapting hormone', a term used to indicate that fish in fresh water, whether stenohaline or euryhaline, show active pituitary prolactin cells (Wendelaar Bonga and van der Meij, 1981). They require prolactin to control the permeability of the integument to water and ions. Importantly, low ambient calcium levels are sensed and define prolactin cell activity (more active in softer water). The joined action of ambient calcium (directly) and prolactin release, determine integumental quality (Wendelaar Bonga et al., 1984a). The degree to which a fish relies on prolactin (whether the fish adapts or tolerates hypocalcic conditions) defines its eventual success to survive in fresh water. The hypercalcemic actions of prolactin in freshwater fish further substantiate the importance of plasma calcium levels in osmoregulation. Clearly both external and (prolactin-dependent) internal, plasmatic calcium concentrations need tight control. The functioning of fish as a 'calcium selectrode' is a wonderful starting paradigm to study original functions of prolactin in calcium physiology.

Few studies have addressed direct actions of prolactin in fish. Levels of prolactin range between 10 and 20 ng ml^{-1} in most fishes (Ogasawara et al., 1996; Auperin et al., 1997; Hogasen and Prunet, 1997; Sakamoto et al., 1997; Prunet et al., 2000). For tilapia it was shown that treatment of the fish with exogenous prolactin (doses up to 12.5 picomole per g fish) induces hypercalcemia (Flik et al., 1986b; Flik et al., 1994a). Prolactin-induced hypercalcemia coincides with enhanced calcium-ATPase activity in basolateral plasma membrane preparations of gill epithelium as well as calcium pump activity in vesicles prepared of these membranes. Moreover, the hypercalcemia induced by prolactin enhances bone density, reflecting that the extra calcium taken up is stored in bone. This of course is further in line with a predicted reduction of integumental permeability to calcium.

5.2.2 Parathyroid hormone related protein and parathyroid hormone

For a long time it was thought that fish only needed control over calcium influx, an anti-hypercalcemic control with hypocalcemic effects, as the water is an infinite source of calcium to be taken up by the gills. Calcium would thus never be in short supply, only calcium influx needed to be controlled. This may however, be a too simplistic approach to understanding calcium handling in fishes, and in vertebrates. All cells we know, from prokaryotic to vertebrate, can live with millimolar ambient calcium levels, and the vertebrate extracellular fluid calcium activity is kept constant to guarantee proper functioning of many key physiological processes including neuronal activity, muscular function, secretion processes and so on. Homeostatic control over plasma calcium levels then requires both hypo- and hyper-regulatory mechanisms to control set points for calcium regulation. This requires also internal control, beyond the control of uptake of calcium from the water. Additional control is needed over fluxes between internal compartments, and distribution of calcium over internal compartments. Calcemic control in fishes is therefore not simply a matter of anti-hypercalcemic control mediated by stanniocalcin (see below). It seems logical then that a fish or vertebrate will not only rely on hypocalcemic or anti-hypercalcemic control mechanisms but on a balance between hypocalcemic and anti-hypercalcemic and hypercalcemic mechanisms to guarantee calcium homeostasis.

Indeed, hypercalcemic hormones that we know from mammals, such as parathyroid hormone related protein (PTHrP) and parathyroid hormone (PTH), are found in fishes (Danks et al., 1998; Hogan et al. 2005). They are thus at least as old as fishes and must have original functions in these vertebrates for them to survive the 450 million years of evolution since the rise of the fishes in the late Ordovician. The gene encoding for PTHrP was long considered to be the 'older' gene that gave rise to the PTH gene in mammals after the water-land transition of the vertebrates. Both PTHrP and PTH-genes were found in zebrafish (Hogan et al., 2005). Nothing is known yet about the function of the PTH-gene products. The (unexpected) presence of PTH-genes next to PTHrP-genes in fishes, however, indicates early evolutionary pressure on hypercalcemic regulatory genes and apparent subfunctionalisation of genes, which are thus best studied in fishes. The function of the PTH-gene product in fishes awaits further research, so far only the messenger RNA for the gene was demonstrated in zebrafish. The fact that PTHrP and PTH signal via shared receptors (Hoare et al., 2000) (and have highly identical N-terminal sequences) would suggest that targets and functions of the proteins are closely related.

PTHrP exerts hypercalcemic actions in fish. Gilthead sea bream larvae exposed to PTHrP in seawater, drink the water with the hormone and absorb the hormone (protein hormones are known to remain bioactive after intestinal absorption in fishes) to exert hypercalcemic effects; the larvae accumulate more calcium as a result of stimulated (branchial) calcium influx from the water, a typical action of hypercalcemic hormones in fishes (Guerreiro et al., 2001).

In adult fishes the effects of PTHrP are more difficult to assess (Abbink et al., 2004; Abbink et al., 2006; Abbink and Flik, 2007; Abbink et al., 2007). In all likelihood this results from the powerful control underlying calcium homeostasis and involving counteracting and compensating endocrine actions. Injection of recombinant, homologous full-length or N-terminal variants of fish PTHrP only rarely induces a significant hypercalcemia. Moreover, treatments such as prolonged feeding of diets low in calcium (combined with low ambient calcium levels) or diets low in vitamin D3, aimed to induce hypocalcemia, affect PTHrP-gene activities in surprising ways (see below). Apparently hypercalcemic function and action of hormones are not easily or predictably assessable, and specific actions may even be masked by other powerful homeostatic control mechanisms.

Among the multiple actions of PTHrP (Guerreiro et al., 2007), permissive endocrine actions in calcium physiology may not be surprising. PTHrP was proven to be a key signal in fish vitellogenesis (Bevelander et al., 2006) as well as bone physiology (Redruello et al., 2005; Rotllant et al., 2005b), processes where estradiol acts in concert with PTHrP. Estradiol is well known to induce overt hypercalcemia in fishes as a result of stimulation of vitellogenesis; estrogen-induced vitellogenesis is potentiated by PTHrP, which is strong evidence for the liver as a PTHrP target and concerted actions *via* shared second messenger pathways (Bevelander *et al.*, 2006). The vitellogenin produced by the liver to provide the eggs (and future embryos) developing in the ovary with an energy source, binds significant amounts of calcium and phosphate, which is reflected by increased total plasma levels of calcium that easily reach 10 millimolar. Effects of exogenous estradiol are thus easily demonstrated by the measurement of plasma calcium (and/or phosphate) and vitellogenin. Once assays became available to reliably determine PTHrP (Rotllant *et al.*, 2003; Anjos *et al.*, 2005) in fish plasma, it became clear that estradiol-induced hypercalcemia is likely mediated though enhanced PTHrP activity, with PTHrP stimulating calcium uptake from the water (Fuentes *et al.*, 2006; Fuentes *et al.*, 2007).

Problematic in the appreciation of PTHrP as an endocrine signal in fish is that its multifaceted identity (Canario *et al.*, 2006) and the source of endocrine PTHrP is under debate (Abbink *et al.*, 2006; Abbink and Flik, 2007; Abbink *et al.*, 2007). Many epithelia express exuberant amounts of PTHrP mRNA as well as protein, and in the case of epithelial production para-, auto- or intracrine functions seem indicated. In gilthead sea bream PTHrP was also found in the pituitary pars intermedia. It is restricted to a subpopulation of somatolactin cells, which in zebrafish are recognised as somatolactin-alpha cells (Zhu *et al.*, 2004). This PTHrP, possibly co-released with somatolactin, could be an endocrine hypercalcemic signal in fishes. Indeed, hypercalcemic functions for the somatolactin cells were suspected long before PTHrP was demonstrated in these cells (van Eys and Wendelaar Bonga, 1984; Wendelaar Bonga *et al.*, 1984b; Wendelaar Bonga *et al.*, 1986) and later proven and confirmed (Varsamos *et al.*, 2006). In sea bream an experimental hypocalcemia is induced by exposure of the fish to low-calcium water and low-calcium diets or prolonged exposure to vitamin-D3 deficient diets. In fish made hypocalcemic this way, the mRNA for PTHrP in the pituitary gland is down-regulated and plasma PTHrP levels (tend to) decrease. This counterintuitive observation was interpreted to indicate a lower PTHrP turnover as growth is hampered in these fish. Interestingly, the genes for PTHrP, its receptor and a calcium-sensing receptor in branchial (chloride) cells are up-regulated. From these observations it was concluded that independent PTHrP systems with the potential for hypercalcemic actions are operational in the fish (Abbink *et al.*, 2004; Abbink *et al.*, 2006).

A second mode of action of PTHrP to exert hypercalcemic effects is stimulation of osteoclastic activity. In gilthead sea bream it was demonstrated that PTHrP induces calcium release from scales *via* the PTHrP type-I receptor, and down-regulates the expression of the osteonectin gene that codes for an important calcium-binding bone glycoprotein, conform to a 'classical' (in the mammalian sense) hypercalcemic mode of action (Redruello *et al.*, 2005; Rotllant *et al.*, 2005b).

An intriguing observation on the pleiotropic PTHrP is its stimulatory effect on interrenal cortisol producing cells (Rotllant *et al.*, 2005a; Guerreiro *et al.*, 2006). A link between the calcium regulatory PTHrP and cortisol implies that calcium regulatory actions of PTHrP may require support of cortisol that organises metabolism *via* control over energy flows in the body. It further shows the deep dedication of an organism to calcium homeostasis.

5.2.3 Calcitriol

Fish produce vitamin D, the precursor of calcitriol: cod liver oil is a well-known, rich source of the vitamin and was widely used to prevent rickets, a disease mainly caused by vitamin D deficiency. Vitamin D is hydroxylated in liver and dihydroxylated in the kidney to form the bioactive hormone 1,25-dihydroxy-vitamin D3, also called calcitriol. For long, the role of calcitriol in fish calcium handling was enigmatic as hypercalcemic effects of exogenous calcitriol are generally mild and not consistently found (Sundell *et al.*, 1992; Sundell *et al.*, 1993; Lock *et al.*, 2007). This likely relates, again, to the powerful calcium homeostatic machinery, of which calcitriol is only one of many players. However, with the recent unequivocal demonstration of vitamin D receptors (VDRs) in fish (Lock *et al.*, 2007), doubts on its physiological relevance were taken away and targets for calcitriol can now be defined unequivocally. Indeed, in Atlantic salmon VDRs are found in all tissues involved in calcium regulation. However, our understanding of the actions of calcitriol is only starting to develop. In mammals VDRs are known to heterodimerize with similar receptors (transcription factors) for vitamin A metabolites and this opens a field of research that is largely unexplored in fishes. Calcitriol-target genes should contain VDR-responsive elements and this property may further refine and speed up our search for the role of calcitriol in fish calcium handling. Calcitriol not only steers VDRs, a genomic mode of action that requires hours to take effect, but may also activate plasma membrane bound receptors to rapidly influence calcium handling. In cod calcitriol stimulates intestinal calcium transport *via* such a pathway. Also for the other dihydroxylated vitamin D metabolite, 24,-25-dihydroxy-vitamin D3 plasma membrane bound receptor mediated effects were described (Sundell and Björnsson, 1990; Larsson *et al.*, 1995; Larsson *et al.*, 1998). We are only starting to understand the complex endocrinology of the vitamin-D metabolites that likely developed in fishes, and are at the basis of vertebrate calcium physiology.

5.3 Hypocalcemic regulation

5.3.1 Calcitonin

Calcitonin was first isolated from salmon ultimobranchial glands and the purified protein proved exceptionally useful in humans (Copp, 1992), in particular in the treatment of menopausal osteoporosis. Salmon calcitonin is sufficiently similar to human calcitonin not to evoke strong immune responses; at the same time, although heterologous, it is not well recognised in the liver and therefore cleared slowly. The well-established hypocalcemic effects of calcitonin in mammals, effects that result from a stimulated calcium deposition in bone, have not been unequivocally confirmed in fish (Wendelaar Bonga, 1980; Wendelaar Bonga,

1981): mild hypocalcemic effects of exogenous calcitonin could only be shown in fish challenged with calcium- poor water and supraphysiological doses were required to do so. A few reports (Fouchereau-Peron *et al.*, 1981; Wagner *et al.*, 1997a) demonstrated inhibitory effects of calcitonin on gill calcium influx, which result indeed corroborates a hypocalcemic role of the hormone. Inhibitory actions of calcitonin on fish osteoclastic activity have, to the best of our knowledge, not been described. A role for calcitonin as an analgesic, as in higher vertebrates (Fabbri *et al.*, 1983; Bazarra-Fernandez, 2007), awaits experimentation in fishes. Still, we may be confronted here with the consequences of anthropomorphic thinking and be overlooking the original function(s) of calcitonin in fishes? Phylogenetically, calcitonin was proven to pre-date the rise of fishes (450 million years ago) as it is found in insects (rise of insects: one billion years ago); calcitonin is member of a family of proteins that includes corticotrophin releasing factor, peptides with a well-accepted role in regulation of stress and anxiety (Lovejoy, 2006; Lovejoy *et al.*, 2006). Maybe the role of calcitonin targeting osteoblasts is a function that only fully evolved after the water-to-land transition. Studies on zebrafish do show that mono- and multi-nucleated bone dissolving cells (osteoclasts) are present in jaw bone and involved in bone remodeling (Witten *et al.*, 2001), a function well conserved then. Calcitonin remains an enigmatic protein and the search for its function(s) (Zaidi *et al.*, 2002) is on-going. Recently Yaoi and colleagues (Yaoi *et al.*, 2004) presented evidence for a whole new pathway of control of calcium handling in which calcitonin *via* its G-protein-coupled receptor regulates otoconin-22 expression, a protein involved in aragonite deposition in bull frog. An exciting and still poorly explored field of research lies open for those interested in calcium handling in vertebrates.

5.3.2 Stanniocalcin

In the 1980s a product extracted from the corpuscles of Stannius received ample attention for its powerful hypocalcemic effects. The laboratory of Copp and his colleagues, who were the first to isolate calcitonin and show its hypocalcemic potency in mammals (Copp, 1992; Azria *et al.*, 1995), not surprisingly, also focused their activities on what we now call stanniocalcin. Extracts of the corpuscles of Stannius contain not only stanniocalcin(s) (McCudden *et al.*, 2001) but also PTHrP (Danks *et al.*, 1998; Ingleton, 2002) and this may have confounded the early research. The first presumed hypocalcemic protein isolated and described was called teleocalcin (Wagner *et al.*, 1986; Wagner *et al.*, 1988). Teleocalcin inhibited branchial calcium influx and was shown to inhibit a presumed calcium ATPase. Later, we demonstrated that the teleocalcin-sensitive ATPase was in fact a non-specific phosphatase with uncertain function in calcium transport (Verbost *et al.*, 1993a; Verbost *et al.*, 1993b; Flik, 2001). Also the apparent molecular radius of teleocalcin was much smaller than that of the native stanniocalcin that was later shown to be the bioactive hypocalcemic/antihypercalcemic moiety. Possibly, truncation of the stanniocalcin molecule (and loss of the glycol-moiety) occurred during isolation procedures and explains association of bioactivity with small molecules. The bulk endocrine protein in corpuscles of Stannius was then shown to inhibit calcium influx across trout gills and called hypocalcin (Lafeber *et al.*, 1988a; Lafeber *et al.*, 1988b). Hypocalcin showed up as a glycoprotein with an apparent 27 kDa molecular mass when separated by sodium dodecyl sulphate polyacrylamide gel electrophoresis under reducing conditions. An uneven number of cysteines in the reduced (glyco-) protein suggested that native hypocalcin could be a homodimer, and this was confirmed by analysis of the product under non-reducing conditions. The hypocalcemic potency of hypocalcin results from inhibitory effects on branchial calcium influx (Lafeber and Perry, 1988), and soon the notion grew that hypocalcin should better be considered an antihypercalcemic hormone: it prevents the hypercalcemia that develops when corpuscles of Stannius are surgically removed (Hanssen *et al.*, 1989). The antihypercalcemic activity of the molecule resides in the N-terminal sequence of the monomer. Small synthetic N-terminal fragments proved to counteract hypercalcemia in eels from which the corpuscles of Stannius were removed. The relevance of dimerisation remains unknown. The glycosylation of the hormone serves a role in recognition in liver and metabolic clearance of the hormone (Hanssen *et al.*, 1993).

Research on hypocalcin really made a leap forward when the gene was (serendipitously!) cloned by Butkus and colleagues (Butkus *et al.*, 1987a; Butkus *et al.*, 1987b). It was when molecular biology made its start. The corpuscles of Stannius were chosen as object for cloning based on the histology of the tissue that shows an extravagant storage of hormone. It was reasoned that the tissue must express an abundance of code for the protein stored and thus be ideal to practice the then very new and not yet very sensitive molecular biological techniques. Hypocalcin was in the centre of interest again and several groups in Europe and Canada made rapid progress. Hypocalcin was renamed stanniocalcin during a meeting in Edmonton, chaired by the late Peter K.T. Pang, one of the pioneers in comparative research on calcium regulating hormones. Whereas the Dutch research group had to change focus to stress endocrinology (Wendelaar Bonga, 1997) and left the area of stanniocalcin research, Wagner and colleagues (Wagner *et al.*, 1992) became, and still are the leaders in stanniocalcin research. Stanniocalcin was well-characterized as an anti-hypercalcemic hormone in a variety of fishes, and its prime function in fishes is an inhibitory control over calcium channels in the apical membrane of the calcium transporting chloride cells in the gills. A remarkable gap in our knowledge concerns the receptor(s) for stanniocalcin. Although the site of stanniocalcin receptors was shown indirectly with a 'stanniocalcin-alkaline phosphatase tandem protein' (McCudden *et al.*, 2002; Paciga *et al.*, 2003; McCudden *et al.*, 2004; Tanega *et al.*, 2004), no direct evidence, i.e. cloning of the stanniocalcin receptor can be found in the literature.

Stanniocalcin, rather first its gene, was then found in humans (Wagner *et al.*, 1995; Olsen *et al.*, 1996) which gave a further boost to stanniocalcin research and the Wagner laboratory was pivotal in this development (Gerritsen and Wagner, 2005). Calcium and phosphate homeostasis depend on and intricate interplay of regulator proteins (Renkema *et al.*, 2008). Not surprising therefore, is the role of stanniocalcin in human and rat renal phosphate handling (Olsen *et al.*, 1996), another well-conserved function: stanniocalcin stimulates phosphate reabsorption in flounder renal proximal tubules (Lu *et al.*, 1994a; Lu *et al.*, 1994b) as it does in mammals. The opposite (Lu *et al.*, 1994b) effects of stanniocalcin on calcium flux (inhibition) and phosphate flux (stimulation) suggest independent regulatory pathways and reflect an uncoupling of calcium and phosphate transport. In isolated fish (killifish, zebrafish, sea bream) renal tubules stanniocalcin counteracts the stimulatory control of PTH/PTHrP on endothelin- regulated multidrug resistance protein-2-mediated transport, important in clearance of xenobiotics (Wever *et al.*, 2007). Cross-talk of second messengers of PTH/PTHrP and stanniocalcin could underlie this effect, an observation that warrants further studies in fish and mammals alike.

The apical membrane of the chloride cell in fish gills thus is equipped with a stanniocalcin-sensitive epithelial calcium channel that belongs to the large transient receptor potential (TRP) channel superfamily (Mensenkamp *et al.*, 2006; Hoenderop and Bindels, 2008) encountered in all vertebrates. Most probably this channel is also present in the apical membranes of calcium transporting epithelia in the intestine and renal tubules. The intestinal Ca^{2+} transporting pathway was functionally characterized in fish (Klaren *et al.*, 1993; Klaren *et al.*, 1997) long before the discovery of the TRP-channels in mammals, for which molecular biological techniques were so instrumental. However, there is convincing evidence for similar channels in fish (Perry *et al.*, 2003). Apparently all these key regulatory proteins find their origin in fishes, the earliest true vertebrates, or their ancestors. With the water-to-land transition of the vertebrates, gills were lost, but intestinal and renal contributions to calcium and magnesium handling changed quantitatively more so than qualitatively. This notion should stimulate comparative physiologists to find models in fish, amphibians and on to mammals to better understand calcium and magnesium handling, processes so pivotal in general physiology. Members of the TRP channel protein family in mammals are regulated by the 'new' hormone klotho (van de Graaf *et al.*, 2006; van der Eerden *et al.*, 2007), named after the Greek goddess that spun the thread of life (klotho was first described as the hormone prolonging life in mice). Klotho is a beta-glucuronidase (van der Eerden *et al.*, 2007) with proteolytic activity regulating TRP channel insertion and activation (Chang *et al.*, 2005). But klotho is a truly pleiotropic regulator. In the mammalian parathyroid cells hypocalcemia triggers klotho secretion and this leads to enhanced recruitment and activity of sodium pumps. As a consequence of the sodium pump activity the electrochmical gradient for sodium increases and causes release of the hypercalcemic parathyroid hormone (Imura *et al.*, 2007). Such controls may be predicted to have evolved in fishes, they possess all the ingredients including klotho (Hayashi *et al.*, 2007), but maybe with PTHrP producing cells as target when it comes to calcium regulation. Is there a role for klotho in recruitment of sodium pumps in chloride cells? The dependence of calcium extrusion from the chloride cell on the sodium pump and sodium–calcium exchange (Flik *et al.*, 1996) makes this a plausible option. With expression of PTHrP in chloride cells (Abbink and Flik, 2007) we could even define a new feedback loop for chloride cell mediated calcium transport. We predict that klotho's thread of life is at least as long as vertebrate life on earth (450 million years since the origin of fishes), but can only hope that it will be longer; the future will tell.

Acknowledgements

The authors thank Dr F.B. Eddy for his sincere friendship and scientific exchange for over 20 years. Support of the Smart Mix Programme of the Netherlands Ministry of Economic Affairs and the Netherlands Ministry of Education, Culture and Science is gratefully acknowledged.

References

Abbink, W. and Flik, G. (2007). Parathyroid hormone-related protein in teleost fish. Gen Comp Endocrinol 152: 243–251.

Abbink, W., Bevelander, G. S., Hang, X. M., Lu,W. Q., Guerreiro, P. M., Spanings,T., Canario, A. V. M. and Flik, G. (2006). PTHrP regulation and calcium balance in sea bream (*Sparus auratus* L.) under calcium constraint. J Exp Biol 209: 3550–3557.

Abbink, W., Bevelander, G. S., Rotllant, J., Canario, A. V. M. and Flik, G. (2004). Calcium handling in *Sparus auratus*: effects of water and dietary calcium levels on mineral composition, cortisol and PTHrP levels. J Exp Biol. 207: 4077–4084.

Abbink, W., Hang, X. M., Guerreiro, P. M., Spanings, F. A. T., Ross, H. A., Canario, A. V. M. and Flik, G. (2007). Parathyroid hormone-related protein and calcium regulation in vitamin D-deficient sea bream (Sparus auratus). J Endocrinol 193: 473–480.

Anjos, L., Rotlant, J., Guerreiro, P. M., Hang, X., Canario, A. V. M., Balment, R. and Power, D. M. (2005). Production and characterisation of gilthead sea bream (*Sparus auratus*) recombinant parathyroid hormone related protein. Gen Comp Endocrinol 143: 57–65.

Auperin, B., Baroiller, J. F., Ricordel, M. J., Fostier, A. and Prunet, P. (1997). Effect of confinement stress on circulating levels of growth hormone and two prolactins in freshwater-adapted tilapia (*Oreochromis niloticus*). Gen Comp Endocrinol 108: 35–44.

Azria, M., Copp, D. H. and Zanelli, J. M. (1995). 25 Years of salmon calcitonin – from synthesis to therapeutic use. Calcified Tiss Internat 57: 405–408.

Ba, J., Brown, D. and Friedman, P. A. (2003). Calcium-sensing receptor regulation of PTH-inhibitable proximal tubule phosphate transport. Am J Physiol 285: F1233–F1243.

Bazarra-Fernandez, A. (2007). Analgesic efficacy of calcitonin for vertebral fracture pain. Calcified Tiss Internat 80: S116–S117.

Berridge, M. J. (1994). The biology and medicine of calcium signaling. Mol Cell Endocrinol 98: 119–124.

Bevelander, G. S., Hang, X., Abbink, W., Spanings, T., Canario, A. V. M. and Flik, G. (2006). PTHrP potentiating estradiol-induced vitellogenesis in sea bream (*Sparus auratus*, L.). Gen Comp Endocrinol 149: 159–165.

Beyenbach, K. W. (1990). Transport of magnesium across biological membranes. Magnesium Trace Elem 9: 233–254.

Beyenbach, K. W. (2000). Renal handling of magnesium in fish: From whole animal to brush border membrane vesicles. Frontiers Biosci 5: D712–D719.

Beyenbach, K. W. (2004). Kidneys sans glomeruli. Am J Physiol 286: F811–F827.

Beyenbach, K. W., Freire, C. A., Kinne, R. K. H. and Kinne-Saffran, E. (1993). Epithelial transport of magnesium in the kidney of fish. Miner Electro Metab 19: 241–249.

Bijvelds, M. J. C., Flik G. and Kolar, Z. I. (1998a). Cellular magnesium transport in the vertebrate intestine. Magnesium Res 11: 315–322.

Bijvelds, M. J. C., Flik, G., Kolar, Z. I. and Wendelaar Bonga, S. E. (1996a). Uptake, distribution and excretion of magnesium in *Oreochromis mossambicus*: Dependence on magnesium in diet and water. Fish Physiol Biochem 15: 287–298.

Bijvelds, M. J. C., Flik, G. and Wendelaar Bonga, S. E. (1997). Mineral balance in *Oreochromis mossambicus*: dependence on magnesium in diet and water. Fish Physiol Biochem 16: 323–331.

Bijvelds, M. J. C., Kolar, Z. I. and Flik, G. (2001). Electrodiffusive magnesium transport across the intestinal brush border membrane of tilapia (Oreochromis mossambicus). Eur J Biochem 268: 2867–2872.

Bijvelds, M. J. C., Kolar, Z. I., Wendelaar Bonga, S. E. and Flik, G. (1996b). Magnesium transport across the basolateral plasma membrane of the fish enterocyte. J Membrane Biol 154: 217–225.

Bijvelds, M. J. C., van der Velden, J. A., Kolar, Z. I. and Flik, G. (1998b). Magnesium transport in freshwater teleosts. J Exp Biol 201: 1981–1990.

Butkus, A., Darling, P. E., Fernley, R. T., Haralambidis, J., John, M., Mcdonald, M. R., Penschow, J. D., Roche, P. J., Ryan, C. B., Thorley, B. R., Trahair, J. F., Tregear, G. W., Xuereb, L. and Coghlan, J. P. (1987a). Purification, isolation and sequence of the protein from the corpuscles of Stannius of *Anguilla australis*. Aust NZ J Med 17: 152.

Butkus, A., Roche, P. J., Fernley, R. T., Haralambidis, J., Penschow, J. D., Ryan, G. B., Trahair, J. F. Tregear G. W. and Coghlan J. P. (1987b). Purification and cloning of a corpuscles of Stannius protein from *Anguilla australis*. Mol Cell Endocrinol 54: 123–133.

Canario, A. V. M., Rotllant, J., Fuentes, J., Guerreiro, P. M., Teodosio, H. R., Power, D. M. and Clark M. S. (2006). Novel bioactive parathyroid hormone and related peptides in teleost fish. FEBS Lett 580: 291–299.

Chang, Q., Hoefs, S., van der Kemp, A. W., Topala, C. N., Bindels, R. J. M. and Hoenderop, J. G. J. (2005). The β-glucuronidase klotho hydrolyzes and activates the TRPV5 channel. Science 310: 490–493.

Copp, D. H. (1992). The discovery of calcitonin. Bone Miner 16: 157–159.

Danks, J. A., Trivett, M. K., Power, D. M., Canario, A.V. M., Martin T. J. and Ingleton P. M. (1998). Parathyroid hormone-related protein in lower vertebrates. Clin Exp Pharmacol P 25: 750–752.

de Ruiter, A. J. H. and Mein, C. G. (1982). Testosterone-dependent transformation of nephronic tubule cells into serous and mucous gland cells in stickleback kidneys *in vivo* and *in vitro*. Gen Comp Endocrinol 47: 70–83.

Fabbri, A., Fraioli,F., Gnessi, L., Moretti, C., Bini, G., Cruccu, G. and Manfredi, M. (1983). Is calcitonin an analgesic hormone? Arch Neurol 40: 64–64.

Flanagan, J. A., Bendell, L. A., Guerreiro, P. M. Clark,M. S., Power, D. M., Canario, A. V. M., Brown, B. L. and Ingleton, P. M. (2002). Cloning of the cDNA for the putative calcium-sensing receptor and its tissue distribution in sea bream (*Sparus aurata*). Gen Comp Endocrinol 127: 117–127.

Flik, G. (2001). The role of scales in calcium metabolism of *Oreochromis mossambicus*. Bone 28: S249–S249.

Flik, G., Fenwick, J. C., Kolar, Z., Mayer-Gostan, N. and Wendelaar Bonga, S. E. (1985). Whole-body calcium flux rates in cichlid teleost fish *Oreochromis mossambicus* adapted to fresh water. Am J Physiol 249: R432–R437.

Flik, G., Fenwick, J. C., Kolar, Z., Mayer-Gostan, N. and Wendelaar Bonga, S. E. (1986a). Effects of low ambient calcium levels on whole-body Ca^{2+} flux rates and internal calcium pools in the fresh-water cichlid teleost, *Oreochromis mossambicus*. J Exp Biol 120: 249–264.

Flik, G., Fenwick, J. C., Kolar, Z., Mayer-Gostan, N. and Wendelaar Bonga, S. E. (1986b). Effects of ovine prolactin on calcium uptake and distribution in *Oreochromis mossambicus*. Am J Physiol 250: R161–R166.

Flik, G., Fenwick, J. C., Kolar, Z., Mayer-Gostan, N. and Wendelaar Bonga, S. E. (1986c). Effects of low ambient calcium levels on whole body Ca^{2+} flux rates and internal calcium pools in the fresh-water cichlid teleost, *Oreochromis mossambicus*. J. Exp Biol 120: 249–264.

Flik, G., Kaneko, T., Greco, A. M., Li, J. and Fenwick, J. C. (1997). Sodium dependent ion transporters in trout gills. *Fish Physiol Biochem* 17: 385–396.

Flik, G., Klaren, P. H. M., Schoenmakers, T. J. M., Bijvelds, M. J. C., Verbost, P. M. and Wendelaar Bonga, S. E. (1996). Cellular calcium transport in fish: Unique and universal mechanisms. Physiol Zool 69: 403–417.

Flik, G., Rentier-Delrue, F. and Wendelaar Bonga, S. E. (1994a). Calcitropic effects of recombinant prolactins in *Oreochromis mossambicus*. Am J Physiol 266: R1302–R1308.

Flik, G., Schoenmakers, T. J. M., Groot, J. A., van Os, C. H. and Wendelaar Bonga, S. E. (1990). Calcium absorption by fish intestine – the involvement of ATP-dependent and sodium-dependent calcium extrusion mechanisms. J Membrane Biol 113: 13–22.

Flik, G., van der Velden, J. A., Dechering, K. J., Verbost, P. M., Schoenmakers, T. J. M. Kolar, Z. I. and Wendelaar Bonga, S. E. (1993). Ca^{2+} and Mg^{2+} transport in gills and gut of tilapia, *Oreochromis mossambicus* – a review. J Exp Zool 265: 356–365.

Flik, G., Varsamos, S., Guerreiro, P. M., Fuentes, X., Huising, M. O. and Fenwick, J. C. (2002). Drinking in (very young) fish. Symp Soc Exp Biol 54: 31–47.

Flik, G. and Verbost, P. M. (1993). Calcium transport in fish gills and intestine. J Exp Biol 184: 17–29.

Flik, G., Verbost, P. M., Atsma, W. and Lucu, C. (1994b). Calcium transport in gill plasma membranes of the crab *Carcinus maenas* – evidence for carriers driven by ATP and a Na^+ gradient. J Exp Biol 195: 109–122.

Fouchereau-Peron, M., Moukhtar, M. S., Legal, Y. and Milhaud, G. (1981). Demonstration of specific receptors for calcitonin in isolated trout gill cells. Comp Biochem Physiol A 68: 417–421.

Freire, C., Kinne, R. K. H., Kinne-Saffran, E. and Beyenbach, K. W. (1995). Evidence for a magnesium channel in renal proximal tubules. J Am Soc Nephrol 6: 948–948.

Freire, C., Kinne, R. K. H., Kinne-Saffran, E. and Beyenbach, K. W. (1996). Electrodiffusive transport of Mg across renal membrane vesicles of the rainbow trout *Oncorhynchus mykiss*. Am J Physiol 39: F739–F748.

Fuentes, J. and Eddy, F.B. (1997). Drinking in marine, euryhaline and freshwater teleost fish. In: Ionic Regulation in Animals, Hazon, N., Eddy, F.B. and Flik, G. (eds). Springer, Heidelberg/New York: 135–149.

Fuentes, J., Figueiredo, J., Power, D. M. and Canario, A. V. M. (2006). Parathyroid hormone-related protein regulates intestinal calcium transport in sea bream (*Sparus auratus*). Am J Physiol 291: R1499–R1506.

Fuentes, J., Guerreiro, P. M., Modesto, T., Rotllant, J., Canario, A. V. M. and Power, D. M. (2007). A PTH/PTHrP receptor antagonist blocks the hypercalcemic response to estradiol–17b. Am J Physiol 293: R956–R960.

Gerritsen, M. E. and Wagner, G. F. (2005). Stanniocalcin: No longer just a fish tale. Vitamin Horm 70: 105–135.

Grubbs, R. D. and Walter, A. (1994). Determination of cytosolic Mg^{2+} activity and buffering in Bc3h–1 cells with Mag–Fura–2. Mol Cell Biochem 136: 11–22.

Guerreiro, P. M., Fuentes, T., Power, D. M., Ingleton, P. M., Flik, G. and Canario, A. V. M. (2001). Parathyroid hormone-related protein: a calcium regulatory factor in sea bream (*Sparus aurata* L.) larvae. Am J Physiol 281: R855–R860.

Guerreiro, P. M., Renfro, J. L., Power, D. M. and Canario, A. V. M. (2007). The parathyroid hormone family of peptides: structure, tissue distribution, regulation, and potential functional roles in calcium and phosphate balance in fish. Am J Physiol 292: R679–R696.

Guerreiro, P. M., Rotllant, J., Fuentes, J., Power, D. M. and Canario, A. V. M. (2006). Cortisol and parathyroid hormone-related peptide are reciprocally modulated by negative feedback. Gen Comp Endocrinol 148: 227–235.

Handy, R. D., Ellis, D., Gow, I. F. and Flatman, P. W. (1996a). Regulation of intracellular ionized magnesium concentration by $Na^+–Mg^{2+}$ exchange in isolated rat ventricular myocytes. J Physiol 495P: P168–P168.

Handy, R. D., Gow, I. F. Ellis, D. and Flatman, P. W. (1996b). Na-dependent regulation of intracellular free magnesium concentration in isolated rat ventricular myocytes. J Mol Cell Cardiol 28: 1641–1651.

Hanssen, R. G. J. M., Lafeber, F. P. J. G., Flik, G. and Wendelaar Bonga, S. E. (1989). Ionic and total calcium levels in the blood of the European eel (*Anguilla anguilla*) – effects of stanniectomy and hypocalcin replacement therapy. J Exp Biol 141: 177–186.

Hanssen, R. G. J. M., Mayer-Gostan, N., Flik, G. and Wendelaar Bonga, S. E. (1993). Stanniocalcin kinetics in fresh-water and seawater European eel (*Anguilla anguilla*). Fish Physiol Biochem 10: 491–496.

Hayashi, Y., Okino, N., Kakuta, Y., Shikanai, T., Tani, M., Narimatsu, H. and Ito, M. (2007). Klotho-related protein is a novel cytosolic neutral beta-glycosylceramidase. J Biol Chem 282: 30889–30900.

Hoare, S. R., Rubin, D. A., Juppner, H. and Usdin, T. B. (2000). Evaluating the ligand specificity of zebrafish parathyroid hormone (PTH) receptors: comparison of PTH, PTH-related protein, and tuberoinfundibular peptide of 39 residues. Endocrinology 141: 3080–3086.

Hoenderop, J. G. J. and Bindels, R. J. M. (2008). Calciotropic and magnesiotropic TRP channels. Physiology 23: 32–40.

Hogan, B. M., Danks, J. A., Layton, J. E., Hall, N. E. Heath, J. K. and Lieschke, G. J. (2005). Duplicate zebrafish pth genes are expressed along the lateral line and in the central nervous system during embryogenesis. Endocrinology 146: 547–551.

Hogasen, H. R. and Prunet, P. (1997). Plasma levels of thyroxine, prolactin, and cortisol in migrating and resident wild arctic char, *Salvelinus alpinus*. Can J Fish Aquat Sci 54: 2947–2954.

Igal, R. A., Dumm, I. N. T. D. and Goya, R. G. (1998). Modulation of rat liver lipid metabolism by prolactin. Prostag Leukotr Ess 59: 395–400.

Imura, A., Tsuji, Y., Murata, M., Maeda, K., Kubota, R., Iwano, A., Obuse, C., Togashi, K., Tominaga, M., Kita, N., Tomiyama, K., Iijima, J., Nabeshima, Y., Fujioka, M., Asato, R., Tanaka, S., Kojima, K., Ito, J., Nozaki, K., Hashimoto, N., Ito, T., Nishio, T., Uchiyama, T., Fujimori, T. and Nabeshima, Y. I. (2007). alpha-klotho as a regulator of calcium homeostasis. Science 316: 1615–1618.

Ingleton, P. M. (2002). Parathyroid hormone-related protein in lower vertebrates. Comp Biochem Physiol B 132: 87–95.

Kass, G. E. N. and Orrenius, S. (1999). Calcium signaling and cytotoxicity. Envir Health Perspect 107: 25–35.

Klaren, P. H. M., Flik, G., Lock, R. A. C. and Wendelaar Bonga, S. E. (1993). Ca^{2+} transport across intestinal brush-border membranes of the cichlid teleost *Oreochromis mossambicus*. J Membrane Biol 132: 157–166.

Klaren, P. H. M., Wendelaar Bonga, S. E. and Flik, G. (1997). Evidence for P_2-purinoceptor-mediated uptake of Ca^{2+} across a fish (*Oreochromis mossambicus*) intestinal brush border membrane. Biochem J 322: 129–134.

Lafeber, F. P. J. G., Flik, G., Wendelaar Bonga, S. E. and Perry, S. F. (1988a). Hypocalcin from Stannius corpuscles inhibits gill calcium uptake in trout. Am J Physiol 254: R891–R896.

Lafeber, F. P. J. G., Hanssen, R. G. J. M., Choy, Y. M., Flik, G., Herrmann-Erlee, M. P. M., Pang, P. K. T. and Wendelaar Bonga, S. E. (1988b). Identification of hypocalcin (teleocalcin) isolated from trout Stannius corpuscles. Gen Comp Endocrinol 69: 19–30.

Lafeber, F. P. J. G. and Perry, S. F. (1988). Experimental hypercalcemia induces hypocalcin release and inhibits branchial Ca^{2+} influx in fresh-water trout. Gen Comp Endocrinol 72: 136–143.

Larsson, D., Björnsson, B. T. and Sundell, K. (1995). Physiological concentrations of 24,25-dihydroxyvitamin D_3 rapidly decrease the in vitro intestinal calcium uptake in the Atlantic cod, *Gadus morhua*. Gen Comp Endocrinol 100: 211–217.

Larsson, D., Lundgren, T. and Sundell, K. (1998). Ca^{2+} uptake through voltage-gated L-type Ca^{2+} channels by polarized enterocytes from Atlantic cod *Gadus morhua*. J Membrane Biol 164: 229–237.

Li, J., Eygensteyn, J., Lock, R. A. C., Wendelaar Bonga, S. E.and Flik, G. (1997). Na^+ and Ca^{2+} homeostatic mechanisms in isolated chloride cells of the teleost *Oreochromis mossambicus* analysed by confocal laser scanning microscopy. J Exp Biol 200: 1499–1508.

Lock, E. J., Ornsrud, R., Aksnes, L. Spanings, F. A. T., Waagbø, R. and Flik, G. (2007). The vitamin D receptor and its ligand 1α,25-dihydroxyvitamin D_3 in Atlantic salmon (*Salmo salar*). J Endocrinol 193: 459–471.

Lovejoy, D. A. (2006). Structure and function of the teneurin C-terminal associated peptides (TCAP). J Exp Zool 305A: 151–151.

Lovejoy, D. A., Al Chawaf, A. and Cadinouche, M. Z. A. (2006). Teneurin C-terminal associated peptides: An enigmatic family of neuropeptides with structural similarity to the corticotropin-releasing factor and calcitonin families of peptides. Gen Comp Endocrinol 148: 299–305.

Lu, M., Renfro, J. L. and Wagner, G. F. (1994a). Effects of stanniocalcin on phosphate transport by flounder renal proximal tubule in primary culture. FASEB J 8: A837–A837.

Lu, M. Q., Wagner, G. F. and Renfro, J. L. (1994b). Stanniocalcin stimulates phosphate reabsorption by flounder renal proximal tubule in primary culture. Am J Physiol 36: R1356–R1362.

Madsen, K. L., Tavernini, M. M., Yachimec, C. Mendrick, D. L., Alfonso, P. J., Buergin, M., Olsen, H. S., Antonaccio, M. J., Thomson, A. B. and Fedorak, R. N. (1998). Stanniocalcin: a novel protein regulating calcium and phosphate transport across mammalian intestine. Am J Physiol 274: G96–G102.

McCudden, C. R., James, K. A., Hasilo, C. and Wagner, G. F. (2002). Characterization of mammalian stanniocalcin receptors - mitochondrial targeting of ligand and receptor for regulation of cellular metabolism. J Biol Chem 277: 45249–45258.

McCudden, C. R., Kogon, M. R., DiMattia, G. E. and Wagner, G. F. (2001). Novel expression of the stanniocalcin gene in fish. J Endocrinol 171: 33–44.

McCudden, C. R., Majewski, A., Chakrabarti, S., and Wagner, G. F. (2004). Co-localization of stanniocalcin-1 ligand and receptor in human breast carcinomas. Mol Cell Endocrinol 213: 167–172.

McWilliams, P. G. and Potts, W. T. W. (1978). Effects of pH and calcium concentrations on gill potentials in brown trout, *Salmo trutta*. J Comp Physiol 126: 277–286.

Mensenkamp, A. R., Hoenderop, J. G. J. and Bindels, R. J. M. (2006). Recent advances in renal tubular calcium reabsorption. Curr Opin Nephrol Hy 15: 524–529.

Molina, A. S., Paladini, A. and Gimenez, M. S. (1997). Hormonal influence on lipid-protein interactions in biological membranes - Lactation effects on alkaline phosphatase activity and intestinal brush border membrane properties in rat. Horm Metab Res 29: 159–163.

Motoyama, H. I. and Friedman, P. A. (2002). Calcium-sensing receptor regulation of PTH-dependent calcium absorption by mouse cortical ascending limbs. Am J Physiol 283: F399–F406.

Ogasawara, T., Sakamoto, T. and Hirano, T. (1996). Prolactin kinetics during freshwater adaptation of mature chum salmon, *Oncorhynchus keta*. Zool Sci 13: 443–447.

Olsen, H. S., Cepeda, M. A., Zhang, Q. Q., Rosen, C. A., Vozzolo, B. L. and Wagner, G. F. (1996). Human stanniocalcin: A possible hormonal regulator of mineral metabolism. Proc Nat Acad Sci USA 93: 1792–1796.

Paciga, M., McCudden, C. R., Londos, C., DiMattia, G. E. and Wagner, G. F. (2003). Targeting of big stanniocalcin and its receptor to lipid storage droplets of ovarian steroidogenic cells. J Biol Chem 278: 49549–49554.

Perry, S. F. (1997). The chloride cell: Structure and function in the gills of freshwater fishes. Annu Rev Physiol 59: 325–347.

Perry, S. F. and Flik, G. (1988). Characterization of branchial trans-epithelial calcium fluxes in fresh-water trout, *Salmo gairdneri*. Am J Physiol 254: R491–R498.

Perry, S. F., Goss, G. G. and Fenwick, J. C. (1992a). Interrelationships between gill chloride cell morphology and calcium uptake in fresh-water teleosts. Fish Physiol Biochem 10: 327–337.

Perry, S. F., Goss, G. G. and Laurent, P. (1992b). The interrelationships between gill chloride cell morphology and ionic uptake in four fresh-water teleosts. Can J Zool 70: 1775–1786.

Perry, S. F., Shahsavarani, A., Georgalis,T., Bayaa, M., Furimsky, M. and Thomas, S. L. Y. (2003). Channels, pumps, and exchangers in the gill and kidney of freshwater fishes: Their role in ionic and acid-base regulation. J Exp Zool A 300: 53–62.

Power, D. M., Ingleton, P. M. and Clark, M. S. (2002). Application of comparative genomics in fish endocrinology. Int Rev Cytol 221: 149–190.

Prunet, P., Sandra, O., Le Rouzic, P., Marchand, O. and Laudet, V. (2000). Molecular characterization of the prolactin receptor in two fish species, tilapia Oreochromis niloticus and rainbow trout, *Oncorhynchus mykiss*: a comparative approach. Can J Fish Physiol Pharm 78: 1086–1096.

Pu, Y. M., Luo, K. Q. and Chang, D. C. (2002). A Ca^{2+} signal is found upstream of cytochrome c release during apoptosis in HeLa cells. Biochem Biophys Res Comm 299: 762–769.

Redruello, B., Estevao, M. D., Rotllant, J., Guerreiro, P. M., Anjos, L. I., Canario, A. V. M. and Power, D. M. (2005). Isolation and characterization of piscine osteonectin and downregulation of its expression by PTH-related protein. J Bone Min Res 20: 682–692.

Renkema, K. Y., Alexander, R. T., Bindels, R. J. M. and Hoenderop, J. G. J. (2008). Calcium and phosphate homeostasis: Concerted interplay of new regulators. Ann Med 40: 82–91.

Rotllant, J., Guerreiro, P. M., Anjos, L., Redruello, B., Canario, A. V. M. and Power, D. M. (2005a). Stimulation of cortisol release by the N-terminus of teleost parathyroid hormone-related protein in interrenal cells in vitro. Endocrinology 146: 71–76.

Rotllant, J., Redruello, B., Guerreiro, P. M., Fernandes, H., Canario, A. V. M and. Power, D. M. (2005b). Calcium mobilization from fish scales is mediated by parathyroid hormone related protein via the parathyroid hormone type 1 receptor. Regul Peptides 132: 33–40.

Rotllant, J., Worthington, G. P., Fuentes, J., Guerreiro, P. M., Teitsma, C. A., Ingleton, P. M. Balment, R. J., Canario, A. V. M. and Power, D. M. (2003). Determination of tissue and plasma concentrations of PTHrP in fish: development and validation of a radioimmunoassay using a teleost 1–34 N-terminal peptide. Gen Comp Endocrinol 133: 146–153.

Sakamoto, T., Shepherd, B. S., Madsen, S. S., Nishioka, R. S., Siharath, K., Richman, N. H., Bern, H. A. and Grau, E. G. (1997). Osmoregulatory actions of growth hormone and prolactin in an advanced teleost. Gen Comp Endocrinol 106: 95–101.

Schoenmakers, T. J. M. and Flik, G. (1992). Sodium-extruding and calcium-extruding sodium calcium exchangers display similar calcium affinities. J Exp Biol 168: 151–159.

Shahsavarani, A., McNeill, B., Galvez, F., Wood, C. M., Goss, G. G., Hwang, P. P. and Perry, S. F. (2006). Characterization of a branchial epithelial calcium channel (ECaC) in freshwater rainbow trout (Oncorhynchus mykiss). J Exp Biol 209: 1928–1943.

Shahsavarani, A. and Perry, S. F. (2006). Hormonal and environmental regulation of epithelial calcium channel in gill of rainbow trout (Oncorhynchus mykiss). Am J Physiol 291: R1490–R1498.

Sundell, K., Bishop, J. E., Björnsson, B. T. and Norman, A. W. (1992). 1,25-Dihydroxyvitamin-D_3 in the Atlantic cod. Plasma levels, a plasma-binding component, and organ distribution of a high-affinity receptor. Endocrinology 131: 2279–2286.

Sundell, K. and Björnsson, B. T. (1990). Effects of vitamin-D_3, 25(OH) vitamin-D_3, 24,25(OH)$_2$ vitamin-D_3, and 1,25(OH)$_2$ vitamin-D_3 on the in vitro intestinal calcium absorption in the marine teleost, Atlantic cod (Gadus morhua). Gen Comp Endocrinol 78: 74–79.

Sundell, K., Norman, A. W. and Björnsson, B. T. (1993). 1,25(OH)$_2$ Vitamin-D_3 increases ionized plasma calcium concentrations in the immature Atlantic cod Gadus morhua. Gen Comp Endocrinol 91: 344–351.

Takei, Y. (2008). Exploring novel hormones essential for seawater adaptation in teleost fish. Gen Comp Endocrinol_157: 3–13.

Takei, Y., Tsuchida, T. and Tanakadate, A. (1998). Evaluation of water intake in seawater adaptation in eels using a synchronized drop counter and pulse injector system. Zool Sci 15: 677–682.

Tanega, C., Radman, D. P., Flowers, B., Sterba, T. and Wagner, G. F. (2004). Evidence for stanniocalcin and a related receptor in annelids. Peptides 25: 1671–1679.

Toribio, R. E., Kohn, C. W., Capen, C. C. and Rosol, T. J. (2003). Parathyroid hormone (PTH) secretion, PTH mRNA and calcium-sensing receptor mRNA expression in equine parathyroid cells, and effects of interleukin (IL)–1, IL–6, and tumor necrosis factor a on equine parathyroid cell function. J Mol Endocrinol 31: 609–620.

van de Graaf, S. F. J., Hoenderop, J. G. J. and Bindels, R. J. M. (2006). Regulation of TRPV5 and TRPV6 by associated proteins. Am J Physiol 290: F1295–F1302.

van der Eerden, B. C. J., Chang, Q., Hoenderop, J. G. J., Pols, H. A. P., Bindels, R. J. M. and van Leeuwen, J. P. T. (2007). The β-glucuronidase klotho diminishes osteoclastogenesis and subsequent osteoclastic bone resorption. Calcified Tiss Internat 80: S32–S33.

van der Velden, J. A., Flik, G., Spanings, F. A. T., Verburg, T. G., Kolar Z. I. and Wendelaar Bonga, S. E. (1992). Physiological effects of low-magnesium feeding in the common carp, *Cyprinus carpio*. J Exp Zool 264: 237–244.

van der Velden, J. A., Spanings, F. A. T., Flik, G. and Wendelaar Bonga, S. E. (1991). Early life stages of carp (*Cyprinus carpio* L) depend on ambient magnesium for their development. J Exp Biol 158: 431–438.

van Eys, G. J. J. M. and Wendelaar Bonga, S. E. (1984). Responses of the PAS-positive pars intermedia cells in the cichlid fish *Sarotherodon mossambicus* to ambient calcium and background adaptation. Cell Tissue Res 236: 181–187.

Varsamos, S., Xuereb, B., Commes, T., Flik G. and Spanings-Pierrot, C. (2006). Pituitary hormone mRNA expression in European sea bass *Dicentrarchus labrax* in seawater and following acclimation to fresh water. J Endocrinol 191: 473–480.

Verbost, P. M., Bryson, S. E., Wendelaar Bonga, S. E. and Marshall, W. S. (1997). Na$^+$-dependent Ca^{2+} uptake in isolated opercular epithelium of *Fundulus heteroclitus*. J Comp Physiol B 167: 205–212.

Verbost, P. M., Butkus, A., Atsma, W., Willems, P., Flik, G. and Wendelaar Bonga, S. E. (1993a). Studies on stanniocalcin - characterization of bioactive and antigenic domains of the hormone. Mol Cell Endocrinol 93: 11–16.

Verbost, P. M., Butkus, A., Willems, P. and Wendelaar Bonga, S. E. (1993b). Indications for two bioactive principles in the corpuscles of Stannius. J Exp Biol 177: 243–252.

Verbost, P. M., Flik, G., Fenwick, J. C., Greco, A. M., Pang, P. K. T. and Wendelaar Bonga, S. E. (1993c). Branchial calcium uptake - possible mechanisms of control by stanniocalcin. Fish Physiol Biochem 11: 205–215.

Verbost, P. M., Lafeber, F. P. J. G., Spanings, F. A. T., Aarden, E. M. and Wendelaar Bonga, S. E. (1992). Inhibition of Ca^{2+} uptake in fresh-water carp, *Cyprinus carpio*, during short-term exposure to aluminum. J Exp Zool 262: 247–254.

Verbost, P. M., Schoenmakers, T. J. M., Flik, G. and Wendelaar Bonga, S. E. (1994). Kinetics of ATP-driven and Na^+-gradient-driven Ca^{2+} transport in basolateral membranes from gills of fresh water-adapted and seawater-adapted tilapia. J Exp Biol 186: 95–108.

Verbost, P. M., van Rooij, J., Flik, G., Lock, R. A. C. and Wendelaar Bonga, S. E. (1989). The movement of cadmium through fresh-water trout branchial epithelium and its interference with calcium transport. J Exp Biol 145: 185–197.

Vonck, A. P. M. A., Wendelaar Bonga, S. E. and Flik, G. (1998). Sodium and calcium balance in Mozambique tilapia, *Oreochromis mossambicus*, raised at different salinities. Comp Biochem Physiol A 119A: 441–449.

Wagner, G. F., Copp, D. H. and Friesen, H. G. (1988). Immunological studies on teleocalcin and salmon corpuscles of Stannius. Endocrinology 122: 2064–2070.

Wagner, G. F., Dimattia, G. E., Davie, J. R., Copp, D. H. and Friesen, H. G. (1992). Molecular cloning and cDNA sequence analysis of coho salmon stanniocalcin. Mol Cell Endocrinol 90: 7–15.

Wagner, G. F., Guiraudon, C. C., Milliken, C. and Copp, D. H. (1995). Immunological and biological evidence for a stanniocalcin-like hormone in human kidney. Proc Nat Acad Sci USA 92: 1871–1875.

Wagner, G. F., Hampong, M., Park, C. M. and Copp, D. H. (1986). Purification, characterization, and bioassay of teleocalcin, a glycoprotein from salmon corpuscles of Stannius. Gen Comp Endocrinol 63: 481–491.

Wagner, G. F., Jaworski, E. M. and Radman, D. P. (1997a). Salmon calcitonin inhibits whole body Ca^{2+} uptake in young rainbow trout. J Endocrinol 155: 459–465.

Wagner, G. F., Vozzolo, B. L., Jaworski, E., Haddad, M., Kline, R. L. Olsen, H. S., Rosen, C. A., Davidson, M. B. and Renfro, J. L. (1997b). Human stanniocalcin inhibits renal phosphate excretion in the rat. J Bone Min Res 12: 165–171.

Wendelaar Bonga, S. E. (1980). Effect of synthetic salmon calcitonin and low ambient calcium on plasma calcium, ultimobranchial cells, Stannius bodies, and prolactin cells in the teleost *Gasterosteus aculeatus*. Gen Comp Endocrinol 40: 99–108.

Wendelaar Bonga, S. E. (1981). Effect of synthetic salmon calcitonin on protein-bound and free plasma calcium in the teleost *Gasterosteus aculeatus*. Gen Comp Endocrinol 43: 123–126.

Wendelaar Bonga, S. E. (1997). The stress response in fish. Physiol Rev 77: 591–625.

Wendelaar Bonga, S. E., Flik, G., van der Meij, J. C., Kolar, Z. and Fenwick, J. C. (1984a). Prolactin and calcium metabolism in the teleost fish *Sarotherodon mossambicus*. Gen Comp Endocrinol 53: 494–494.

Wendelaar Bonga, S. E. and Pang, P. K. T. (1991). Control of calcium regulating hormones in the vertebrates - parathyroid hormone, calcitonin, prolactin, and stanniocalcin. Int Rev Cytol 128: 139–213.

Wendelaar Bonga, S. E. and van der Meij, J. C. A. (1981). Effect of ambient osmolarity and calcium on prolactin cell activity and osmotic water permeability of the gills in the teleost *Sarotherodon mossambicus*. Gen Comp Endocrinol 43: 432–442.

Wendelaar Bonga, S. E., van der Meij, J. C. A. and Flik, G. (1986). Response of PAS-positive cells of the pituitary pars intermedia in the teleost *Carassius auratus* to acid water. Cell Tissue Res 243: 609–617.

Wendelaar Bonga, S. E., van der Meij, J. C. A., van der Krabben, W. A. W. A. and Flik, G. (1984b). The effect of water acidification on prolactin cells and pars intermedia PAS-positive cells in the teleost fish *Oreochromis* (formerly *Sarotherodon) mossambicus* and *Carassius auratus*. Cell Tissue Res 238: 601–609.

Wever, K. E., Masereeuw, R., Miller, D. S., Hang, X. M. and Flik, G. (2007). Endothelin and calciotropic hormones share regulatory pathways in multidrug resistance protein 2-mediated transport. Am J Physiol 292: F38–F46.

Witten, P. E., Hansen, A. and Hall, B. K. (2001). Features of mono- and multinucleated bone resorbing cells of the zebrafish *Danio rerio* and their contribution to skeletal development, remodeling, and growth. J Morph 250: 197–207.

Yaoi, Y., Onda, T., Hidaka, Y., Yajima, S., Suzuki, M. and Tanaka, S. (2004). Developmental expression of otoconin-22 in the bullfrog endolymphatic sac and inner ear. J Histochem Cytochem 52: 663–670.

Zaccone, G., Wendelaar Bonga, S. E., Flik, G., Fasulo, S., Licata, A., Locascio, P., Mauceri, A. and Lauriano, E. R. (1992). Localization of calbindin D28k-like immunoreactivity in fish gill – a light microscopic and immunoelectron histochemical study. Regul Peptides 41: 195–208.

Zaidi, M., Moonga, B. S. and Abe, E. (2002). Calcitonin and bone formation: a knockout full of surprises. J Clin Invest 110: 1769–1771.

Zhu, Y., Stiller, J. W., Shaner, M. P., Baldini, A. Scemama, J. L. and Capehart, A. A. (2004). Cloning of somatolactin alpha and beta cDNAs in zebrafish and phylogenetic analysis of two distinct somatolactin subtypes in fish. J Endocrinol 182: 509–518.

Chapter 6

The effect of inorganic contaminants and cyanobacterial toxins on cation homeostasis in freshwater fish

Nicolas R. Bury and James C. McGeer

Keyword: Teleost fish, pollution, toxicity, natural toxins, toxicology, epithelial sodium channel (ENaC), sodium proton exchanger (NHE), soidu/potassium ATPase (Na$^+$/K$^+$-ATPase), sodium/potassium/chloride co-transporter (NKC), sodium/bicarbonate co-transporter (NBC1), epithelial calcium channel (ECaC), Na$^+$/Ca^{2+} Exchanger (NXC), Ca^{2+}-ATPase (PCMA, silver, copper, cadmium, zinc, lead, Biotic ligand model, macroarray, gene expression

Abstract

The gills of freshwater fish are a multifunctional organ. The branchial architecture ensures a large surface area and coupled with a thin epithelial covering enables rapid oxygen uptake and excretion of metabolic waste gases. However, because the internal milieu of freshwater fish is hyperosmotic to their surroundings the thin epithelium increases the likelihood of ionic losses and water absorption. To compensate for the ionic loss the gills are the site of active ion acquisition from the water, and the ion uptake processes are a target for environmental pollutants. For example, increasing concentrations of waterborne metals are known to severely perturb ion balance and fish compensate by altering ion uptake dynamics in the continued presence of metals. In addition, increased eutrophication of freshwaters has seen the rise in the incidences of cyanobacterial blooms, and an associated increase in the production of toxic metabolites, such as microcystin, by various cyanobacterial speceis that have been found to affect branchial ion ATPase activity. Because the gills are in the 'frontline' of pollutant exposure they are an attractive organ to develop predictive tools for aquatic environmental monitoring and risk assessment. This is exemplified by the development of the biotic ligand model (BLM) to predict acute metal toxicity based on the interactions of metals with the gill and the use of primary gill cell cultures in conjunction with gene expression profiling to identify specific genetic responses to classes of pollutants.

6.1 Introduction

The gill epithelium of freshwater teleost fish is in contact with the aquatic environment and is thus the interface between the internal and external milieu, as well as a major site of the organism's interaction with waterborne pollutants (MacKay and Fraser, 2003; Niyogi and Wood, 2004; Malbrouck and Kestemont, 2006). Chapter 1 provides a general overview of the responses of teleost fish to osmotic challenges, as well as suggesting ideas for the future research that is necessary to build a fuller understanding of teleost fish osmoregulation. This chapter will focus on the uptake processes for the major cations, Na^+, Ca^{2+}, Mg^{2+}, K^+, across the fish gill in freshwater (a review comparing osmoregualtory strategies in freshwater and marine fish has recently been published by Marshall and Grosell, 2005, and will concentrate on how inorganic contaminants and cyanobacterial toxins disrupt these uptake processes. The chapter will conclude by showing how empirical studies investigating the way in which inorganic contaminants affect gill function have been integral in the development of computer based tools to predict acute metal toxicity. In addition, we will give an example of how a freshwater fish primary gill cell cultures can be used as a biomonitoring tool for environmental assessment of pollutants.

6.2 Branchial cation uptake in freshwater fish

6.2.1 Freshwater fish branchial architecture and cell types

The gills of freshwater fish are involved in a number of essential processes including oxygen uptake, acid–base balance, metabolic waste excretion and ion exchange (Evans *et al.*, 2005). The features of the gill that facilitate gas exchange, an increase in surface area and a thin epithelial covering to aid gas transfer to the blood (Laurent, 1982), create conditions which challenge the ionoregulatory capacity of fish. This is because, in freshwater, fish maintain their internal milieu at levels that are hyperosmotic to the environment, and thus continually lose ions and gain water across the gill epithelium. In response to this osmotic challenge, fish in freshwater drink very little (Fuentes *et al.*, 1996), produce copious quantities of dilute urine (Brown *et al.*, 1980), and to counteract the loss of ions the gill lamellae actively sequester ions from the water.

The branchial epithelium has three main cell types, respiratory, mucus producing and mitochondria rich cells (MRC). The majority of cells (~90%) are respiratory cells, also termed pavement cells and their appearance under scanning electron microscope shows an intricate pattern of microridges on the surface. The mucus cells secrete glycoproteins to form the stabilized boundary layer on the external surface of the gill. This boundary layer protects the epithelium and can be altered in response to stressors (see Chapter 7 for more details). The third cell type is the MRC which in the past have sometimes been refereed to as chloride cells (Evans *et al.*, 2005). These cells are characterized by a large number of mitochondria, indicative of their primary function, ion transport (Evans *et al.*, 2005). There appear to be subtypes of MRC within the gills of rainbow trout, distinguishable based on their ability to bind to peanut lectin agglutinin (PNA). Cells that are PNA positive show transmission electron microscopic image characteristics of MR chloride cells with additional protrusions from the surface epithelium that form microvilli and increase the surface area of the apical membrane. MRC that are PNA negative have features more similar to pavement cells (Galvez et al., 2002). The role of these two cell types in ion uptake (Parks et al., 2007) has yet to be fully determined.

6.2.2 Sodium and Potassium uptake in freshwater fish

There has been much debate as to the proteins involved in apical entry of sodium in freshwater fish. For Na^+, two uptake models have been proposed, both involving linkages with proton transfer. One model describes an apical epithelial sodium channel (ENaC) which is electrogenically coupled to a proton pump (V-type H^+-ATPase) and the other is a Na^+/H^+ exchanger (NHE; Evans et al., 2005, Marshall and Grosell, 2005). Avella and Bornancin (1989) questioned the thermodynamic properties of a NHE mechanism in freshwater fish and thus the H^+-ATPase coupled ENaC model has generally been favoured in recent years. Pharmacological studies using known mammalian inhibitors of Na^+ ion transporters and also V-type ATPases have confirmed the linkage between H^+-ATPase and Na^+ uptake. Phenamil, a derivative of the drug amiloride (which is recognized as an inhibitor of Na^+ uptake), has a high affinity for ENaCs, and has been shown to inhibit Na^+ uptake by freshwater fish in vivo (Bury and Wood, 1999; Boisen et al., 2003). This observation coupled with the result that bafilomycin, a V-type ATPase inhibitor, also reduces apical Na^+ uptake supports the hypothesis of Na^+ uptake via an ENaC (Bury and Wood, 1999; Reid et al., 2003). Interestingly, the two MRC subtypes show pharmacological differentiation and only PNA negative cell Na^+ uptake is sensitive to bafilomycin and phenamil (Reid et al., 2003) (see Figure 1).

In spite of the convincing evidence from the pharmacological studies, a dichotomy exists. Compared to the mammalian in vitro studies, the concentrations of amiloride or its derivatives required to block sodium transport in freshwater fish are often orders of magnitude higher, for example 10^{-4} M for amiloride (Wilkie and Wood, 1994), and 10^{-6} M for phenamil (Bury and Wood, 1999). At these concentrations, using mammalian studies as a reference point, the drugs potentially lose their specificity (Kleyman and Cragoe, 1990) and therefore the interpretation of findings in fish studies is not always clear. Furthermore, while evidence of the degenerin/ENaC family of proteins occurs from Caenorhabditis elgans to Drosphila melanogaster to mammals (Syntichaki and Tavernarakis, 2004), to date no ENaC subunit homolog has been cloned from a teleost fish species. Similarly, there is no evidence from the sequenced genomes of various teleost fish including: zebrafish (Danio rerio, version Zv7), puffer fish (Tetraodon nigrividis, version Tetraodon 3 and Takifugu rubripes, version Fugu 4.0), medaka (Oryzias latipes, version HdrR), stickleback (Gasterosteus aculeatus, version Broad S1), and cartilaginous fish (Elephant Shark, Callorhinchus milii, Venkatesh et al., 2007). Amiloride sensitive acid-sensing ion channels (ASICs) have been identified in zebrafish, but these are not expressed at the gill and are thought to be involved in neural communication (Paukert *et al.*, 2004).

The uncertainty over a H⁺-ATPase linked ENaC Na⁺ uptake mechanism in fish makes consideration of other uptake processes relevant. In this regard it is interesting that recent studies suggest that there are several isoforms of an NHE transporter in the mammalian kidney cell and that specific expression of these isoforms exists, suggesting potential divergence of function (Wagner *et al.*, 2004). By use of heterologous antibodies, NHE has been located to the apical membrane of freshwater fish gills (Wilson *et al.*, 2002). It would appear that further studies will be required in order to fully ascertain the proteins involved in apical Na⁺ entry and their transport characteristics.

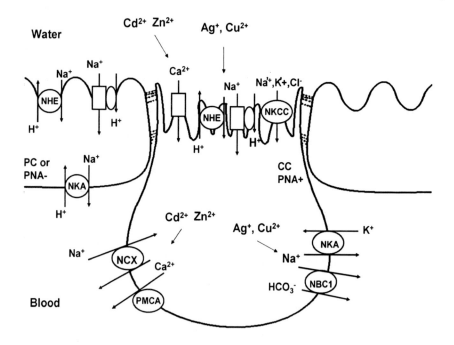

Figure 1. *Major cation uptake routes across the freshwater fish gill*

    Controversy exists as to the precise mechanism for sodium uptake this either occurs via a Na⁺ channel linked to a V-type ATPase, a Na⁺/H⁺ exchanger (NHE) (Marshall and Grosell, 2006), or a Na⁺/K⁺/2Cl⁻ co-transporter (NKCC) (Wu et al., 2003). This either occurs via the mitochondrial rich cells (MRC) or pavement cells (PC) (Evans, 2005), and possible only via peanut lectin agglutin negative (PNA-) cells (Reid et al., 2003). Basolateral extrusion occurs via a Na⁺/K⁺-ATPase (NKA) (Evans, 2005) or via a Na⁺/HCO₃⁻ co-transporter (NBC1), (Perry et al., 2003; Hirata et al., 2003). Calcium apical entry is via an epithelial calcium channel (Qui and Hogstrand, 2004) and extrusion via either a Ca²⁺-ATPase (PCMA) or Na⁺/Ca²⁺ exchanger (NCX) (Verbost et al., 1994). Metals are known to interfere with cation uptake and these can be loosely split into two categories those that affect calcium uptake and homeostasis (e.g Cd²⁺ and Zn²⁺) and those that affect sodium uptake and homeostasis (e.g. Ag⁺ and Cu²⁺; see text for more details).

There is little dispute that the main Na^+ transport route across the basolateral membrane involves the enzyme Na^+/K^+-ATPase (Evans et al., 2005). This enzyme transports two Na^+ from the cell in exchange for three K^+, and the energy required for this is obtained via the dephosphorylation of adenosine triphosphate (ATP). Pharmacological sensitivity, namely inhibition by ouabain, confirms the presence of this enzyme system. Na^+/K^+-ATPase has also been shown as an essential component for cell/volume regulation (Hoffman et al., 2007). Na^+ transport may also occur via an electrogenic Na^+/HCO_3^- co-transporter (NBC1) and recent work by Perry et al. (2003) as well as Hirata et al. (2003) identified this transport mechanism in the basolateral membrane of rainbow trout and Japanese dace, respectively. Expression of NBC1 is increased during respiratory acidosis (Perry et al., 2003) and thus may play a more prominent role in acid/base balance (see Figure 1).

In comparison to Na^+ uptake, there is a paucity of information with which to develop a mechanistic understanding of K^+ uptake in freshwater fish. The reason for little work being conducted on freshwater acquisition of K^+ is probably because radiotracers for K^+ are not commercially available. K^+ is however, an analogue of 137Cs, and studies investigating the accumulation of ^{137}Cs by freshwater fish following the Chernobyl nuclear accident in 1987 suggest that the diet is the main uptake route of this element, and thus by association is probably the main route for K^+ acquisition (Koulikov and Meili, 2003). However, immunohistological studies using mammalian antibodies has shown the presence of a Na^+, K^+, $2Cl^-$ co-transporter (NKCC) on the apical membrane of the gills of freshwater adapted tilapia (Wu et al., 2003), suggesting a mechanism for branchial uptake of K+ (see Figure 1).

6.2.3 Calcium and magnesium uptake in freshwater fish

Divalent cation metabolism in fish is discussed in more detail in chapter 5. Uptake of calcium against its concentration gradient occurs on the apical membrane of the gill via the epithelial calcium channel (ECaC) proteins. ECaC is derived from the transient receptor potential (TRP) gene family and is closely related to the mechanically gated DEG/ENaC proteins (Syntichaki and Tavernarakis, 2004). Identification of ECaC homologues has been done in rainbow trout (Shasavarani et al., 2006) and pufferfish (Qui and Hogstrand, 2004) and therefore suggests that apical entry of calcium is via this channel. Support for this comes from the results of in vivo studies where calcium uptake was inhibited by the voltage-independent Ca^{2+} channel blocker, lanthanum, as well as being reduced following treatment with the hypocalcaemic hormone, stanniocalcin (Perry and Flik, 1988). More recently, vitamin D3 has been shown to stimulate ECaC expression with a concomitant stimulation of calcium uptake (Qui and Hogstrand, 2004). Initial, localisation studies suggested that calcium uptake occurred via the MRC (Perry and Flik, 1988), but in situ hybridisation and immunohistochemcial studies have shown ECaC to be more widespread in the rainbow trout gill (Shasavarani et al., 2006). Basolateral extrusion of calcium from the gill cell into the blood is via either an ATP-dependent plasma Ca^{2+}-ATPase, PMCA, or a Na^+/Ca^{2+} exchanger, NCX (Verbost et al., 1994) (see Figure 1).

In comparison to Ca^{2+} uptake, a mechanistic understanding of Mg^{2+} uptake from freshwater by fish has seldom been studied. A branchial uptake mechanism for Mg^{2+} is probable because a low magnesium diet will induce uptake of this cation from the water (Bijvelds et al., 1998). Recent mammalian studies have identified TRPM6, related to the Ca^{2+} channel, as the protein involved in Mg^{2+} renal re-absorption (Voets et al., 2004). Further studies are required to ascertain whether TRPM6 homologs in fish are also Mg^{2+} channels.

6.3. The effects of inorganic pollutants on freshwater fish osmoregulation

6.3.1 The acute effects of metals on osmoregulation in freshwater fish

Sources of elevated metal concentrations in the aquatic environment include both natural and anthropogenic enrichment, the former arising from geological sources, volcanic emission and forest fires (Rasmussen, 1996). Anthropogenic sources include point discharges such as effluents and stack emission as well as diffuse sources. Point sources such as mine and smelter releases can provide significant inputs to the environment (Thornton, 1996). Diffuse sources arise from the fact that metals are used in many everyday household products, construction, vehicles, and a host of other products and processes such that urban and road run-off are increasingly becoming a concern as the human population expands (United States Commission on Ocean Policy, 2004). These concerns have evolved over time and much of the current focus is on long term cumulative impacts caused by relatively low concentrations, in addition to short term acute effects that might occur, for example at the high concentrations in a spill or unexpected release scenario.

In aquatic organisms the acute effects of metals arise from uptake across the gills. Free metal ions are generally considered the most bioavailable and therefore the toxic form. Uptake of non-essential metals usually occurs via transport processes designed for essential ions such as Na^+, Ca^{2+} and Mg^{2+} (Bury and Wood, 1999; Niyogi and Wood, 2004). This is because the non-essential metal possesses similar characteristics to the essential ion, such as ionic radius and/ or charge, and has been termed ionic mimicry (Bridges and Zalups, 2005). The substitution of metal ions into essential cation transport processes disrupts internal ion balance and is often the primary cause of acute toxicity (Niyogi and Wood, 2004). However, it is difficult to make generalizations about the relative transport capabilities of fish gills for metals, because environmental conditions influence the relative proportion of free ions, and determine the extent of competition for uptake sites between essential and non-essential elements (Niyogi and Wood, 2004).

While uptake via ionic mimicry is generally considered to occur for most metals, there are exceptions to this toxicity by mimicry paradigm. For example, Ni^+ toxicity is via respiratory toxicity based on bioaccumulation induced structural damage in the gill (Pane et al., 2003). Similarly, extremely elevated exposures cause severe irritation to the fish gill epithelium resulting in excessive mucus production, epithelial lifting, oedemas and cell necrosis (Mallat, 1985). In these cases death is likely to follow due to suffocation. Most of the metals that cause toxicity via the disruption of ionoregulatory processes can be loosely classed as those that effect either Na^+ or Ca^{2+} uptake pathways. Physiological studies have shown that a variety of divalent metal ions such as Zn^{2+} (Hogstrand et al., 1994), Co^{2+} (Comhaire et al., 1998), Cd^{2+} (Verbost et al., 1988) and Pb^{2+} (Rogers and Wood, 2004) share an apical uptake route with calcium. This uptake is probably mediated via ECaC (Qiu and Hogstrand, 2004), but molecular biology studies have shown the presence of a number of Zn^{2+} uptake mechanisms at the gill (Feeney et al., 2005) and a divalent metal transporter (DMT1, Gunshin et al., 1997), for which various divalent metals may act as substrates (Cooper et al., 2006). Both Cd^{2+} (Verbost et al., 1988) and Zn^{2+} (Hogstrand et al., 1996) have been found to competitively inhibit the uptake of Ca^{2+} into basolateral membrane vesicle preparations of freshwater fish gills. These two metals along with Pb^{2+} have also been shown to inhibit brachial Ca^{2+}-ATPase activity (Rogers and Wood, 2004). In the latter work, a waterborne concentration of 2.3 µM Pb^+ resulted in a 40% reduction in Ca^{2+} uptake (Rogers and Wood, 2004). It is also theorized that elevated levels of divalent metals may also displace Ca^{2+} from tight junctions, thus increasing the general permeability of the gill epithelium and exacerbating the loss of ions to the environment.

The metals that affect the sodium uptake pathway include Cu^{2+} and Ag^+ (Pelgrom et al., 1995, McGeer and Wood, 1998, Bury et al., 1999), and both metals have been shown to enter fish from the surrounding water via a sodium-sensitive uptake pathway (Bury and Wood, 1999; Grosell and Wood, 2002). In the case of Cu^{2+}, the study of Pelgrom et al. (1995) showed that exposure to 3.3 µM resulted in a 50% reduction in Na^+ uptake in tilapia, while for Ag^+ a concentration of 0.03 µM resulted in a similar reduction in rainbow trout (Bury et al., 1999). While this comparison of Cu^{2+} and Ag^+ inhibition of Na^+ uptake generally illustrates the different sensitivities that fish have to these two metals it is difficult to draw comparisons across studies because of the effect of exposure conditions. For example, the study of Bury et al. (1999) illustrated that Ag^+ induced inhibition of Na^+ uptake in rainbow trout ranged from 0% to > 50% depending on the Cl^- concentration, dissolved organic content, or the Na^+ concentrations.

Copper usually occurs in the divalent state in the aquatic environment, but due to its redox cycling, it is often the monovalent form that is relevant in biological situations. Cu^{2+} ions possess the same charge and similar ionic radius as Na^+, thus it is able to mimic Na^+ at uptake sites. It is important to highlight that there are also sodium-insensitive uptake pathways: for example, this has been shown for Cu^{2+} (Grosell and Wood, 2002) and is presumed to occur via the copper transporter 1 (CTR1), which has been cloned in zebrafish (Mackenzie et al., 2004). While mechanisms such as these are important for nutritional requirements it is questionable that such mechanisms are implicated in toxicity responses as transport capacities are generally thought to be lower than the rates of uptake required to induce acute lethality. In spite of the fact that the affinity of metal cations for Ca^{2+} and/or Na^+ is comparatively lower than nutritional transporters, the capacity of these pathways is sufficient to allow for the uptake required to produce acute toxicity when waterborne exposure levels are elevated. Additionally, it is the disruption of ionic balance, at least in part via competitive reduction of either Ca^{2+} or Na^+ uptake, that is associated with toxicity and this does not occur via metal specific transport mechanisms.

Once taken up via an apical Na^+ pathway into the epithelial cell both Ag^+ and Cu^{2+} can bind to and disrupt the activity of the basolateral Na^+/K^+-ATPase. Both Ag (Christer Hogstrand personnel communication) and Cu^{2+} (Li et al., 1996) have been shown to disrupt Mg^{2+} ATP binding resulting in irreversible inhibition of enzyme activity.

The aetiology of the acute lethal effect that follows metal induced disruption of ionoregulatory mechanisms is complex. Hogstrand and Wood (1996) proposed a process by which the effects of Ag^+ on Na^+ balance leads to acute mortality and this serves as a general example/hypothesis that could be applicable to the lethal effects of other metals. Briefly, branchial ion losses cause a reduction in plasma volume, and an increase in plasma protein resulting in increased blood viscosity (Wood et al., 1996). Concomitantly, a first phase (release of catecholamines) and second phase (release of cortisol) stress response is elicited. This also affects haematological and vascular properties by causing splenic contraction and an increase in haematocrit that further contributes to increased blood viscosity. Catecholamines also induce vascular vasoconstriction and tachycardia resulting in increased blood pressure. The resulting combination of reduced plasma volume, increased blood viscosity and vasoconstriction with tachycardia, if severe, will lead to acute cardiovascular collapse.

6.3.2 The chronic effects of metals on osmoregulation in freshwater fish

While there is agreement on the sites of metal uptake and the mechanisms of acute toxicity in the gills of freshwater fish, those for chronic toxicity are less well understood. Routes of uptake remain the same but metal movement through the gill tissue and distribution via the circulation, at least to some degree, means accumulation in all tissues and organs. Understanding the toxicokinetics of chronic accumulation and how that leads to physiological impacts is an essential component of linking exposure and environmental risk (McCarty and MacKay, 1993). Numerous studies have contributed to the understanding of how chronic metal exposure and exposure can impact on osmoregulatory responses (see for example Alsop et al., 1999; Hollis et al., 1999; Taylor et al., 2000; McGeer et al., 2000a,b; Chowdhury et al., 2005a). These and other studies have also illustrated that metal accumulation patterns, responses, and physiological impacts can be complex, particularly for essential metals such as Cu^{2+} and Zn^+ (Cousins, 1985; Vallee and Falchuk, 1993). Within the context of these responses, osmoregulatory adjustments can be subtle and temporary (e.g. McGeer et al., 2000a).

Ion regulation, particularly Ca^{2+} and/or Na^+ balance is disrupted by chronic sublethal metal exposure, however, because of the relatively low concentrations (compared to acute toxicity exposure) the effect is transient. The organism's response to ion disruption during chronic low level metal exposure follows the damage-repair model proposed by McDonald and Wood (1993). This model has two responses that combine to re-establish ionic balance; the first of these is the production and mobilization of metal binding proteins, such as metallothionein or glutathione that sequester and detoxify metal (Mason and Jenkins, 1995; Hogstrand and Wood, 1996; Chowdhury et al., 2005a); the second is to repair and compensate for the physiological disruption caused by metal accumulation.

A variety of physiological changes associated with the second phase response can be induced through chronic exposure and the acclimation processes are complex, involving an integrated response that varies with the metal of exposure. Changes related to osmoregulation include: reduced apical metal uptake into the gill and through into the blood, increased clearance from blood to tissues, modulation of cationic uptake to restore ion homeostasis, accumulation in tissues and finally excretion via the gills, liver or kidney (Grosell et al., 1997; Bury, 2005). For example, the number and affinity of cation transport (uptake) proteins such as Na^+/K^+-ATPase (Lauren and McDonald, 1987; Bury, 2005) is altered while plasma clearance and biliary excretion of is enhanced (Grosell et al., 1997; 2001) during chronic sublethal exposure to Cu^{2+}. These responses are not just restricted to chronic Cu^{2+} and Ag^+ exposure, and rainbow trout show faster plasma clearance of Cd^{2+} following sublethal exposure to Cd^{2+} (Chowdhury et al., 2005b) and reduced gill uptake (Hollis et al., 1999).

These responses clearly illustrate that the process of acclimation to metals result in a new physiological equilibrium, which includes an alteration in osmoregulatory status. Metal accumulation induced changes do not necessarily change the resting set-point for essential plasma and tissue ion levels, but mechanisms by which these homeostatic concentrations are maintained are altered dramatically. As such the process of acclimation involves establishing a new equilibrium in terms of physiological mechanisms involved in ion regulation and this new set-point ensures that plasma and tissue ion concentrations return to the pre-existing levels.

The physiological changes in metal handling and cation regulation associated with exposure to sublethal concentration of a specific metal has been shown to confer increased tolerance to Cd^{2+} (Hollis et al., 1999), Zn^{2+} (Alsop et al., 1999) and Cu^{2+} (Taylor et al., 2000). Depending on the mechanisms induced by a particular metal, it is feasible that the acclimation response would confer an ability to resist subsequent exposure to other metals and this has been shown to occur for Cu^{2+} and Zn^{2+} acclimated rainbow trout during acute challenges with Cd^{2+} (McGeer et al., 2007). A few other studies have shown this cross acclimation phenomenon in fish (Xie and Kerks, 2003) and invertebrates (Howell, 1985; Lopes et al., 2005). The theorized mechanisms for cross-tolerance is that exposure to a single metal induces physiological alteration that addresses the disruptions to ion regulation. One potential non-specific metal protection mechanism is via metal detoxification (e.g. metallothionein/glutathione production).

6.4 The effect of cyanobacterial toxins on osmoregulation in freshwater fish

The prevalence of cyanobacterial (blue-green algal) blooms have increased over recent years, due to anthropgenic input of nutrients and increased eutrophication (Jacoby et al., 2000). In some instances the blooms form unsightly scums on the surface, which reach concentrations as high as 57 g l⁻¹ (cyanobacterial scum densities, dry weight per scum volume; Cook et al., 2004), and block the sunlight reaching the upper epiliminion and reducing other phytoplankton productivity. The diurnal pattern of photosynthesis and respirations causes major fluctuations in dissolved oxygen content and pH during these blooms that may be stressful to other resident biota within the lake (Scott et al., 2005). On senescence of a bloom, decomposition by microbes further reduces oxygen content and causes the release of nitrogenous breakdown products (e.g. ammonia) providing additional stresses to the ecosystem.

Strains of the cyanobacteria, for example Microcystis, Anabaena, and Oscillotoria can produce secondary metabolites termed microcystins (MC; Carmichael, 1992). MC are monocyclic heptapeptides, that possess a (2S,3S,8S,9S)-3-amino-9-methoxy-2,6,8-trimethyl-10-phenyldeca-4,6,-dienoic acid at position 5, a N-methyl dehydroalanine (MDha) at position 7 and two variable L-amino acids at position 2 and 4 (Malbrouck and Kestemont, 2006). There are 65 different forms of MC, due to the variation in amino acid toxins, with the species containing leucine (L) and arginine (R) being the most common (Malbrouck and Kestemount, 2006). During a bloom the MCs are kept within the cyanobacterial cells and levels in the lake are close to detection limits, however on senescence of a bloom the MC are released and levels may reach μg l⁻¹ concentrations (Rodger et al., 1994).

The main toxic action of MC is associated with the inhibition of protein phosphatases 1 and 2A activity (Mackintosh et al., 1990) via interactions with serine and threonine phosphorylations. PP 1 and 2 A are integral in helping maintain cellular integrity and inhibitions causes profound alteration to the cytoskeleton that leads to cell necrosis. MC do not readily cross membranes and uptake is thought to be due to MC mimicking bile salts at their sites of transport in the intestine (Eriksson et al., 1990). Consequently, the toxin enters the hepatic-portal vein and accumulates in the liver, and vertebrates, including fish, exposed to the MC show signs of hepatotoxicosis (Rodger et al., 1994; Carbis et al., 1996).

There have also been histopathological records of damage to the osmoregulatory organs, including gills (Rodger et al., 1994) and kidney (Carbis et al., 1996). Rodger et al. (1994) found that following a bloom of Anabaena flos-aquae in Loch Leven, over 1000 dead brown trout was retrieved from the shoreline. The A. flos-aquae bloom had a concentration of 539 μg MC-LR equivalents per gram dry weight of cyanobacterial scum and the water concentrations following lysis of the scum were 16–19 μg MC-LR l⁻¹. The gill pathology showed epithelial ballooning and oedema, a number of necrotic cells and widespread secondary lamellar clubbing (Rodger et al., 1994). These branchial pathologies are characteristics of severe irritation, but it was not possible to determine whether cyanobacterial cells, the MC released following lysis of the blue-green algal cells, or other water quality parameters (pH was measured at 9.35 in the surface waters during this period) were the causative agents.

In addition to the gross histopathological changes, MCs may directly affect ion transport and cell volume regulations. PPs have been shown to be important in NKCC1 (Darman *et al.*, 2001) and Na^+/K^+-ATPase activity (Lecuona *et al.*, 2000), and thus by inference antagonists of PPs (e.g. MCs) may be toxic. In fish Gaete *et al.* (1994) provided direct evidence that purified MC-LR could inhibit branchial ion pump enzymes activity in vitro. In this study carp (*Cyprinus carpio*) gill microsomal fractions enriched in ATPase activity were collected via differential centrifugation. Ouabain sensitive Na^+/K^+-ATPase activity, Ca^{2+}-ATPase and HCO_3^--ATPase activity was measured in the presence and absence of purified MC-LR, and results showed that 4 µg of toxin caused severe inhibition of ATPase activity (Na^+/K^+-ATPase activity reduced by 90%; Ca^{2+}-ATPase activity by 18% and HCO_3^--ATPase activity by 39%). A subsequent study by Zambrano and Canelo (1996) showed that MC-LR caused a reduction in the K^+-dependent hydrolysis of Na^+ dependent phosphorylation of the Na^+/K^+-ATPase enzymes as well as increasing the release of the bound inhibitor ouabain. This suggests that in addition to the inhibition of serine and theronine phosphorylation, MC-LR can also inhibit the aspartic acid dephosphorylation step of this ion pump.

However, the potency of MC-LR to specifically affect osmoregulation has also been questioned. In laboratory studies, no brown trout fry mortalities were recorded on exposure to purified MC-LR, lysed cells from a strain of *Microcystis aeruginosa* that produces the toxins, 7813, or a strain of cells that does not CYA43, at concentrations similar levels to those measured in Loch Leven for 63 days; there was a reduction in growth rate, and only minor perturbations to ionoregulation with a significant increase in fry whole body Na^+ and Cl^- content at the end of the exposure period (Bury *et al.*, 1995). However, no effect was observed on direct Na^+ influx or efflux measurements in either a short term exposure (4 h) or at the end of the 63 days (Bury *et al.*, 1995). A subsequent study with slightly larger brown trout (11–90 g) exposed to lysed cells from *M. aeruginosa* 7820 (a strain producing MCs) showed a drop in plasma Na^+ and Cl^- levels over the first 8 h of exposure that then returned to pre-exposure levels by 24 hours. This was associated with a highly significant rise in plasma cortisol concentration and subsequent rise in plasma glucose levels in these fish. These results taken together suggest that ion balance in brown trout is only subtly affected by lysed cyanobacterial cells, and this effect may or may not be due to the direct action of compounds in the lysate, or a secondary effect of a stimulated stress response (Bury *et al.*, 1996).

In a sequence of studies by Bury and colleagues (Bury *et al.*, 1996; 1998), they found that purified MC-LR (verified by HPLC and mouse toxicity assay) did not inhibit branchial ATPase activity in tilapia (*Oreochromis mossambicus*). However, other cytotoxic compounds were present in the extracts of the cyanobacteria. In these studies tilapia were initially exposed to extracts from M. aeurginosa 7820, CYA43 and an equivalent concentration of MC-LR for 24 h and Ca^{2+} influx rate measured, only the cyanobacterial extracts were found to cause an inhibition of Ca^{2+} uptake. In vitro studies using basolateral membrane vesicles enriched in ATPase activity and permeabilised isolated cells to measure SERCA Ca^{2+}-ATPase activity and mitochondrial uptake of Ca^{2+} also showed an inhibitory effect of extracts from the cyanobacterial and no effect of purified MC-LR. In addition, K^+-dependent pNPPase activity of branchial BLMV was also inhibited by extracts of either strain of cyanobacteria, but not the purified toxin. Various other studies have also identified a number of cytotoxic fractions from cyanaobacterial extracts (Namikoshi and Reinhart, 1996).

It is evident that compounds within cynaobacteria have the potential to disrupt ion balance in freshwater fish. However, the nature of these compounds and mechanisms of inhibition are uncertain. There is conflicting evidence as to whether MCs have a direct effect on these transport processes, but there is evidence that cytotoxic compounds, probably lipid in origin, can affect fish. Whether, there is direct action on the branchial surface and ion uptake pathways, or an indirect effect via stimulus of the stress response (Bury et al., 1996) awaits further investigation. There are other water quality issues associated with cyanobacterial blooms, such as fluctuations in water pH, dissolved oxygen, and on senescence an increase in ammonia; these in addition to perturbed to ionoregulation will impact on physiological homeostasis and be stressful to the fish.

6.5. Development of models and *in vitro* techniques to monitor the effects of pollutants on fish gills

6.5.1 Development of the Biotic Ligand Model

The understanding of the physiology of metal uptake and impacts on ionic homeostasis was instrumental in establishing models for predicting acute metal toxicity in freshwater systems. The Biotic Ligand Model (BLMs) is a good example. An equilibrium modeling approach is applied, first to establish the relative concentrations of free and complexed forms of the metal in solution, and then to estimate the relative uptake of free ions into the gill. The prediction of accumulation is done through the development of equilibrium constants that describe both the uptake onto the biotic ligand (i.e. gills) as well as the competition with essential cations. A number of different BLMs have been recently published, including for the acute effects of Zn^{2+}, Cu^{2+}, Ag^+, Ni and Cd^{2+} (reviewed by McGeer, 2008). However, shortcomings have been expressed; the BLM does not account for the different sensitivities of different aquatic organisms, and it does not recognize that organisms acclimate to their exposure conditions, for example a fish in soft water has a much different ionoregulatory profile compared to one in hard water. In spite of this, the BLM does have a mechanistic basis and therefore the theoretical approach applied (ionoregulatory impairment leading to acute effects) is robust. Although the end points will be different, this type of approach serves as a good example of how to develop an understanding of chronic toxicity prediction.

6.5.2 The use of primary gill cell cultures for pollutant monitoring

Primary gill cell cultures grown on membrane supports where initially developed by Part and colleagues (Part et al., 1993). The diffusive 'tightness' of the epithelium is part of the basic functional physiology of the gill and measured transepithelial resistance (TER) of ~20 kΩ cm^{-2} when cultured on membrane supports resembles those measured in vivo (Walker et al., 2007). Because the cultures are polarised they allow for water to be placed on the apical surface whilst bathing the basolateral membrane in media (Fletcher et al., 2000). The establishment of a cultured branchial epithelium was seen as a potential useful model to study branchial ionic regulation. Despite various methodological advances, for example the development of double seeded preparation that contain MR cells to replace the original single seeded cultures that are exclusively 'pavement-like' cells (Fletcher et al., 2000; Walker et al., 2007), active ion transport across these primary gill cells has only been demonstrated in a few cases (Avella, 1999; Zhou et al., 2003; Kelly and Wood, 2008). However, it is emerging that these primary gill cultures possess similar metal binding characteristics (Zhou et al., 2005) and respond at a transcriptomic level to aquatic metal exposure in a manner that resembles the response of the intact animal.

Zhou et al. (2005) demonstrated that silver binding to the cultured rainbow trout gill epithelial was influenced by water chemistry, mimicking the binding characteristics of the intact trout gill (Janes and Playle, 1995). Walker and colleagues (Walker et al., 2007; 2008) have recently used molecular biological techniques to evaluate the use of the cultured epithelium to assess bioreactive metal concentrations in water. Vertebrate cells possess a metal sensing protein termed metal transcription factor-1 (MTF-1). MTF-1 senses an increase in labile intracellular Zn^{2+} concentrations (Laity and Andrews, 2007; Bury et al., 2008). Zn^{2+} bound MTF-1 then acts as a transcription fact binding to metal response elements in target genes, one being MT. A dose-dependent expression of MT in cultured gill cells on exposure to metal has been observed (Mayer et al., 2003). Walker et al. (2007; 2008) were able to link MT gene expression in the cultured gill epithelium to the effect of metal exposure to the whole organisms. In these studies the water chemistry (hardness, dissolved organic matter) was altered to manipulate zinc and silver speciation. In parallel studies the effect of altering water chemistry on zinc and silver inhibition of rainbow trout Ca^{2+} and Na^+ influx, respectively, was assessed and compared to the expression levels of MT and another MTF-1 stimulated gene zinc transporter 1 (ZNT-1) in cultured gill cells in the same water. The response of the cultured gills cells (degree of increased gene expression) correlated to response of the whole animal (degree of inhibition of cation influx), suggesting that these cells were able to determine the presence of bioreactive metal in the water. A further development using a rainbow trout micorarray derived from a subtractive suppression hybridisation of rainbow trout fry treated with or without Cd, has shown unique gene expression profiles for culture epithelium exposed to Cd, Cu^{2+} and Ag^+ (Walker et al., 2008).

There is potential to transfer the gill cell culture technology to the field, whereby site-specific cell response could be monitored in real-time. This would provide a versatile in vitro technique that could be developed as 'a biological component' of a biomonitoring tool kit to assess water quality in situ.

Acknowledgements

The authors would like to thanks Emily-Jane Costa for help in preparing and organizing the manuscript. JCM acknowledges the contributions of NSERC Discovery and CRD programs, the latter in partnership with the International Lead Zinc Research Organization (ILZRO), International Zinc Association (IZA), International Copper Association (ICA), Copper Development Association (CDA), Nickel Producers Environmental Research Association (NiPERA), Noranda-Falconbridge (now Xtrata), Teck Cominco, and Inco (now Vale Inco Limited).

References

Alsop, D. H., McGeer, J. C., McDonald, D. G. and Wood, C. M. (1999). Assessing the costs and consequences of chronic waterborne zinc exposure to juvenile rainbow trout in hard and soft water. Environ Toxicol Chem 18: 1014–1025.

Avella, M. and Bornancin, M. (1989). A new analysis of ammonia and sodium-transport through the gills of freshwater rainbow trout (*Salmo gairdneri*). J Exp Biol 142: 155–175.

Avella, M., Part, P. and Ehrenfeld, J. (1999). Regulation of Cl⁻ secretion in seawater fish (*Dicentrarchus labrax*) gill respiratory cells in primary culture. J Physiol 516: 353–363.

Bijvelds, M. J. C., Van der Velden, J. A., Kolar, Z. I. and Flik, G. (1998). Magnesium transport in freshwater teleosts. J Exp Biol 201: 1981–1990.

Boisen, A. M. Z., Amstrup, J., Novak, I., and Grosell, M. (2003). Sodium and chloride transport in zebrafish soft water and hard water acclimated (*Danio rerio*). Biochim Biophys Acta 1618: 207–218.

Bridges, C. C. and Zalups, R. K. (2005). Molecular and ionic mimicry and the transport of toxic metals. Toxicol Appl Pharmacol 204:274–308.

Brown, J. A., Oliver, J. A., Hanerson, I. W. and Jackson, B. A. (1980). Angiotensin and single nephron glomerular function in trout *Salmo gairdneri*. Am J Physiol 239: R509–R514.

Bury, N. R. (2005). The changes to apical silver membrane uptake, and basolateral membrane silver export in the gills of rainbow trout (*Oncorhynchus mykiss*) on exposure to sublethal silver concentrations. Aquat Toxicol 72: 135–145.

Bury, N. R., Eddy, F. B. and Codd, G. A. (1995). The effects of the cyanobacterium *Microcystis aeruginosa*, the cyanobacterial hepatotoxin micorcystin-LR and ammonia on the growth rate and ionic regulation of brown trout. J Fish Biol 46: 1042–1054.

Bury, N. R., Flik, G., Eddy, F. B. and Codd, G. A. (1996). The effects of cyanobacteria and the cyanobacterial toxin microcystin-LR on Ca^{2+} transport and Na^+/K^+-ATPase in tilapia gills. J Exp Biol 199: 1319–1326.

Bury, N. R., Codd, G. A., Wendelaar Bonga, S. E., Eddy, F. B. and Flik, G. (1998). Fatty acids from the cyanobacterium *Microcystis aeruginosa* with potent inhibitory effects on fish gill Na^+/K^+-ATPase activity. J Exp Biol 201: 81–89.

Bury, N. R. and Wood, C. M. (1999). Mechanism of branchial apical silver uptake by rainbow trout is via the proton-coupled Na^+ channel. Am J Physiol 277: R1385–R1391.

Bury, N. R., Galvez, F. and Wood, C. M. (1999). Effects of chloride, calcium, and dissolved organic carbon on silver toxicity: Comparison between rainbow trout and fathead minnows. Environ Toxicol Chem 18: 56–62.

Bury, N. R., Chung, M. J., Sturm, A., Walker, P. A. and Hogstrand, C. (2008). Cortisol stimulates the zinc signaling pathway and expression of metallothion-eins and ZnT1 in rainbow trout gill epithelial cells. Am J Physiol 295: R623–R629.

Carbis, C. R., Rawlin, G. T., Mitchell, G. F., Anderson, J. W. and McCauley, I . (1996). The histopathology of carp, *Cyprinus carpio* L, exposed to microcystins by gavage, immersion and intraperitoneal administration. J Fish Dis 19: 199–207.

Carmichael, W. W. (1992). Cyanobacteria secondary metabolites. J Appl Bacteriol 72: 445–459.

Chowdhury, M. J., Baldisserotta, B. and Wood, C.M. (2005a). Tissue specific cadmium and metallothionein levels in rainbow trout chronically acclimated to waterborne or dietary cadmium. Arch Environ Contam Toxicol 48: 381–390.

Chowdhury, M. J., Grosell, M., McDonald, D. G. and Wood, C.M. (2005b). Plasma clearance of cadmium and zinc in non-acclimated and metal-acclimated trout. Aquat Toxicol 64: 259–275.

Comhaire, S., Blust, R., van Ginneken, L., Verbost, P. M. and Vanderborght O. L. J. (1998). Branchial cobalt uptake in the carp, *Cyprinus carpio*: Effect of calcium channel blockers and calcium injection. Fish Physiol Biochem 18: 1–13.

Cook, C. M., Vardaka, E. and Lanaras, T. (2004). Toxic cyanobacteria in Greek freshwaters, 1987–2000: Occurrence, toxicity, and impacts in the Mediterranean region. Acta Hydrochim Hydrobiol 32: 107–124.

Cooper, C. A., Handy, R. D. and Bury, N. R. (2006). The effects of dietary iron concentration on gastrointestinal and branchial assimilation of both iron and cadmium in zebrafish (*Danio rerio*). Aquat Toxicol 79:167–175.

Cousins, R. J. (1985). Absorption, transport, and hepatic metabolism of copper and zinc: special reference to metallothionein and ceruloplasmin. Physiol Rev 65: 238–309.

Darman, R. B., Flemmer, A. and Fortush, B. (2001). Modulation of ion transport by direct targeting of protein phosphatase type 1 to the Na-K-Cl cotransporter. J Biol Chem 276: 34359–34362.

Evans, D. H., Piermarini, P. M. and Choe, K. P. (2005). The multifunctional fish gill: Dominant site of gas exchange, osmoregulation, acid–base regulation, and excretion of nitrogenous waste. Physiol Rev 85: 97–177.

Eriksson, J. E., Gronberg, L., Nygard, S., Slotte, J. P. and Meriluoto, J. A. O. (1990). Hepatocellular uptake of 3H-dihydromicrocystin-LR a cyclic peptide toxin. Biochim Biophys Acta 1025: 60–66.

Feeney, G. P., Zheng, D. L., Kille, P. and Hogstrand, C. (2005). The phylogeny of teleost ZIP and ZnT zinc transporters and their tissue specific expression and response to zinc in zebrafish. Biochim Biophys Acta 1732: 88–95.

Fletcher, M., Kelly, S. P., Part, P., O'Donnell, M. J. and Wood, C. M. (2000). Transport properties of cultured branchial epithelia from freshwater rainbow trout: A novel preparation with mitochondria-rich cells. J Exp Biol 203: 1523–1537.

Fuentes, J., Bury, N. R., Carroll, S. and Eddy, F. B. (1996). Drinking in Atlantic salmon presmolts (*Salmo salar* L) and juvenile rainbow trout (*Oncorhynchus mykiss* Walbaum) in response to cortisol and sea water challenge. Aquaculture 141: 129–137.

Gaete, V., Canelo, E., Lagos, N. and Zambrano, F. (1994). Inhibitory effects of *Microcystis aeruginosa* toxin on ion pumps of the gill of freshwater fish. Toxicon 32: 1221–127.

Galvez, F., Reid, S. D., Hawkings, G. and Goss, G. G. (2002). Isolation and characterization of mitochondria-rich cell types from the gill of freshwater rainbow trout. Am J Physiol 282: R658–668.

Grossell, M., Hogstrand, C. and Wood, C. M. (1997). Cu^{2+} uptake and turnover in both Cu-acclimated and non-acclimated rainbow trout. Aquat Toxicol 38: 257–276.

Grosell, M., McGeer, J. C. and Wood, C. M. (2001). Plasma copper clearance and biliary copper excretion are stimulated in copper acclimated trout. Am J Physiol 280: R796–R806.

Grosell, M. and Wood, C. M. (2002). Copper uptake across rainbow trout gills: mechanisms of apical entry. J Exp Biol 205: 1179–1188.

Gunshin, H., Mackenzie, B., Berger, U. V., Gunshin, Y., Romero, M. F., Boron, W. F., Nussberger, S., Gollan, J. L. and Hediger, M. A. (1997). Cloning and characterization of a mammalian proton-coupled metal-ion transporter. Nature 388: 482–488.

Hirata, T., Kaneko, T., Ono, T., Nakazato, T., Furukawa, N., Hasegawa, S., Wakabayashi, S., Shigekawa, M., Chang, M. H., Romero, M. F. and Hirose, S. (2003). Mechanism of acid adaptation of a fish living in a pH 3.5 lake. Am J Physiol 284: R1199–R1212.

Hoffmann, E. K., Schettino, T. and Marshall, W. S. (2007). The role of volume-sensitive ion transport systems in regulation of epithelial transport. Comp Biochem Physiol 148A: 29–43.

Hogstrand, C. and Wood, C. M. (1996). The physiology and toxicology of zinc in fish. In: Taylor, E. W. (ed) Toxicology and Aquatic Pollution: Physiological, Cellular and Molecular Approaches. Cambridge University Press, London: 61–84.

Hogstrand, C., Wilson, R. W., Polgar, D. and Wood, C. M. (1994). Effects of zinc on the kinetics of branchial calcium uptake in freshwater rainbow trout during adaptation to waterborne zinc. J Exp Biol 186: 55–73.

Hogstrand, C., Verbost, P. M., Wendelaar Bonga, S. E. and Wood, C. M. (1996). Mechanisms of zinc uptake in gills of freshwater rainbow trout: Interplay with calcium transport. Am J Physiol. 270: R1141–R1147.

Hollis, L. M., McGeer, J. C., McDonald, D. G. and Wood, C. M. (1999). Cadmium accumulation, gill Cd^{2+} binding, acclimation and physiological effects during long term sublethal Cd^{2+} exposure in rainbow trout. Aquat Toxicol 46: 101–119.

Howell, R. (1985). Effect of zinc on cadmium toxicity to the amphipod *Gammarus pulex*. Hydrobiol 123: 245–249.

Jacoby, J. M., Collier, D. C., Welch, E. B., Hardy, F. J. and Crayton, M. (2000). Environmental factors associated with a toxic bloom of *Microcystis aeruginosa*. Can J Fish Aquat Sci 57: 231–240.

Kelly, S. P. and Wood, C. M. (2008). Cortisol stimulates calcium transport across cultured gill epithelia from freshwater rainbow trout. In Vitro Cell Dev Biol 44; 96–104.

Kleyman, T. R. and Cragoe, E. J. (1990). Cation transport probes: the amiloride series. Methods Enzymol 191: 739–755.

Koulikov, A. O. and Meili, M. (2003). Modelling the dynamics of fish contamination by Chernobyl radiocaesium: an analytical solution based on potassium mass balance. J Environ Radioactivity 66: 309–326.

Laity, J. H. and Andrews, G. K. (2007). Understanding the mechanisms of zinc-sensing by metal response element binding transcription factor-1 (MTF-1). Arch Biochem Biophys 462: 201–210.

Lauren, D. J. and McDonald, D. G. (1987). Acclimation to copper by rainbow trout, *Salmo gairdneri*: physiology. Can J Fish Aquat Sci 44: 99–104.

Laurent, P. (1982). Structure of vertebrate gills. In: Houlihan, D. F., Rankin, J. C. and Shuttleworth, T. J. (eds) Gills, Cambridge University Press, Cambridge: 25–43.

Lecuona, E., Carcia, A. and Sznajder, J. I. (2000). A novel role for protein phosphatase 2A in the dopaminergic regulation of Na,K-ATPase. FEBS Lett 481: 217–220.

Li, J., Lock, R. A. C., Klaren, P. H. M., Swarts, H. G. P., Stekhoven, F. M. A. H. S., Wendelaar Bonga, S. E. and Flik, G. (1996). Kinetics of Cu^{2+} inhibition of Na^+/K^+-ATPase. Toxicol Lett 87: 31–38.

Lopes, I., Baird, D. J. and Bibiero, R. (2005). Genetically determined resistance to lethal levels of copper by *Daphnia longispina*: association with sublethal response and multiple/coresistance. Environ Toxicol Chem 24: 1414–1419.

Mackenzie, N. C., Brito, M., Reyes, A. E. and Allende, M. L. (2004). Cloning, expression pattern and essentiality of the high-affinity copper transporter 1 (ctr1) gene in zebrafish. Gene 328: 113–120.

Mackintosh, C., Beattie, K. A., Klumpp, S., Cohen P. and Codd, G. A. (1990). Cyanobacterial microcystin-LR is a potent and specific inhibitor of protein phosphatase 1 and 2A from both human and higher plants. FEBS Lett 264: 187–192.

Mallat, J. (1985). Fish gill structural changes induced by toxicants and other irritants: a statistical review. Can J Fish Aquat Sci 42: 630–648.

Marshall, W. S. and Grosell, M. (2005). Ion transport, osmoregulation and acid–base balance. In Physiology of Fishes. Vol. 3: 177–230 , Evans, D. and Claiborne, J. B. (eds), CRC Press, Boca Raton .

Mason, A. Z. and Jenkins, K. D. (1995). Metal detoxification in aquatic organisms. In: Tessier, A. and Turner, D. R. (eds) Metal Speciation and Bioavailability in Aquatic Systems. Wiley, Chichester, UK: 479–608.

Malbrouck, C. and Kestemont, P. (2006). Effects of microcystins on fish. Environ Toxicol Chem 25: 72–86.

Mayer, G. D., Leach, A., Kling, P., Olsson, P. E. and Hogstrand, C. (2003). Activation of the rainbow trout metallothionein–A promoter by silver and zinc.

Comp Biochem Physiol 134B: 181–184.

McCarty, L. S. and Mackay, D. (1993). Enhancing ecotoxicological modeling and assessment. Environ Sci Technol 27: 1719–1728.

McDonald, D. G. and Wood, C. M. (1993). Branchial mechanisms of acclimation to metals in freshwater fish. In: Rankin, J. C. and Jensen, F. B. Fish Ecophysiology, Chapman and Hall, London: 297–321.

McGeer, J. C. (2008). The biotic ligand model as a tissue residue approach for metals. In: Meador, J. and Adams, W. J. (eds) Tissue Residue Approach for Toxicity Assessment: Invertebrates and Fish. SETAC Press, Pensacola FL: in press.

McGeer, J. C., Nadella, S. R., Alsop, D. H., Hollis, L., Taylor, L. N., McDonald, D. G. and Wood, C. M. (2007). Influence of acclimation and cross-acclimation of metals on acute Cd^{2+} toxicity and Cd^{2+} uptake and distribution in rainbow trout (*Oncorhynchus mykiss*). Aquat Toxicol 84: 190–197.

McGeer, J. C., Szebedinszky, C., McDonald, D. G. and Wood, C. M. (2000a). Effects of chronic sublethal exposure to waterborne Cu^{2+}, Cd^{2+} or Zn^{2+} in rainbow trout 1: Iono-regulatory disturbance and metabolic costs. Aquat Toxicol 50: 231–243.

McGeer, J. C., Szebedinszky, C., McDonald, D. G. and Wood, C. M. (2000b). Effects of chronic sublethal exposure to waterborne Cu^{2+}, Cd^{2+} or Zn^{2+} in rainbow trout 2: Tissue specific metal accumulation. Aquat Toxicol 50: 245–256.

McGeer, J. C. and Wood, C. M. (1998). Protective effects of water Cl^- on physiological responses to waterborne silver in rainbow trout. Can J Fish Aquat Sci 55: 2447–2454.

MacKay, D. and Fraser, A. (2003). Bioaccumulation of persistent organic chemicals: mechanisms and models Environ Pollut 110: 375–391.

Namikoshi, M. and Rinehart, K. (1996). Bioactive compounds produced by cyanobacteria. J Industr Micro Biotechnol 17: 373–384.

Niyogi, S. and Wood, C. M. (2004). The Biotic Ligand Model, a flexible tool for developing site-specific water quality guidelines for metals. Environ Sci Technol 38: 6177–6192.

Pane E. F., Richards, J. G. and Wood, C. M. (2003). Acute waterborne nickel toxicity in the rainbow trout (*Oncorhynchus mykiss*) occurs by a respiratory rather than an ionoregulatory mechanism. Aquat Toxicol 63: 65–82.

Parks, S. K., Tresguerres, M. and Goss, G. G. (2007). Interactions between Na^+ channels and Na^+-HCO_3^- cotransporters in the freshwater fish gill MR cell: a model for transepithelial Na^+ uptake. Am J Physiol 292: C935–C944.

Part, P., Norrgen, L., Bergstrom, E. and Sjoberg, P. (1993). Primary culture of epithelial cells from rainbow trout gills. J Exp Biol 175: 219–232.

Paukert, M., Sidi, S., Russell, C., Siba, M., Wilson, S. W., Nicolson, T. and Gründer, S. (2004). A family of acid-sensing ion channels from the zebrafish: widespread expression in the central nervous system suggests a conserved role in neuronal communication. J Biol Chem 279: 18783–18791.

Pelgrom, S. M. G. J., Lock, R. A. C., Balm, P. H. M. and Wendelaar Bonga, S. E. (1995). Integrated physiological response of tilapia *Oreochromis mossambicus* to sublethal copper exposure. Aquat Toxicol 32: 303–320.

Perry, S. F. and Flik, G. (1988). Characterization of branchial trans-epithelial calcium fluxes in freshwater trout *Salmo gairdneri*. Am J Physiol 254: R491–R498.

Perry, S. F., Furimsky, M., Bayaa, M., Georgalis, T., Shahsavarani, A., Nickerson, J. G. and Moon, T. W. (2003). Integrated responses of Na^+/HCO_3^- cotransporters and V-type H^+-ATPases in the fish gill and kidney during respiratory acidosis. Biochim Biophys Acta 1618: 175–184.

Qiu, A. D. and Hogstrand, C. (2004). Functional characterisation and genomic analysis of an epithelial calcium channel (ECaC) from pufferfish, *Fugu rubripes*. Gene 342: 113–123.

Rasmussen, P. (1996). Trace metals in the environment : a geological perspective. Geological Survey of Canada, Ottawa, GSC Bulletin 429.

Reid, S. D., Hawkings, G. S., Galvez, F. and Goss, G. G. (2003). Localization and characterization of phenamil-sensitive Na^+ influx in isolated rainbow trout gill epithelial cells. J Exp Biol 206: 551–559.

Rodger, H. D., Turnbull, T., Edwards, C. and Codd, G. A. (1994). Cyanobacterial (blue-green algal) bloom associated pathology in brown trout, *Salmo trutta* L in Loch Leven, Scotland. J Fish Dis 17: 177–181.

Rogers, J. T. and Wood, C. M. (2004). Characterization of branchial lead-calcium interaction in the freshwater rainbow trout *Oncorhynchus mykiss* J Exp Biol 207: 813–825.

Scott, D. M., Lucas, M. C. and Wilson, R.W. (2005). The effect of high pH on ion balance, nitrogen excretion and behaviour in freshwater fish from an eutrophic lake: A laboratory and field study. Aquat Toxicol 73: 31–43.

Shahsavarani, A., McNeill, B., Galvez, F., Wood, C. M., Goss, G. G., Hwang, P. P. and Perry, S.F. (2006). Characterization of a branchial epithelial calcium channel (ECaC) in freshwater rainbow trout (*Oncorhynchus mykiss*). J Exp Biol 209: 1928–1943.

Syntichaki, P. and Tavernarakis, N. (2004). Genetic models of mechanotransduction: the nematode *Caenorhabditis elegans*. Physiol Rev 84: 1097–153.

Taylor, L. N., McGeer, J. C., Wood, C. M. and McDonald, D. G. (2000). The physiological response of rainbow trout (*Oncorhynchus mykiss*) exposed to sublethal copper concentrations in hard and soft water. Environ Toxicol Chem 19: 2298–2308.

Thornton, I. (1996). Impacts of mining on the environment; some local, regional and global issues. Appl Geochem 11: 355–261.

United States Commission on Ocean Policy (2004). An Ocean Blueprint for the 21st Century. Washington, DC; final report.

Venkatesh, B., Kirkness, E. F., Loh, Y. H., Halpern, A. L., Lee, A. P., Johnson, J., Dandona, N., Viswanathan, L. D., Tay, A., Venter, J. C., Strausberg, R.

L. and Brenner, S. (2007). Survey sequencing and comparative analysis of the elephant shark (*Callorhinchus milii*) genome. PLoS Biol 5(4):e101.

Verbost, P. M., Schoenmakers, T. J. M., Flik, G. and Wendelaar Bonga, S. E. (1994). Kinetics of ATP-driven and Na^+ gradient driven Ca^{2+} transport in basolateral membranes from gills of freshwater adapted and seawater adapted tilapia. J Exp Biol 186: 95–108.

Verbost, P. M., Flik, G., Lock, R. A. C. and Wendelaar Bonga, S. E. (1988). Cadmium inhibits plasma membrane calcium transport. J Membrane Biol 102: 97–104.

Voets, T., Nilius, B., Hoefs, S., van der Kemp, A. W. C. M., Droogmans, G., Bindels, R. J. M. and Hoenderop, J. G. J. (2004). TRPM6 forms the Mg^{2+} influx channel involved in intestinal and renal Mg^{2+} absorption. J Biol Chem 279: 19–25.

Wagner, C. A., Finberg, K. E., Breton, S., Marshansky, V., Brown, D. and Geibel, J. P. (2004). Renal vacuolar H^+-ATPase. Physiol Rev 84: 1263–1314.

Walker, P. A., Bury, N. R. and Hogstrand, C. (2007). Influence of culture conditions on metal-induced responses in a cultured rainbow trout gill epithelium. Environ Sci Technol 41: 6505–6513.

Walker, P. A., Kille, P., Scott, A., Bury, N. R. and Hogstrand, C. (2008). An in vitro method to assess toxicity of waterborne metals to fish. Toxicol Appl Pharmacol 230: 67–77.

Wilkie, M. P. and Wood, C. M. (1994). The effects of extremely alkaline water (pH 9.5) on rainbow trout fill function and morphology. J Fish Biol 45: 87–98.

Wilson, J. M., Whiteley, N. M. and Randall, D. J. (2002). Ionoregulatory changes in the gill epithelia of coho salmon during seawater acclimation. Physiol Biochem Zool 75: 237–249.

Wood, C. M., Hogstrand, C., Galvez, F. and Munger, R. S. (1996). The physiology of waterborne silver toxicity in freshwater rainbow trout (*Oncorhynchus mykiss*) .1. The effects of ionic Ag^+. Aquat Toxicol 35: 93–109.

Wu, Y. C., Lin, L. Y. and Lee, T. H. (2003). $Na^+,K^+,2Cl^-$-cotransporter: A novel marker for identifying freshwater- and seawater-type mitochondria-rich cells in gills of the euryhaline tilapia, *Oreochromis mossambicus*. Zool Studies 42: 186–192.

Xie, L. and Klerks, P. L. (2003). Responses to selection for cadmium resistance in the least killifish, *Heterandria Formosa*. Environ Toxicol Chem 22: 313–320.

Zambrano, F. and Canelo, E. (1996). Effects of microcystin-LR on the partial reactions of the Na^+-K^+ pump or the gill of carp (*Cyprinus carpio* Linneo.). Toxicon 34: 451–458.

Zhou, B. S., Kelly, S. P., Ianowski, J. P. and Wood, C. M. (2003). Effects of cortisol and prolactin on Na^+ and Cl^- transport in cultured branchial epithelia from freshwater rainbow trout. Am J Physiol 285: R1305–R1316.

Zhou, B. S., Nichols, J., Playle, R. C. and Wood, C. M. (2005). An in vitro biotic ligand model (BLM) for silver binding to cultured gill epithelia of freshwater rainbow trout (*Oncorhynchus mykiss*). Toxicol Appl Pharmacol 202: 25–37.

Chapter 7

The biological roles of mucus: importance for osmoregulation and osmoregulatory disorders of fish health

Richard D. Handy and Richard J. Maunder

Keywords: mucus, fish, sodium, chloride, mucoprotein, ion exchange, osmoregulation, diagnostics

Abstract

Mucus is far from a simple protein solution, and contains many solutes and other materials. This paper critically assesses the composition of mucus, and the relationship between structure and function, especially in the context of osmoregulation and fish health. Mucus typically contains about 95% or more of water, with about 1% by weight of salts and other small solutes, 0.5–1% of free protein, and around 1% of mucins. The mucins are carbohydrate-rich glycoproteins and are partly responsible for the physical properties of mucus. Several models of mucus structure occur in nature, and the dynamic model takes into account the myriad of electrolytes, sugars, lipids, free amino acids, peptides, and other non-mucin components of mucus. Mucus has important immunological roles. The immune components are briefly reviewed and include antimicrobial enzyme activity, antibodies, lectins, histones, and interleukins. Mucus has major functions in osmoregulation, including the establishment of an unstirred layer (USL) that concentrates ions on the epithelial surface and prevents ion depletion. However, there are concerns that the gel forming properties of mucus will slow ion diffusion rates. Values for the diffusion coefficients of various solutes through mucus are reviewed, and for Na^+ or Cl^- ions in fish mucus, the diffusion coefficients are only slightly different to the water or control salines, but this may not be true for other types of mucus or other solutes. Anion exclusion from the polyanionic matrix of mucus does not prevent Cl^- uptake, and charge screening effects can explain free anion permeability through mucus layers. The relationship between mucus ion content and rheology also suggest links between osmoregulation and locomotion in some animals. Mucus has great potential as a non-invasive diagnostic tool for fish health. Data from a range of solutes are examined, and several analytes including glucose, sodium and cortisol may be useful, and may also reflect events in the blood. Mucus composition is modulated by body size/age, diet, stress and other factors in the immediate history of the animal, and any diagnostic application could account for these effects by establishing reference ranges for mucus.

7.1 Introduction

Mucus is often assumed to be a simple mixture of mucus proteins and water that provides a protective slime over the exterior surfaces of the organism. In fact, mucus is a chemically complex secretion that has many different biological functions (reviews; Clamp *et al.*, 1978; Lundgren, 1992; Shephard, 1994; Litchenberger 1995; Quraishi *et al.*, 1996). In addition to water and the mucus proteins (mucins), mucus secretions also contain a range of electrolytes (Schlichter, 1981; Handy, 1989), antibodies and other immune components (Fast *et al.*, 2002; Bromage *et al.*, 2006), respiratory gases (Ultsch and Gros, 1979), enzymes (Subramanian *et al.* 2007), secreted waste products from metabolism (e.g., acids and ammonia, Wright *et al.*, 1986), and other foreign substances (e.g., toxic metals, Handy and Eddy, 1990; Handy, 1992). This chemical complexity has led to the suggestion that mucus has many biological roles including the control of water diffusion and ion gradients across epithelia (Shephard, 1981; 1982; Handy, 1989), a defence against infection or an immunological barrier (e.g., in the gut, Swidsinski *et al.*, 2007), the control and coupling of gas diffusion across epithelia (e.g., Wright *et al.*, 1989; Saldena *et al.*, 2000), the prevention of dessication of soft bodied animals (e.g. tree frogs, Barbeau and Lillywhite, 2005; clams during exposure to air, Vosloo and Vosloo, 2006), and in locomotion (e.g., gliding on pedal mucus in snails, Denny, 1989).

Despite these varied roles of mucus in animals, the major glycoproteins that constitute most of the mucus proteins are highly conserved across species. Many organisms typically have mucus glycoproteins rich in sialic acid, carboxylic acid or sulphate residues (e.g., Warren, 1963; Clamp, 1978; Handy, 1989). This raises the possibility that it is the sum of the more minor components of mucus (e.g. electrolytes, immunoglobulins etc.) rather than just the major glycoproteins that infers the functions of mucus in a particular organism. The composition of the mucus secretion is also influenced by its hydration state. When the mucus is first secreted from the mucous cells (sometimes called 'native' mucus), it becomes hydrated by the external medium (i.e., the external environment). This hydrated mucus can have a different composition to the native mucus (Handy, 1989), and this raises the concern that the composition of mucus is also strongly influenced by the chemical composition of the external environment. It may even be possible that materials are incidentally incorporated into hydrated mucus from the external environment, and add complexity to the chemistry, but have no biological function. Such issues become important when considering the practical applications of mucous chemistry in animal health and veterinary diagnostics. It is clearly important to differentiate what has come from inside the organism, compared to what has been incidentally deposited in the mucus. Alternatively, perhaps the material deposited into the mucus from the external environment can be exploited in biomonitoring tools for environmental protection (Handy and Eddy, 1990). The composition of the mucus is also influenced by biological factors such as dietary status and acclimation states (Handy and Eddy, 1990). Clearly, there is some debate over what gets into the mucus from the organism and the role of the external environment in defining the composition of mucus. This may be particularly important where materials must be moved through a mucus layer to get into, or out of, the organism. This is certainly the case for ion and water movements across mucous epithelia, and the fish gill has been a useful tool to explore this phenomenon, where both cations and anions must negotiate the mucus layer prior to transport across the gill epithelium (review, Handy and Eddy, 2004).

The overall aim of this paper is to critically assess the composition of mucus, with a particular focus on relating composition/structure with biological functions in fish. Then, using the example of osmoregulation, the relationship between function and composition of mucus will be examined in detail. Finally, the practical application of such knowledge on mucus will be discussed, and in particular, one aspect that is currently topical is the use of mucus as a non-invasive method for diagnosing osmoregulatory disorders of fish health.

7.2 Composition and functions of mucus

7.2.1 Mucins

Mucus typically contains about 95% or more of water, with about 1% by weight of salts and other small solutes, 0.5–1% of free protein, and around 1% of mucins (Creeth, 1978). The mucins are the carbohydrate-rich glycoprotein component of mucus (sometimes called 'mucoproteins') and are responsible for the physical properties of mucus (Creeth, 1978). Mucins are high molecular weight glycoproteins with numerous (hundreds) covalently attached oligosaccharide units. These oligosaccharide units include L-fucose, D-galactose, N-acetyl-D-glucosamine, N-acetyl-D-galactosamine and sialic acids (Clamp et al., 1978). The sialic acid component refers mainly to neuraminic acid derivatives, and N-acetylneuraminic acid is commonly found in mucus from humans to fish (Warren, 1963; Asakawa, 1974; Clamp et al., 1978; Arillo et al., 1979; Handy, 1989). Similar to other glycoproteins, the protein backbone of mucin is synthesised in the endoplasmic reticulum and the glycosylation occurs in the Golgi complex via glycosyl-transferase enzymes, and sialy-transferase and sulpho-transferase enzymes to produce sialic acid-containing mucoproteins and sulphate-containing mucoproteins respectively (review, Phelps, 1978). The glycosylated components are attached to the protein backbone often by serine (Ser) and threonine (Thr) residues. Consequently mucins tend to have a high content of Ser and Thr (e.g., one third or half of the amino acids present, Clamp et al., 1978), and with each of these carrying a chain of sugar residues it is no surprise that the molecular weights of mucins are high (e.g., 105–106).

The functions of mucins have been interpreted from their physico-chemical properties. These properties fall into two broad categories: (i) properties associated with the number, or polymerisation of, the glycoprotein sub units that make up the mucin, and (ii) the chemical reactivity and ion exchange properties of the glycosylated residues. In most mucins, a portion of the protein core (usually one end of it) is not glycosylated, and it is therefore possible to bind several glycoproteins together via disulphide bridges to form a mucin. For example, native pig gastric mucus contains four glycoprotein sub-units to make the mucin (Clamp et al., 1978; Figure 1). It is the spatial arrangement of these sub-units and the presence of their glycosylated side chains that infer the rheological properties of mucus. Mucins in water will form a liquid phase at low concentrations, but when the mucin concentration rises to tens of mg/ml a viscous (or even solid) gel will form. The precise mucin concentration required to form the gel phase will depend on the ionic strength of the solution and the precise number of glycoprotein sub-units in the mucin, but gel formation at mucin concentrations of 30 mg/ml and above are fairly typical (Clamp et al., 1978). The importance of the sub-units in the gel forming properties are easily illustrated by breaking the disulphide bridges that hold the sub-units together; treatment with mercaptoethanol (for example) results in solubilisation of the gel and a reduction in viscosity (Sheffner, 1963; Clamp et al., 1978; Bell et al., 1985). Similarly, treatments that break the covalent bonds that attach the glycosylated side chains (e.g., homogenisation, use of detergents), also results in the loss of the gel forming properties (Morris and Rees, 1978).

The biological function of the intact native mucin has therefore been associated with gel forming properties and their role of mucus as a protective barrier on the organisms, or delicate surfaces of organisms such as gills or gut epithelium. However, the glycoprotein residues also have some ion exchange properties that infer a role for mucins in trapping solutes in the mucus, or altering the diffusion of material through mucus. These ion exchange properties are partly derived from the net charge of the carbohydrate moieties at physiological pH, and the effects of changing ionic strength, and therefore charge screening of the residues with ions in the solution (Scott, 1968; Scott, 1989). The residues are mainly anionic at physiological pH including carboxyl, ester sulphate, and sialic acid residues. For the latter, the pK_a is <3 and so these residues will be strongly negatively charged at neutral pH values. Stith (1984a) titrated frog mucus with Na^+ ions and estimated the negative charge to be around -49 equivalents $mole^{-1}$. Mucin is therefore a polyanion that is fixed in the mucus gel, and will bind ions according to their charge density and mobility in solution relative to H+ ions (Scott, 1968; Handy and Eddy, 1991; Handy and Eddy, 2004). Ion binding to mucus will also be a function of the ions present in the solution, and under normal physiological conditions at neutral pH, the mucus will bind the main bulk cations (i.e., Na^+, K^+, Ca^{2+} and Mg^{2+}) according to their relative concentrations, and charge density (Handy, 1989).

7.2.2 Solutes, lipids and free proteins

Some examples of the non-mucin components of mucus are illustrated in Table 1. Mucus clearly contains a range of electrolytes, sugars, lipids, and amino acids. There are also larger non-mucin proteins such as enzymes and peptides. The general assumption is that complex biological molecules such as lipids, amino acids and so on, are derived from the organism secreting the mucus rather than from adsorption of material into the mucus from the external environment. However, this is more difficult to establish experimentally for substances found in both the mucus and environment in significant concentrations, such as electrolytes where some of the ions may have come directly from the water. The composition of the mucus will be influenced by the sampling method. The literature sometimes does not always report the exact details of how the mucus was collected, and whether or not the mucus was a hydrated form, or a native form straight from the mucus cells (i.e., not hydrated by external water or saline). Nonetheless, some general patterns emerge in the composition of mucus. The electrolyte concentrations are a few mmol l^{-1} in mucus, except where either seawater or physiological salines have been used to raise the NaCl concentrations to around 100 mmol l^{-1} or more. The pH of mucus is normally circum-neutral. Fish mucus at least, contains a few mmol l^{-1} of glucose and triglycerides. These substances must originate from within the secreted mucus since native mucus has higher concentrations than hydrated mucus, and of course, water in the external environment does not normally contain millimolar levels of these substances. Mucus also contains free amino acids, and most of these are essential amino acids. It seems unlikely that these amino acids are mainly derived from the breakdown of mucins, since intact mucins are isolated from fresh mucus and that additions of amino acids to the diet can also modify the amino acid composition of the mucus (Saglio and Fauconneau, 1985). However, mucus does contain glycosidase activity, and it is possible that some of the carbohydrate content of mucus solutions are derived from degradation of the glycoprotein side chains of the mucin molecules. Mucus also contains other enzymes such as lysozyme, alkaline phosphatase, and proteases (Table 1).

The functions of these various non-mucin components are open to debate. The concensus view for bulk electrolytes is that the mucus layer supports ion gradients, and therefore slows diffusive losses of electrolytes from the epithelia (see Handy, 1989 and below). However, given that the tertiary structure of mucin influences the gel forming properties of mucus, and this in turn is a function of ionic strength (Bell et al., 1985). It is clear that ions also have a role in the formation of mucus gels. This is apparent in clinical disorders where abnormal NaCl secretion contributes to very viscous mucus (e.g., airway mucus in cystic fibrosis patients, Baconnais et al., 2005). However, the routine biological role of ions in mucus rheology is less clear for animals (see below on rheology).

The glucose, lipids and free amino acids are assumed to be simply incidental products of the mucus-secreting cells. However, while this may seem a reasonable assumption for many solutes and small molecules in mucus, there are some materials that have well known biological roles, for example, the many immunological components of mucus (Table 2 and below).

Table 1. Some of the non-mucin components of mucus from fish and other vertebrates

Component/ analyte	Type of mucus/ species	Notes	Author
Ions/small solutes			
Cations and anions	Canine gastric mucus	Ranges for the following ions (in mEq l⁻¹); Na⁺, 114–148; K⁺, 2.5–6.9; Ca²⁺, 2.4–5.0; Mg²⁺, 1.3–3.1; Cl⁻, 96–144; HCO₃⁻, 6.5–29.8; pH, 7.43–8.88.	Hollander (1963)
Cations and anions	Tortoise intestinal mucus (*Testudo hermanni hermanni* Gmelin)	Mean values ± S.D. (in mEq Kg⁻¹); Na⁺ 110.9 ± 2.1; K⁺ 5.4 ± 0.7; Cl⁻ 170.2 ± 6.1; pH 7.63 ± 0.29; water content 98.47 ± 0.22 %.	Gilles-Baillien (1981)
Sodium	Frog skin mucus (*Rana pipiens*)	3.35 mmol l⁻¹ in the mucus compared to 2.97 mmol l⁻¹ in the external solution.	Stith (1984a)
Cations and anions	Foot mucus from pond snails (*Lymnaea stagnalis*)	Single values (mmol l⁻¹ of mucus); Na⁺, 32.6; K⁺, 3.6; Ca²⁺, 16.2; Mg²⁺, 6.8; Cl⁻, 28.4; NH₄⁺, 0.66. All values were higher than those in the haemolymph.	Schlichter (1981)
Cations and anions	Skin mucus from rainbow trout (*Oncorhynchus mykiss*)	Total ion concentrations in mucus from fish in freshwater, mean values ± S.E., n = 7–10 fish (in mmol l⁻¹); Na⁺, 2.01 ± 0.18; K⁺, 0.84 ± 0.06; Ca²⁺, 0.21 ± 0.01; Mg²⁺, 0.04 ± 0.005; Cl⁻, 2.18 ± 0.21; SO₄²⁻, 0.45 ± 0.09; PO₄³⁻, 0.26 ± 0.03; pH 6.95 ± 0.03.	Handy (1989)

Table 1. Some of the non-mucin components of mucus from fish and other vertebrates

Component/ analyte	Type of mucus/ species	Notes	Author
Lipids and free sugars			
Glucose	Skin mucus from eels (*Anguilla anguilla*)	In wild fish collected in month of November caught by electrofishing, 0.98 µmol g^{-1} of freeze dried mucus.	Fauconneau and Saglio (1984)
Glucose and total triglycerides	Skin mucus from mullet (*Chelon labrosus*)	In fed fish for native and hydrated mucus respectively (mean ± S.D., n = 5–7). Glucose (in mmol l^{-1}); 7.2 ± 4.9 (native); 5.5 ± 2.1 (hydrated). Triglycerides (in mmol l^{-1}); 45.9 ± 41.7 (native); 5.2 ± 2.7 (hydrated).	Handy and Newell unpublished.
Glucose and total triglycerides	Skin mucus from carp (*Cyprimus carpio*)	In fed fish for native and hydrated mucus respectively (mean ± S.D., n = 5–7). Glucose (in mmol l^{-1}); 6.0 ± 4.8 (native); 1.0 ± 0.7 (hydrated). Triglycerides (in mmol l^{-1}); 19.5 ± 9.1 (native); 1.9 ± 0.8 (hydrated).	Handy and Newell unpublished.
Free amino acids and peptides			
Free amino acids	Skin mucus from goldfish (*Carassius auratus*)	In recently fasted fish, unfed for 15 days. Numerous amino acids measured including (µmoles g^{-1} of freeze dried extract); taurine, 18.1; serine, 25.3; glutamic acid, 17.5; glycine, 11.4; alanine11.5; lysine 9.8; total free amino acids, 136.9. The total free amino acid content of the mucus increased with age of the fish and may be influenced by diet and fasting.	Saglio and Fauconneau (1985)
Free amino acids	Skin mucus from eels (*Anguilla anguilla*)	In wild fish collected in month of November caught by electrofishing. Numerous amino acids measured including (µmoles g^{-1} of freeze dried mucus); taurine, 5.15; serine, 5.28; glutamic acid, 9.87; glycine, 5.97; alanine 0.83; lysine 3.04; total free amino acids, 59.27. Only slight seasonal effects were observed November-May.	Fauconneau and Saglio (1984)

Table 1. Some of the non-mucin components of mucus from fish and other vertebrates

Component/ analyte	Type of mucus/ species	Notes	Author
Enzymes			
Glycosidase activity	External mucus from various species of fish	Range of values and enzymes reported for mucus samples extracted in acetone. Examples (ranges across species) include β-N-acetylhexosaminidase, 1.0–8.1 units g^{-1} extract; β-galactosidase, 0.1–1.4 units g^{-1} extract.	Nakagawa *et al.* (1987)
Alkaline phosphatase	Skin mucus from various salmonid fish	Alkaline phosphatase was detected in skin mucus from seawater-adapted Rainbow trout, Coho salmon, and Atlantic salmon with specific activities of (mean values, U/mg protein): 1.04 ± 0.90, 0.75 ± 0.36, 0.45 ± 0.36 respectively of each species. Alkaline phosphatase was not detected in the mucus from animals kept in freshwater.	Fast *et al.* (2002)
Protease activity	Skin mucous from various salmonid fish	Protease was detected in skin mucus from seawater-adapted Rainbow trout, Coho salmon, and Atlantic salmon with specific activities of (mean values, U mg^{-1} protein): 0.051 ± 0.015, 0.036 ± 0.03, 0.026 ± 0.015 respectively of each species. Protease was not detected in the mucus from animals kept in freshwater.	Fast *et al.* (2002)
Esterase and alkaline phosphatase activity	Skin mucus from olive flounder (*Paralichthys olivaceus*)	Alkaline phosphatase activity (0.376 ± 0.005 units mg^{-1} protein) and esterase activity (0.170 ± 0.006 units mg^{-1} protein) were detected in the skin mucus. Lysozyme, trypsin-like proteases and tranferrin are also reported.	Palaksha *et al.* (2008)

7.2.3 Immunological components of mucus

The mucus secretions of fish and other animals are also considered to a functional component of the immune system (e.g., reviews on humoral immunity, Fast *et al.*, 2002; antibodies, Bromage *et al.*, 2006; lectins, Russell and Lumsden, 2005; innate immunity, Subramanian *et al.*, 2007). Some examples of immunological components in fish skin mucus are illustrated (Table 2), and in terms of mass concentration these would be a significant contribution to the colloidal properties of the non-mucin components of mucus. We should therefore consider that immunological status of mucus may alter its osmotic properties. It is clear that fish mucus is able to support an antibody response to an antigen challenge/infection. Mucus also contains a variety of enzymes that are associated with bacterial killing or antimicrobial activity including lysozyme, amino acid oxidase activity, and protease inhibitors. Some of these are enzymes are well known Fe^{++} and Cu^{++} dependent-enzymes, and so presumably the trace element status of the mucus will influence the bacteriocidal properties of mucus. The mucus also contains essential molecular components of the immune system such as lectins, histones, and interleukins. The latter have been implicated in the regulation of Na^+ uptake in the intestine (Barmeyer *et al.*, 2004). This complexity on immune components alone shows that mucus is far from being a simple protein solution, and perhaps immune function and ionic status may be more closely connected than previously thought. In addition, with differences emerging in the immunological composition of mucus from seawater-adapted and freshwater fish (e.g., Fast *et al.*, 2002; Delamare-Deboutteville *et al.* 2006), it is possible that the osmoregulatory status of the animal will have some influence on immunity via changes in mucus composition.

7.3 Osmoregulation and mucus

The role of surface mucus in fish osmoregulation has a long history of research. The first published studies detailed experiments involving the crude removal of surface mucus from the eel Anguilla anguilla (Portier and Duval, 1922; Negus, 1963) or rock goby *Gobius paganellus* (Raffy, 1950) and making observations on the animal's ability to maintain osmotic stability. These and other experiments (Negus, 1967) led to the general conclusion that the mucosal lining on the skin and gills of fish acts as a physical waterproof barrier that helps to maintain the osmotic gradient between the fish and the surrounding water. This assumption remains despite the fact that it has not been satisfactorily proven experimentally; see Shephard (1994). The role of mucus in osmoregulation has also been inferred by the observation that fish placed in a hypertonic medium display an increased number of mucus secreting goblet cells within the epidermal layer (Ahuja, 1970; Blanc-livini and Abraham, 1970; Wendelaar-Bonga, 1978). The increased number of cells and mucus production does not however explain the mechanisms of how mucus is involved in osmoregulation.

Table 2. Some examples of the immunological components of fish mucus

Type of mucus/ species	Notes	Author
Antibody production	Skin mucus from European eels (*Anguilla anguilla*)	Eels were challenged with *Vibrio vulnificus serovar* E, a bacterial pathogen, and total antibody production in the skin mucus and serum were measured using a dot blotting technique. The immune response in mucus was faster (peak at days 3–4) and than in the serum.	Esteve-Gassent *et al.* (2003)
Antibody production	Skin mucus of white sturgeon (*Acipenser transmontanus* Richardson)	Fish were challenged by several methods, including intraperitoneal immunization with white sturgeon iridovirus (WSIV). Immunoglobulins were detected in mucus, and specificity to WSIV was partly confirmed using immunocytochemistry.	Drennan *et al.* (2007)
Antibody production	Skin mucus from barramundi (*Lates calcarifer*).	Antibody titres in mucus and serum were measured during either acclimation to seawater or freshwater following vaccination with *Streptococcus iniae*. A strong specific antibody response was detected in both mucus and serum. Fish acclimated in seawater prior to vaccination showed a markedly higher specific mucosal antibody response than fish acclimated in freshwater.	Delamare-Deboutteville *et al.* (2006)
Antimicrobial peptides and proteins	Skin mucus from cod (*Gadus morhua*)	The authors extracted a fraction from cod mucus that showed antimicrobial activity against *Bacillus megaterium*, *Escherichia coli* and *Candida albicans*. Separation of the proteins in the extract, and sequence analysis identified the following anti-microbial proteins: histone H2B (13 565 Da), ribosomal protein L40 (6397 Da), ribosomal protein L36A (12 340 Da) and ribosomal protein L35 (14 215 Da).	Bergsson *et al.* (2005)
Congerin	Skin and gut mucus from Japanese conger eels (*Conger myriaster* Brevoort)	Congerin is a lectin (mucosal galectin) and therefore part of the innate immune response. Congerin from mucus could agglutinate rabbit erythrocytes and some gut bacteria. Thus demonstrating its role in immune defences.	Nakamura *et al.* (2007)

Table 2. Some examples of the immunological components of fish mucus

	Type of mucus/ species	Notes	Author
Interleukins	Skin mucus of atlantic salmon (*Salmo salar*)	Gene expression if interleukin-1β in the skin of Atlantic salmon following infection with the parasite, *Gyrodactylus salaris*. The mucous cells are implicated as the likely source of the increased expression in the fish skin.	Lindenstrom *et al.* (2006)
L-amino acid oxidase activity	Skin mucus from rockfish (*Sebastes schlegeli*)	Extraction of an antibacterial component of the mucus was analysed by RT-PCR and western blotting to reveal L-amino acid oxidase activity capable of killing the bacterium, *Photobacterium damselae*.	Kitani *et al.* (2007)
Lysozyme activity	Skin mucus from various salmonid fish	Lysozyme was detected in skin mucus from seawater-adapted rainbow trout, Coho salmon, and Atlantic salmon with specific activities of (mean values, U mg⁻¹ protein): 65 ± 40.8, 19.1 ± 14.2, 13.6 ± 10.2 respectively of each species. Lysozyme was also detected in the mucus from animals kept in freshwater at higher concentrations (values around 110-200 U mg⁻¹ protein).	Fast *et al.* (2002)
Lysozyme activity	Various marine and freshwater fish.	Mean lysozyme values in the mucus range from 16-124 U/ mg protein depending on species. Alkaline phosphatase, cathepsin B, and protease activities are also reported.	Subramanian *et al.* (2007)
Lysozyme content	Skin mucus from channel catfish (*Ictalurus punctatus*)	Pooled measurement from 5 samples; 183 ng ml⁻¹ of mucus. Immunoglobulins also tentatively identified by precipitation methods.	Ourth (1980)
Serine protease inhibitors	Skin mucus of pufferfish (*Takifugu pardalis*)	Two trypsin inhibitors termed TPTI 1 and 2 were purified from skin mucus, and identified as acidic glycoproteins that could inhibit the activity of trypsin and α-chymotrypsin, and were therefore identified as serine protease inhibitors. The role of these inhibitors is likely in the neutralization of serine proteases released by invading pathogens.	Nagashima *et al.* (2004)

7.3.1 Mucus as an unstirred layer

One way that mucus could aid in osmoregulation is its ability to set up an unstirred layer (USL) next to the surfaces involved in ion transport. This USL of water and mucus (micron scale) is distinct from the glycocalyx (nanometer scale) on the exterior surface of the cell membrane, although from the biophysics review point the USL is a continuum that extends to the cell membrane surface. The gel forming properties of mucus and the frictional forces close to the epithelial surface will slow the flow of any water (or other liquid) in the bulk solution to form the USL. The USL is sometimes also regarded as a 'stagnant' layer because it may act as a partial barrier to diffusion so that rapidly permeating substances become trapped or accumulate in the USL. These effects can be so large that the USL could become the rate-limited step in diffusion across an epithelium in some circumstances (Barry and Diamond, 1984). However, the situation is undoubtedly more complex than this, and the flow dynamics at the interphase between the bulk water and mucus will be influenced by peri-kinetic shear forces, the presence of colloids and how the colloids interact with mucins (see recent discussion of colloid chemistry in Handy et al., 2008a; 2008b). There is evidence that the electrolytes within the unstirred layer itself are distributed to facilitate active ion uptake and reduce ion loss across the epithelium. Ion gradients often occur through USLs, with higher ion concentration existing next to the epithelial surface than at the interface with the external medium (Shephard, 1982; Shephard, 1984b; Simonneaux et al., 1987; Handy, 1989). These gradients are often not linear, with large increases in ion concentrations as the membrane surface is approached. This may reflect the role of mucus in preventing ion leak from epithelia, with such ions being trapped against the exterior surface of the cell membrane by the mucus layer (Handy, 1989). The existence of ion gradients through mucus also implies that mucus will alter the diffusion rates of solutes.

7.3.2 Diffusion rates of gases and electrolytes through mucus

In addition to setting up an USL, mucus may also reduce the rate of delivery of ions to the epithelial surface by slowing diffusion. Ultimately, the ion transporters on the cell membrane are dependent on ions being delivered to the binding site on the transport protein, and this will depend on a good supply of ions in the mucus adjacent to the transporter (Handy and Eddy, 2004). Several studies have investigated the diffusion coefficients of the key ions through mucus, and compared the values to a water or saline control medium (Table 3). The experimentally derived values for diffusion coefficients (Table 3) show some variability between studies, but most of this is likely due to type and precise viscosity of mucus used in the experiment, the charge density and ion-binding properties of the diffusible ion, and the method of measurement of the coefficient. For ions with a low charge density such as monovalent electrolytes, the diffusion rates in fish mucus can sometimes be similar to salines, but for metals with a high charge density (e.g., heavy metals) the situation can be very different. For example, the calculated diffusion coefficients of $^{22}Na^+$ and $^{36}Cl^-$ through skin mucus preparations from the marine teleost *Leptocottus armatus* were similar (±15%) to those obtained through control saline solutions (Marshall, 1978). Similarly, the diffusion of calcium through skin mucus of rainbow trout Oncorhynchus mykiss did not differ from that through a control buffer (Part and Lock, 1983). In this same experiment however, there was evidence that the diffusion rate of cadmium and mercury were both reduced in mucus compared to the control. This ability of mucus to reduce diffusion rate has also been found for several other key ions. The reported diffusion coefficients for chloride ions through the oesophagus of both marine and freshwater fish (Shephard, 1984a; 1984b) were considerably lower than reported values for chloride ions through water or saline (Li and Gregory, 1974; Marshall, 1978). Similarly, the reported diffusion coefficients for hydrogen (Williams and Turnberg, 1980; Lucas, 1984; Sarosiek *et al.*, 1984; Lee and Nicholls, 1987; Winne and Verheyen, 1990), sodium (Lucas, 1984) and bicarbonate (Livingston *et al.*, 1995) ions in mammalian mucus preparations were all substantially lower than for the control mediums. The diffusion of a range of other substances through a variety of mucus preparations has also been shown to be reduced compared to controls (see Table 3) and the diffusion coefficients of tritiated water and caffeine were both reduced through solutions containing increasing concentrations of mucus glycoproteins (Marriott, 1989). The study of fluorescently labelled molecules through human nasal mucus has provided evidence that suggests it is the molecule size of the substance that affects its diffusion rate, with small molecules (flurorescein, MW ~300 Da) diffusing through mucus and unstirred water at similar rates, while medium (serum albumin, MW ~68000 Da) and larger (IgG, MW ~146000 Da) molecules showed increasingly slower diffusion rates through mucus compared to water (Radomsky *et al.*, 1990).

Overall, the experimentally derived values for diffusion coefficients may have some merit in a general understanding of the role played by mucus. However there are limitations and the measured diffusion coefficients in such experiments may not exactly match the diffusion coefficient *in vivo*. Some of the experimental methods used to test the diffusional properties of mucus involve removal of the mucus, its dilution, or at best the manipulation or alteration of mucus conditions in situ. These methods will inevitably alter the chemical status of the mucus, and it's USL forming properties, as well as the precise distribution of ions through it. The experiments that have attempted to make measurements in situ on the epithelia are likely to be closest to the *in vivo* state, but even the introduction of the tip of a microelectrode into the USL might change the flow dynamics at the recording site, and there is no perfect way to eliminate such experimental artefacts. Nonetheless, the delivery of millimolar amounts of electrolytes into the mucus should normally provide enough ions in excess so the ion concentrations are not rate limiting for transporters with micromolar affinities.

7.3.3 Anion exclusion

Perhaps a larger problem in the investigation of the role of mucus in osmoregulation is how anions are delivered to the epithelial surface. All animals require anions such as Cl⁻, and this is tightly coupled with Na^+ uptake at the cell membrane, once both the Cl⁻ and Na^+ are through the mucus layer (Handy and Eddy, 2004). The chemistry of mucins and the residues on the glycoprotein structure infer that mucus is a matrix of fixed polyanions at normal physiological pH (see sections above). The idea that like charges repel is well know, so some explanation of how negatively charged ions get through the mucus layer in the face of the huge fixed negative charge is needed. It is clear that anions do get through the mucus layer, and Cl⁻ uptake rates across the gills of fish (e.g., trout, around 100 μmol kg^{-1} h^{-1}, Battram and Eddy, 1990) are at the same order of magnitude as Na^+ ions. In fish, the charge density of the mucus has been shown to vary with tissue type and function, with a higher density of fixed negatively charged residues on the gill compared to skin epithelium being identified using histological techniques (Asakawa, 1970; Singh and Thakur, 1975; Whitear, 1977). Thus the fixed negative charge appears to be even stronger on the gills where the majority of water and ion movement takes place. The overall negative electrostatic charge of the mucus layers could be expected to increase the number of cations attracted into the mucus layer, and decrease the number of anions that diffuse into it by simple charge repulsion. This diffusional selectivity of ions based on charge is described theoretically by the Donnan exclusion phenomenon (Bokris and Reddy, 1973), and when the various ions involved reach an equilibrium with the electrochemical difference between the mucus and the external medium (i.e., a Donnan equilibrium; Overbeek, 1956; Tam and Verdugo, 1981), then steady-state ion activities and voltages can be recorded across the interface of the two mediums. The contribution played by Donnan exclusion in ion exchange through mucus has been investigated in a variety of species by the use of micro electrodes sensitive to the small differences in electrical potential (the Donnan potential) that is set up between the mucus layer and the adjacent epithelia, relative to the external medium. Unfortunately, the experimental methods involved require a similar interference or manipulation of the mucus layer as was described for the diffusion coefficient experimentation above, and hence the results carry the same limitations in their interpretation. However, the results from work investigating ion exchange through the mucus of snail footsole (Schlichter, 1982), frog skin (Stith, 1984b), fish oesophagus (Shephard, 1982; Shephard, 1984b; Simonneaux et al., 1987), fish skin mucus (Handy, 1989), and the mucillages in fish eggs (Peterson and Martin-Robichaud, 1986; Shephard, 1987) provide evidence that free anions are present in the mucus, and even though Donnan potentials can be measured, the voltages are not sufficiently high to dramatically alter the rates of ion fluxes, with the possible exception of situations in very soft natural waters (Shepherd, 1987). For example, Handy (1989) measured Cl⁻ activities of around 1.8 mmol l⁻¹ with an +18 mV Donnan potential across the water/mucus interface, and an activity coefficient of 0.82 for Cl⁻ indicated most of the total chloride present was as the free Cl⁻ ion (not surprising, as the mucins have little fixed positive charge). These observations suggest other events are occurring in the mucus chemistry that overcomes anion exclusion.

There are several possible explanations for this apparent discrepancy. One

Table 3. Diffusion rates of gases and electrolytes through mucus

Type of mucus/species	Ion or solute	Diffusion coefficient (×10⁻⁵ cm² s⁻¹)		Author
Mucosal surface of oesophagus of buffalo sculpin *Enophrys bison*	Cl⁻	0.231		Shephard (1984a)
Mucosal surface of oesophagus of minnow *Phoxinus phoxinus*	Cl⁻	0.30 ± 0.029		Shephard (1984b)
Skin surface mucus scraped from Pacific staghorn sculpin *Leptocottus armatus*	²²Na	Mucus	Saline control	Marshall (1978)
		1.06 ± 0.07	1.84 ± 0.12	
			1.05 ± 0.07	
	³⁶Cl	1.51 ± 0.08	1.48 ± 0.03	
		1.91 ± 0.08	1.65 ± 0.06	
Submucosa + mucosa combined layer from conger eel *Conger oceanicus_* swimbladder	Oxygen	0.0039 ± 0.0013 (59× lower than in water)		Lapennas and Schmidtnielsen (1977)
Artificial porcine mucin	H⁺ and Na⁺	Mucin conc %, w/v	H⁺ Na⁺	Lucas (1984)
		0	10.5 16.53	
		10	4.4 7.4	
		20	2.45 2.6	
		30	1.47 0.98	
Canine gastric mucus	H⁺	0.764 ± 0.082 (9× lower than in the 0.155M NaCl control)		Sarosiek *et al.* (1984)

Table 3. *Diffusion rates of gases and electrolytes through mucus*

Type of mucus/species	Ion or solute	Diffusion coefficient (×10⁻⁵ cm² s⁻¹)		Author
Porcine gastric mucus	H⁺	1.75 ± 0.23 (4× lower than in saline)		Williams and Turnberg (1980)
Rat gastric mucus	HCl	5.4 ± 1.3 (6× and 12× lower than in water and saline respectively)		Livingston and Engel (1995)
Rat duodenal mucus	HCO_3^-	0.181 ± 0.12 (11× less than in saline)		Livingston *et al.* (1995)
Porcine gastric mucus (and water comparison)		Mucus	Water	Desai and Vadgama (1991)
	Phloroglucinol	0.24	0.78	
	5-Hydroxy-L-tryptophan	0.14	0.68	
	Phenolphthalein	0.18	0.83	
	5-Hydroxytryptamine	0.14	0.63	
	Phenolphthalein diphosphate			
	NAD	0.33	0.49	
	Glycyrrhizic acid	0.017	0.11	
	Cyanocobalamine	0.27	0.67	
	RNA	0.10	0.26	
	Lysozyme	0.09	1.6	
		0.045	1.2	
Rat intestinal mucus		Mucus gel	Control buffer	Winne and Verheyen (1990)
	L-Phenylalanine	0.41	0.9	
	A-Methyl-glucoside	0.40	1.09	
	Aminopyrine	0.38	1.00	
	Antipyrine	0.44	1.10	
	Benzoic acid	0.56	1.23	
	Urea	0.84	1.66	
	[³H] Water	1.67	3.14	
	Hydrogen ion	0.35	5.31	

Values for diffusion coefficients are single values, or means ± S.E., where given. Reference values for diffusion coefficients (×10⁻⁵ cm² s⁻¹) in dilute solutions at 25 °C at 0.01 M ionic strength; NaCl, 1.545; KCl, 1.917; CaCl₂ 1.188 (Robinson and Stokes, 1959). The apparent diffusion coefficient in seawater for Cl⁻ is about 1.65 (Li and Gregory, 1974).

explanation is that the cations present in the mucus have provided sufficient charge screening of the mucins so that all the fixed negative charges in the mucus have essentially been titrated. Any free Cl⁻ ions, or other free anions, in the mucus matrix would effectively see a mucin with no net charge, and the Cl⁻ would be free to diffuse. Stith (1984a) estimated the negative charge to be around -49 equivalents mole⁻¹ in frog skin mucus, and with mucus protein concentrations of 1–2 g l⁻¹ and the high molecular weights of mucins, this would suggest a few millimoles of cations would be needed for charge screening in most mucus solutions. These concentrations of cations are readily found in mucus (Table 1), and free ion measurements also indicate the cations are in excess (e.g., excess of 1 mmol l⁻¹ Na⁺ activity in fish skin mucus; Handy, 1989).

Adequate charge screening of the mucins seems to be the most likely explanation, but there are other alternatives that could theoretically maintain apparent anion influx. One possibility is that anions leaking out of the epithelium are trapped adjacent to the membrane by the presence of mucus, and are therefore simply recycled. Thus any technique that measures ion uptake by measuring the appearance of the ions in the blood would record the true unidirectional influx across the epithelia. However, techniques that rely on measuring the disappearance of the solute from the external medium (e.g., loss of ²²Na⁺ from the bathing medium for example) could underestimate the unidirectional influx. The solution is to repeat the experiments with unlabelled water and/or measure in the blood to quantify this 'back flux' of ions. Alternatively use Ussing preparations to measure transepithelial potential in short circuit and open circuit conditions in such experiments (Kirschner, 1978), then deduct the Donnan potential to establish the residual voltage. Presumably, drops in the residual voltage in the different experimental conditions will reflect the ion recycling at the membrane. Another theoretical possibility is that the epithelial surface is mostly polyanionic, but that there are patches of neutral or cationic material that will enable anions to enter and move through the mucus. This idea of positive 'patches' within an otherwise negatively charged matrix has been of interest in research on the molecular docking mechanisms and interactions between proteins (Tworowski et al., 2005; Wittemann and Ballbuff, 2006). The idea may seem problematic for epithelia because the patches of mucus that enable anion diffusion would need to be located directly over the anion transporters on the membrane, and yet the mucus is mobile on the epithelial surface. Nonetheless, Nagel et al. (2002) have clearly identified an uneven distribution of Cl⁻ current on the frog skin which can only be explained in terms of a patchy distribution of the transporters in the membrane. These alternatives should therefore not be excluded without further research.

7.3.4 Rheology and osmoregulation

The gel forming properties of mucus is a function of ionic strength or salt concentration in the mucus (Bell et al., 1985). This property establishes a strong relationship between the viscous/rheological properties of mucus and the ionic status of the mucus, and therefore osmoregulation. The theoretical basis of this relationship is clear. The mucins in mucus are polyanions, and the gel forming properties of mucus depend on the spatial arrangement of the mucins (Figure 1). This spatial arrangement will depend on the level of charge screening of the mucins. If enough cations are added to just screen the fixed negative charge, then the anion-repulsion between mucins will decrease and the mucins can be closer together (thicker mucus). However, if far too much salt is added so that salt crystals form, then the mucus proteins can precipitate on the crystals resulting in a denatured mucus with a loss of the rheological properties. There are even suggestions that the mucins themselves can act as nuclei for crystal formation (i.e., biocrystalisation, Humbert et al., 1986). The rheological properties of mucus are significance in locomotion such as gliding on foot mucus in snails (Denny, 1989; Lauga and Hosoi, 2006), and mucus can reduce the drag over the surface of fish skin (Bernadsky et al., 1993). It therefore seems logical that changes in the ionic composition of mucus, that alter rheology, will subsequently alter the efficiency of such locomotor behaviours. Davies and Hutchinson (2005) argue that calcium crystals in snail mucus trails may help the animal orientate in the trail, suggesting a role for these crystals in animal behaviour. However, we do not know if animals are able to actively manage salt concentrations in the mucus so that mucus rheology is controlled in a way that enhances locomotor performance; or whether speed itself (e.g., body lengths per second) would inevitably result in a different dilution and hydration of body surface mucus as the animal moves. Presumably, faster water movement would more rapidly hydrate the mucus, and reduce the viscosity. Further research is required to establish these suggested links between osmoregulation, mucus and locomotion.

7.4 Mucus as a non-invasive diagnostic tool for osmoregulation and fish health

The diagnostics of animal health often relies on analysis of an easily accessible body fluid, and traditionally whole, blood, serum, or plasma has been used for veterinary purposes. However, concerns about the stress involved in collecting blood samples (e.g., Caldwell et al., 2006), and ethical demands to use less invasive methods in research (reduction, refinement, replacement; the 3Rs, Combes et al., 2004), has increased interest in the use of mucus as a less invasive diagnostic tool of animal health. This effort has been mostly on animals such as fish that produce significant quantities of accessible mucus (e.g., Eddy and Fraser, 1982). The fact that fish mucus contains many components of the immune system (Table 2) has also led to the suggestion that skin mucus could be used to monitor immune responses to infection (e.g., Fast et al., 2002). However, perhaps the use of mucus can go further, and the scientific community should move towards using diagnostics in mucus instead of using blood samples for a range of physiological functions including osmoregulation. In order to achieve this goal for osmoregulatory pathologies several assumptions and practical issues need to be resolved, including:

(i)   The mucus should ideally reflect the changes solute concentrations

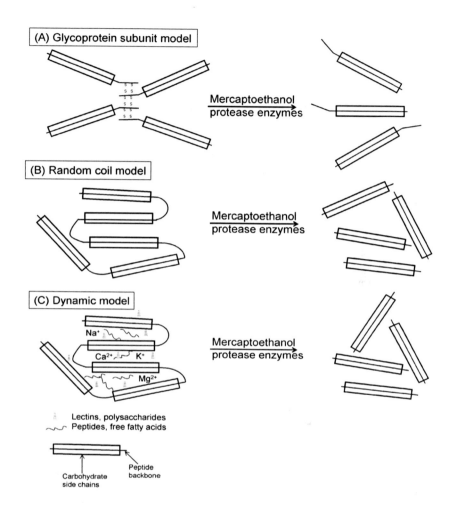

Figure 1. *Possible models for mucin structure*

Mucin polymers are made of glycoproteins which each have a peptide backbone. The peptide backbone is largely covered in carbohydrate side chains, but some areas are exposed where disulphide bridges can form between the glycoproteins. There are several models of how the glycoprotein subunits could be arranged to form a mucin polymer. **(a)** In the 'subunit' model the glycoproteins are arranged to form a distinct protein structure. This model has been proposed for pig gastric mucus which contains 4 glycoprotein subunits (Clamp et al., 1978). **(b)** The random coil model proposes the glycoproteins are attached end to end (disulphide bridges not shown for clarity) to produce a flexible polymeric structure (e.g., cervical mucins, Carlstedt and Sheehan, 1989). **(c)** The dynamic model argues that the other non-mucin components of mucus have some importance in modifying the rheology of the mucus gel, including ions present in the mucus, as well as soluble carbohydrates, free fatty acids, lectins, and small peptides (after Slomiany et al., 1989). In all these models, the polymers of mucin are important for the gel forming properties of mucus, and disruption of disulphide bridges with mercaptoethanol, cleavage of the peptide backbone with proteases/enzymatic digestion, or removed of the side chains with neuraminidases will change rheology to the liquid (or sol) phase.

in the blood, so that the utility of mucus as an alternative to collecting blood can be proven.

(ii)   Changes in mucus composition must reflect changes in the health of the organism. For osmoregulatory disturbances, and other disorders, the diagnostics should detect the early signs of stress, so the assays have practical values in protecting fish stocks.

(iii)   Diagnosis of an osmoregulatory disorder may require the exclusion of other health effects, or factors that modulate osmoregulatory problems. The diagnostics for osmoregulatory pathology (or indeed any conditions), should therefore be part of a suite of assay that cover a range of different conditions including evidence of infection, nutritional pathologies, metabolic disorders, and the effects of foreign compounds (pollutants, drugs), so that the correct diagnosis is achieved.

(iv)   The mucus diagnostics needs to be easy to use, robust, and relatively cheap in order to be accepted for practical veterinary use.

(v)   Issues relating to standard reference ranges of analytes, and acceptable levels of precision and accuracy need to be defined for mucus. These standards need to be at least as robust as existing standards for the analysis of blood. For example, reference ranges for Na^+ in mucus that equate to a known reference range for Na^+ in the blood.

(vi)   Offer new opportunities for diagnosis, or analysis, of substances that are not easy to measure in the blood or other body fluids. For example, trace elements that are normally at low concentration in the blood or water.

The idea that mucus should reflect the blood or other internal fluids has some basis in physiology. Mucus is essentially a secretion that is derived from inside mucous cells, and these cells, like most other cells in the organism, should be influenced by the composition of the extracellular fluids around them. It therefore seems logical that any change in the chemical composition of the blood or extracellular fluid should be partly reflected in the secreted mucus. This should particularly hold true for substances that can move across cell membranes by diffusion (e.g., organic chemicals/some drugs) and therefore easily penetrate both the blood and mucus cells. The situation may be more complex for materials that are partitioned between the intracellular and extracellular compartments via membrane transport processes (e.g., solutes such as metals, glucose, amino acids), but one might expect some relationship between an increasing (or decreasing) level of solute in the blood compared to mucus. Mucous cells are secretory, and have an active endocytotic pathway (Phelps, 1978), and so particulate material (e.g. viruses, bacteria, small proteins) could also penetrate these cells from the extracellular fluid. Viruses can be detected in mucus (e.g. Maggi et al., 2003). Many investigations have attempted to measure the chemical components of mucus, and with exception of immunological studies on mucus (see Table 2), there are few examples in the literature where attempts have been made to measure the composition of the blood and the mucus within the same experiment for diagnostic purposes. However, some data are available that relate to osmoregulation, or the stress hormones involved in osmoregulation. Simontacchi *et al.* (2008) demonstrated a correlation between blood and mucus levels of cortisol in seabass (*Dicentrarchus labrax*) and suggested mucus cortisol could be used to assess stress. Figure 2 shows some data for various solutes in the blood plasma of trout plotted against the same solute in the mucus. The animals were subject to various treatments (controls, handling stress, or low pH exposure) prior to sampling as an experimental tool to force some changes in the body fluids, so that responses over a range of concentrations could be observed for each solute. Several observations can be made from Figure 2. First consider the relationship between blood and mucus regardless of treatment (i.e., all the data in each plot). It is clear from the overall correlation coefficients that the data are not completely random (correlations above the 0.05 threshold), except in the case of K^+. However, only the glucose and Na^+ show convincing trends overall, with levels in the mucus clearly increasing as blood levels also elevate (Figure 2). Now consider the effects of the individual treatments (different symbols in each graph, Figure 2). It is clear that where an overall trend is apparent, the data for individual treatments tends to cluster. For example, in the Na^+ plot (Figure 2e), the low pH episode caused a rise in blood and mucus Na^+ compared to controls. The treatment-effect simply clusters the data along the same overall trend in data series. The level of clustering can of course be reflected in statistical differences between the mean data for blood or mucus in each treatment (Table 4), but there are instances where the correlations are treatment-specific. For example, for lactate there is a clear correlation between mucus and blood in the handling stress experiment (correlation coefficient, -0.659), but not in the controls or low pH experiment (correlation coefficients, 0.232 and -0.035 respectively). This highlights that the diagnostic value of measuring a solute in blood or mucus can depend on the history of the animal. In the case of glucose and Na^+ this does not seem important, as all the data are on a similar trend line regardless of how the animal has been treated. However, this is not the case for lactate (Figure 2a). Clearly, there is some merit in using mucus as a measure to reflect events in the blood, but care should be taken to fully characterise the response of each parameter in a range of stressful conditions. Only when this is done, can we be confident about data interpretation.

The notion that a change in mucus composition should reflect organism health is of fundamental importance. The evidence for this strong in some disciplines, such as immunology (Table 2), but data on osmoregulation is more fragmented. There is some evidence that nutritional status is reflected in the solutes present in the mucus, and diet can influence the free amino acid content of mucus (Fauconneau and Saglio, 1984). The intake of dietary salt also alters the osmoregulatory status of mucus (Handy and Eddy, 1990). However, the measurement of increasing (or decreasing) solute concentration in the blood does not necessarily show a simple linear increase (or decrease) in the mucus (Figure 2). The correlation between

Table 4. *Measurements of solutes in blood and mucus following handling stress, or exposure to low pH*

Parameter	Body Fluid	Treatment		
		Control	Handling Stress	Low pH
Bicarbonate	Blood	2.78 ± 0.29	2.82 ± 0.22	3.50 ± 0.27#
	Mucus	0.93 ± 0.11*	1.73 ± 0.13#	1.49 ± 0.20*#
	Correlation coefficient	0.232	-0.659	-0.035
Lactate	Blood	1.44 ± 0.12	4.51 ± 0.55#	0.71 ± 0.08#
	Mucus	1.37 ± 0.26*	0.47 ± 0.08*#	0.56 ± 0.10#
	Correlation coefficient	0.818	-0.183	0.078
Glucose	Blood	5.86 ± 0.17	3.26 ± 0.20#	3.65 ± 0.54#
	Mucus	0.67 ± 0.01*	0.23 ± 0.01*#	0.51 ± 0.07*
	Correlation coefficient	0.530	-0.477	0.210
Sodium	Blood	141 ± 4.5	139 ± 6.8	180 ± 6.6#
	Mucus	2.86 ± 0.17*	3.20 ± 0.21*	6.79 ± 0.51*#
	Correlation coefficient	-0.600	-0.209	0.268
Potassium	Blood	2.05 ± 0.27	2.23 ± 0.2	2.07 ± 0.1
	Mucus	2.10 ± 0.18	2.43 ± 0.17	4.35 ± 0.38#
	Correlation coefficient	0.630	-0.646	-0.369

Data are means ± S.E. (n = 5-10 fish for each parameter) and expressed as mmol l^{-1}, from Handy unpublished. * Statistically significant difference (t-test, P < 0.05) between blood and mucus for the parameter within each treatment (column). #Statistically significant (t-test, P < 0.05) treatment effect compared to control within body fluid and experiment. Correlation coefficients are indicated for the comparison of blood with mucus within each column for each solute.

levels in the mucus and in the blood are also analyte-specific with some solutes showing good correlations (e.g., Na^+), while others are more variable (e.g., lactate; Figure 2). However, these problems are not new, and concentrations of solutes measured in the blood rarely show a simple linear increase with the respect to the tissues or external medium. For example for solutes in the food, the kinetics of blood measurements following a meal rarely show a simple linear relationship with dietary intake (e.g., glucose, Blasco et al., 1996; dietary salt, Smith et al., 1995).

Evidence of general stress should also be detectable in the mucus. This could be reflected by increases in substances known to be released by organisms during stress, such as cortisol, and this has been reported in mucus (e.g., Simontacchi et al., 2008). Alternatively, diagnostics in blood can sometimes involve measurement of metabolites or products of pathological processes that are not normally present in the body fluids. These could be high levels of reactive oxygen species or

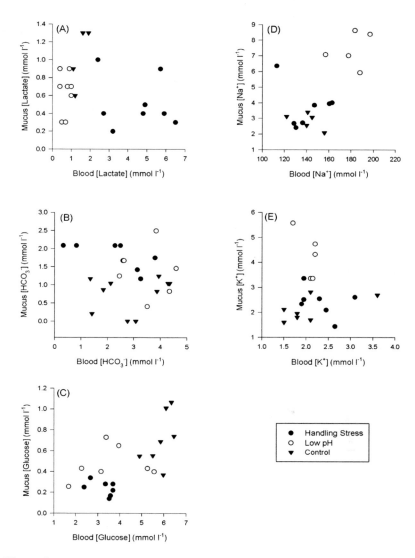

Figure 2.

Solute measurements in blood compared to freshly secreted (native) mucus from adult rainbow trout, (a) lactic acid, (b) bicarbonate, (c) glucose, (d) sodium, (e) potassium. Samples were collected from health animals (controls), fish subject to confinement in a net for 1 hour (handling stress), exposure to an episode of acidified water (pH 6.0, acidified with H₂SO₄) for 16 hours (low pH). For the treated animals, samples were collected at the end of the treatment. The fish tanks were on flow-through single pass to ensure other water quality parameters remained normal. Correlation coefficients for all data within each plot (regardless of treatment) were -0.160, -0.315, 0.657, 0.649, -0.036 for plots A-E respectively. Notably, the glucose and Na⁺ plots give the best correlations overall (see main text for details). The mean data from each treatment are shown in Table 4.

materials released from damaged cells (e.g., cytosolic lactate dehydrogenase). The presence/absence of such materials may also be a useful approach with mucus. For example, haemoglobin is not normally present in mucus, and has long been suggested as an indicator of stress (Smith and Ramos, 1976). The absence of haemoglobin would suggest that the mucus was less likely to be contaminated by ions from blood arising from abrasions on the fish skin. This would be a very important negative control for osmoregulatory investigations. Mucus can also contain, and promote the generation of, reactive oxygen species (e.g., Nakamura *et al.*, 1998). However, the latter is also complicated by dietary status, and is modified by the presence of dietary antioxidants (Ren *et al.*, 2007). The effects of pollutants on osmoregulation is a major concern, and numerous biomarkers have been suggested (Schlenk *et al.*, 2008). Mucus is a route for excretion for trace metals (Varanasi and Markey, 1978; Handy, 1992; Handy and Penrice, 1993).

Mucus production rates are also known to increase during times of stress, and this has been investigated mostly in the context of osmoregulatory or ionic stresses. Mucus production rates are difficult to measure. For fish skin mucus, the approach is to measure the dilution of some unique component of the mucus that is not normally detected in the water, or excreted via other routes from the animal. Measurement of sialic acid meets these requirements (Eddy and Fraser, 1982; Handy, 1989). The presence of low or high levels of such materials in the water might be used for a simplified or semi-quantitative determination of low or high mucus production rates, but more accurate determinations would require a series of time-dependent measurements to be made in laboratory conditions. Mucus production rates are an important aspect of the animals' physiology. High mucus production rates, could contribute to deficiency states where valuable materials are lost through excessive mucus production. For example, stressed rainbow trout can produce 6 ml of mucus kg^{-1} h^{-1} of body mass (Eddy and Fraser, 1982), and with a mucus Na^+ concentration of around 2 mmol l^{-1} (Handy, 1989), this would be a loss of 12 μmol l^{-1} Na^+ kg^{-1} h^{-1}. Given that Na^+ uptake rates across the gills in fish are around 100–200 μmol kg^{-1} h^{-1} (Eddy, 1982), it is clear that salt losses via the mucus could be equivalent to around 10% of the salt taken up by the gills. If Na^+ uptake is inhibited (e.g., unfed fish exposed to pollutants), the mucus secretion would represent an unsustainable loss of electrolytes. Similar arguments apply to mucus protein (e.g., 1.7 g l^{-1} in trout mucus), representing a loss of 10.2 mg protein kg^{-1} h^{-1} through the skin mucus (or 244 mg protein day^{-1} to be replaced by dietary intake).

Any analytical method applied to mucus must be robust, preferably easy to use, and cost-effective. This equally applies to any other diagnostic approach that might use blood, urine, or tissue biopsies. A number of clinical assays have been developed using mucus or mucus smears (e.g., Maggi *et al.*, 2003), and even some of the simple dip-stick type colorimetric tests used for solutes in mammalian blood or urine may work on fish mucus. Some knowledge transfer from the clinical sciences to fish health will aid the development of a 'diagnostic kit' for fish mucus. The precision and accuracy of these tests would also need to be defined for fish mucus.

Another important aspect of diagnostics is agreeing what is 'normal' and defining reference ranges for the analytes measured. These reference ranges are available for osmolytes in the blood of humans, farm animals, and the common species of fish used in aquaculture (e.g., Hille, 1982), and a similar set of reference values need to be established for mucus. Reference ranges are usually established after the collection of data over many years, so that there is sufficient data to be confident about the ranges agreed; and so that ranges can be set for common biotic factors such as species/strain, age, sex or body size. For the rainbow trout at least, there is a significant body of information on skin mucus (e.g., Fast *et al.*, 2002; Handy, 1989; Tables 1 and 2), and it seems feasible to set some initial reference values for this species, including osmoregulatory parameters. Any reference value would need to take into account the hydration state of the mucus or mucus production rate by normalising data to the protein content (or sialic acid content) of the mucus. The hydration state issue can also be overcome by using standard protocols for collecting native mucus, and by denaturing the protein in the sample (e.g., with trichloroacetic acid) so that the liquid supernatant phase can be analysed for solutes (equivalent to collecting a plasma sample from whole blood). Overall, mucus has great potential as a diagnostic tool for osmoregualtion, and is already being applied in some aspects of fish health.

7.5 Conclusions and perspectives

Mucus is far from being a simple solution of proteins, and has numerous other non-mucin components such as electrolytes, amino acids, fatty acids, immunoglobulins, free peptides and enzymes. We are far from understanding the complex interactions between these components in mucus, but mucus has some important biological functions in osmoregulation and fish health. Mucus clearly has a role in preventing ion depletion from epithelia and supports ion gradients for ion uptake in dilute environments. However, the ionic composition of the mucus is also fundamental to the physical properties of the mucus. The relationships between osmoregulation and the function of mucus rheology in the immunological barrier, or in locomotion, require further research. It is also evident that a myriad of chemical reactions could occur in mucus, due to the enzymes present and the role of mucus in concentration solutes. This raises the possibility of chemical sensing, as well as chemical buffering, and the notion that the mucus is involved in chemical perception or detecting the environment. The relationship between biocrystalisation in mucus and locomotion/orientation is also intriguing. Mucus also has some important practical applications in the biosciences, not only as a diagnostic tool for animal health assessment, but also in monitoring low level pollutants that may be concentrated in the mucus layer, but not easily detected in the surrounding water.

References

Ahuja, S. K. (1970). Chloride cell and mucus cell response to chloride-enriched and sulphate-enriched media in gills of *Gambusia affinis affinis* (Baird and Girard) and Catla catla (Hamilton). J Exp Zool 173: 231–250.

Arillo, A., Margiocco, C. and Melodia, F. (1979). Gill sialic acid content as an index of environmental stress in rainbow trout, Salmo gairdneri. J Fish Biol 15: 405–410.

Asakawa, M. (1970). Histochemical studies of the mucus on the epidermis of the eel, *Angilla japonica*. B Jpn Soc Sci Fish 36: 83–86.

Asakawa, M. (1974). Sialic acid containing glycoprotein in external mucus of eel, *Anguilla japonica* - 2. Carbohydrate and amino acid composition. B Jpn Soc Sci Fish 40: 303–308.

Barmeyer, C., Amasheh, S., Tavalali, S., Mankertz, J., Zeitz, M., Fromm, M. and Schulzke, J. D. (2004). IL-1 beta and TNF alpha regulate sodium absorption in rat distal colon. Biochem Biophys Res Comm 317: 500–507.

Baconnais, S., Delavoie, F., Zahm, J. M., Milliot, M., Terryn, C., Castillon, N., Banchet, V., Michel, J., Danos, O., Merten, M., Chinet, T., Zierold, K., Bonnet, N., Puchelle, E. and Balossier, G. (2005). Abnormal ion content, hydration and granule expansion of the secretory granules from cystic fibrosis airway glandular cells. Exp Cell Res 309: 296–304.

Barbeau, T. R. and Lillywhite, H. B. (2005). Body wiping behaviors associated with cutaneous lipids in hylid tree frogs of Florida. J Exp Zool 208: 2147–2156.

Barry, P. H., and Diamond, J. M. (1984). Effects of unstirred layers on membrane phenomena. Physiol Rev 64: 763–872.

Battram, J. C. and Eddy, F. B. (1990). Recovery of chloride uptake in seawater-adadpted rainbow trout (*Salmo gairdneri*) after transfer to freshwater. J Exp Biol 148: 489–493.

Bell, A. E., Sellers, L. A., Allen, A., Cunliffe, W. J., Morris, E. R. and Rossmurphy, S. B. (1985). Properties of gastric and duodenal mucus: Effect of proteolysis, disulfide reduction, bile, acid, ethanol, and hypertonicity on mucus gel structure. Gastroenterology 88: 269–280.

Bergsson, G., Agerberth, B., Jornvall, H. and Gudmundsson, G. H. (2005). Isolation and identification of antimicrobial components from the epidermal mucus of Atlantic cod (*Gadus morhua*). Febs J 272: 4960–4969.

Bernadsky, G., Sar, N. and Rosenberg, E. (1993). Drag reduction of fish skin mucus: relationship to mode of swimming and size. J Fish Biol 42: 797–800.

Blanc-livni, N., and Abraham, M. (1970). Influence of environmental salinity on prolactin and gonadotrophin-secreting regions in pituitary of Mugil (Teleostei). Gen Comp Endocr 14: 184–197.

Blasco, J., Fernandez-Borras, J., Marimon, I. and Requena, A. (1996). Plasma glucose kinetics and tissue uptake in brown trout *in vivo*: Effect of an intravascular glucose load. J Comp Physiol B 165: 534–541.

Bokris, J. O. M., and Reddy, A. K. N. (1973). The electrified interface. In: J. O. M. Bokris, J. O. M. and Reddy, A. K. N. (eds) Modern Electrochemistry. Plenum Press, New York: 623–844.

Bromage, E. S., Ye, J. M. and Kaattari, S. L. (2006). Antibody structural variation in rainbow trout fluids. Comp Biochem Phys B 143: 61–69.

Caldwell, S., Rummer, J. L. and Brauner, C. J. (2006). Blood sampling techniques and storage duration: Effects on the presence and magnitude of the red blood cell beta-adrenergic response in rainbow trout (*Oncorhynchus mykiss*). Comp Biochem Phys A 144: 188–195.

Carlstedt, I. and Sheehan, J. K. (1989). Structure and macromolecular properties of cervical mucus glycoproteins. In: Chantler, E. and Ratcliffe, N. A. (eds) Mucus and Related Topics. The Company of Biologists Limited, Cambridge: 289–316.

Clamp, J. R., Allen, A., Gibbons, R. A. and Roberts, G. P. (1978). Chemical Aspects of Mucus. Brit Med Bull 34: 25–41.

Combes, R. D., Gaunt, I. and Balls, M. (2004). A scientific and animal welfare assessment of the OECD health effects test guidelines for the safety testing of chemicals under the European Union REACH system. Atla-Altern Lab Anim 32: 163–208.

Creeth, J. M. (1978). Constituents of mucus and their separation. Brit Med Bull 34: 17–24.

Davies, M. S. and Hutchinson, S. J. (1995). Crystalline calcium in littorinid mucus trails. Hydrobiologia 309: 117–121.

Delamare-Deboutteville, J., Wood, D. and Barnes, A. C. (2006). Response and function of cutaneous mucosal and serum antibodies in barramundi (*Lates calcarifer*) acclimated in seawater and freshwater. Fish Shellfish Immun 21: 92–101.

Denny, M. W. (1989). Invertebrate mucus secretions: functional alternatives to vertebrate paradigms. In: Chantler, E. and Ratcliffe, N. A. (eds) Mucus and Related Topics. The Company of Biologists Limited, Cambridge: 337–366.

Desai, M. A. and Vadgama, P. (1991). Estimation of effective diffusion coefficients of model solutes through gastric mucus: Assessment of a diffusion chamber technique based on spectrophotometric analysis. Analyst 116: 1113–1116.

Drennan, J. D., LaPatra, S. E., Swan, C. A., Ireland, S. and Cain, K. D. (2007). Characterization of serum and mucosal antibody responses in white sturgeon (*Acipenser transmontanus* Richardson) following immunization with WSIV and a protein hapten antigen. Fish Shellfish Immun 23: 657–669.

Eddy, F. B. (1982) Osmotic and ionic regulation in captive fish with particular reference to salmonids. Comp Biochem Physiol 73:125–141.

Eddy, F. B. and Fraser, J. E. (1982). Sialic acid and mucus production in rainbow trout (*Salmo Gairdneri* Richardson) in response to zinc and sea water. Comp Biochem Phys C 73: 357–359.

Esteve-Gassent, M. D., Nielsen, M. E. and Amaro, C. (2003). The kinetics of antibody production in mucus and serum of European eel (*Anguilla anguilla* L.) after vaccination against *Vibrio vulnificus*: development of a new method for antibody quantification in skin mucus. Fish & Shellfish Immun 15: 51–61.

Fast, M. D., Sims, D. E., Burka, J. F., Mustafa, A. and Ross, N. W. (2002). Skin morphology and humoral non-specific defence parameters of mucus and plasma in rainbow trout, coho and Atlantic salmon. Comp Biochem Phys A 132: 645–657.

Fauconneau, B. and Saglio, P. (1984). Protein bound and free amino acid content in the skin mucus of the European eel, *Anguilla anguilla* (L). Comp Biochem Phys B 77: 513–516.

Gilles-baillien, M. (1981). Na, cycloleucine and insulin compartments in tortoise intestinal mucus: Possible role of the mucus in intestinal absorption processes. Mol Physiol 1: 265–272.

Handy, R. D. (1989). The ionic composition of rainbow trout body mucus. Comp Biochem Phys A 93: 571–575.

Handy, R. D. and Eddy, F. B. (1990). The interactions between the surface of rainbow trout, *Oncorhynchus Mykiss*, and waterborne metal toxicants. Funct Ecol 4: 385–392.

Handy, R. D. and Eddy, F. B. (1991). Effects of inorganic cations on Na^+ adsorption to the gill and body surface of rainbow trout, *Oncorhynchus mykiss*, in dilute solutions. Can J Fish Aquat Sci 48: 1829–1837.

Handy, R. D. (1992). The assessment of episodic metal pollution 1. Uses and limitations of tissue contaminant analysis in rainbow trout (*Oncorhynchus mykiss*) after short waterborne exposure to cadmium or copper. Arch Environ Con Tox 22: 74–81.

Handy, R. D. and Penrice, W. S. (1993). The influence of high oral doses of mercuric chloride on organ toxicant concentrations and histopathology in rainbow trout, *Oncorhynchus mykiss*. Comp Biochem Phys C 106: 717–724.

Handy, R. D. and Eddy, F. B. (2004) Transport of solutes across biological membranes in eukaryotes: An environmental perspective. In: van Leeuwen H. P. and Köster, W. (eds) Physicochemical Kinetics and Transport at Chemical-Biological Interphases, John Wiley, Chichester: 337–356.

Handy, R. D., Kammer, F. v. d., Lead, J. R., Hassellov, M., Owen, R. and Crane, M. (2008a). The ecotoxicology and chemistry of manufactured nanoparticles. Ecotoxicology 17: 287–314.

Handy, R.D., Owen, R., Valsami-Jones, E. (2008b). The ecotoxicology of nanoparticles and nanomaterials: Current status, knowledge gaps, challenges, and future needs. Ecotoxicology 17: 315–325

Hille, S. (1982). A literature review of the blood chemistry of rainbow trout, *Salmo Gairdneri*. J Fish Biol 20: 535–569.

Hollander, F. (1963). The electrolyte pattern of gastric mucinous secretions: Its implication for cystic fibrosis. Ann NY Acad Sci 106: 757–766.

Humbert, W., Kirsch, R. and Simonneaux, V. (1986). Is mucus involved in biocrystallization - study of the intestinal mucus of the sea water eel *Anguilla*

Anguilla L. Cell Tissue Res 245: 599–604.

Kirschner, L. B. (1978). External charged layer and Na⁺ regulation. In: Jørgensen, C. B. and Skadhauge, E. (eds) Osmotic and Volume Regulation (Alfred Benzon Symposium XI, Munksgaard). Academic Press, New York: 310–321.

Kitani, Y., Mori, T., Nagai, H., Toyooka, K., Ishizaki, S., Shimakura, K., Shiomi, K. and Nagashima, Y., (2007). Gene expression and distribution of antibacterial L-amino acid oxidase in the rockfish *Sebastes schlegeli*. Fish Shellfish Immun 23: 1178–1186.

Lapennas, G. N. and Schmidtnielsen, K. (1977). Swimbladder permeability to oxygen. J Exp Biol 67: 175–196.

Lauga, E. and Hosoi, A. E. (2006). Tuning gastropod locomotion: Modeling the influence of mucus rheology on the cost of crawling. Phys Fluids 18: 113102.

Lee, S. P. and Nicholls, J. F. (1987). Diffusion of charged ions in mucus gel: Effect of net charge. Biorheology, 24: 565–569.

Li, Y. H. and Gregory, S. (1974). Diffusion of ions in seawater and in deep sea sediments. Geochim Cosmochim Acta 38: 703–714.

Lichtenberger, L. M. (1995). The hydrophobic barrier properties of gastrointestinal mucus. Annu Revi Physiol 57: 565–583.

Lindenstrøm, T., Sigh, J., Dalgaard, M. B. and Buchmann, K. (2006). Skin expression of IL-1 beta in East Atlantic salmon, *Salmo salar* L., highly susceptible to *Gyrodactylus salaris* infection is enhanced compared to a low susceptibility Baltic stock. J Fish Dis 29: 123–128.

Livingston, E. H. and Engel, E. (1995). Modeling of the gastric gel mucus layer: Application to the measured pH gradient. J Clin Gastroenterol 21: S120–S124.

Livingston, E. H., Miller, J. and Engel, E. (1995). Bicarbonate diffusion through mucus. Am J Physiol-Gastr L 269: G453–G457.

Lucas, M. L. (1984). Estimation of sodium chloride diffusion coefficient in gastric mucin. Digest Dis Sci 29: 336–345.

Lundgren, J. D. (1992). Mucus production in the lower airways. A review of experimental studies. Dan Med Bull 39: 289–303.

Maggi, F., Pifferi, M., Fornai, C., Andreoli, E., Tempestini, E., Vatteroni, M., Presciuttini, S., Marchi, S., Pietrobelli, A., Boner, A., Pistello, M. and Bendinelli, M. (2003). TT virus in the nasal secretions of children with acute respiratory diseases: Relations to viremia and disease severity. J Virol 77: 2418–2425.

Marriott, C. (1989). Drug-mucus actions and interactions. In: Chantler, E. and Ratcliffe, N. A. (eds) Mucus and Related Topics. The Company of Biologists Limited, Cambridge: 163–177.

Marshall, W. S. (1978). Involvement of mucous secretion in teleost osmoregulation. Can J Zool 56: 1088–1091.

Morris, E. R and Rees, D. A. (1978). Princliples of biopolymer gelation. Brit Med Bull 34: 49–53.

Nagashima, Y., Takeda, M., Ohta, I., Shimakura, K. and Shiomi, K. (2004).

Purification and properties of proteinaceous trypsin inhibitors in the skin mucus of pufferfish *Takifugu pardalis*. Comp Biochem Phys B 138: 103–110.

Nagel, W., Somieski, P. and Katz, U. (2002). The route of passive chloride movement across amphibian skin: localization and regulatory mechanisms. BBA-Biomembranes, 1566: 44–54.

Nakagawa, H., Asakawa, M. and Enomoto, N. (1987). Glycosidase activities in the livers of various fishes and mollusks. Nippon Suisan Gakkaishi 53: 1033–1037.

Nakamura, A., Okamoto, T., Komatsu, N., Ooka, S., Oda, T., Ishimatsu, A. and Muramatsu, T. (1998). Fish mucus stimulates the generation of superoxide anion by *Chattonella marina* and *Heterosigma akashiwo*. Fisheries Sci 64: 866–869.

Nakamura, O., Inaga, Y., Suzuki, S. Tsutsui, S., Muramoto, K., Kamiya, H. and Watanabe, T. (2007). Possible immune functions of congerin, a mucosal galectin, in the intestinal lumen of Japanese conger eel. Fish Shellfish Immun 23: 683–692.

Negus, V. E. (1963). The function of mucus. Acta Oto-Laryngol 56: 204–214.

Negus, V. E. (1967). The function of mucus: A hypothesis. Proc R Soc Med 60: 75–77.

Ourth, D. D. (1980). Secretory IgM, lysozyme and lymphocytes in the skin mucus of the channel catfish, *Ictalurus punctatus*. Dev Comp Immunol 4: 65–74.

Overbeek, J. T. (1956). The Donnan equilibrium. Prog Biophy Biophys Chem 6: 58–84.

Palaksha, K. J., Shin, G. W., Kim, Y. R. and Jung, T. S. (2008). Evaluation of non-specific immune components from the skin mucus of olive flounder (*Paralichthys olivaceus*). Fish Shellfish Immun 24: 479–488.

Part, P. and Lock, R. A. C. (1983). Diffusion of calcium, cadmium and mercury in a mucous solution from rainbow trout. Comp Biochem Phys C 76: 259–263.

Peterson, R. H. and Martin-Robichaud, D. J. (1986). Perivitelline and vitelline potentials in teleost eggs as influenced by ambient ionic strengths, natal salinity and electrode electrolyte; and the influence of these potentials on cadmium dynamics within the egg. Can J Fish Aquat Sci 43: 1445–1450.

Phelps, C. F. (1978). Biosynthesis of mucus glycoprotein. Brit Med Bull 34: 43–48.

Portier, P. and Duval, M. (1922). Pression osmotique du sang de l'anguille essuyée en jonction des modifications de salinité du milieu exterieur. C R Hebd Seances Acad Sci 175: 1105–1106.

Quraishi, M. S., Jones, N. S. and Mason, J. (1998). The rheology of nasal mucus: a review. Clin Otolaryngol 23: 403–413.

Radomsky, M. L., Whaley, K. J., Cone, R. A. and Saltzman, W. M. (1990). Macromolecules released from polymers: Diffusion into unstirred fluids. Biomaterials 11: 619–624.

Raffy, A. (1950). Reactions de *Gobius paganellus* à la dessalure. Comptes Rendus des Séances et Mémoires de la Société de Biologie 144: 1649–1651.

Ren, T., Koshio, S., Ishikawa, M. Yokoyama, S., Micheal, F. R., Uyan, O. and Tung, H. T. (2007). Influence of dietary vitamin C and bovine lactoferrin on blood chemistry and non-specific immune responses of Japanese eel, *Anguilla japonica*. Aquaculture 267: 31–37.

Robinson, R. A. and Stokes, R. H. (1959). Electrolyte solutions, Butterworths, London.

Russell, S. and Lumsden, J. S. (2005). Function and heterogeneity of fish lectins. Vet Immunol Immunop 108: 111–120.

Saglio, P. and Fauconneau, B. (1985). Free amino acid content in the skin mucus of goldfish, *Carassius auratus* L: Influence of feeding. Comp Biochem Physiol A 82: 67–70.

Saldena, T. A., Saravi, F. D., Hwang, H. J., Cincunegui, L. M. and Carra, G. E. (2000). Oxygen diffusive barriers of rat distal colon: Role of subepithelial tissue, mucose, and mucus gel layer. Digest Dis Sci 45: 2108–2114.

Sarosiek, J., Slomiany, A., Takagi, A. and Slomiany, B. L. (1984). Hydrogen ion diffusion in dog gastric mucus glycoprotein: Effect of associated lipids and covalently bound fatty acids. Biochem Bioph Res Co 118: 523–531.

Scott, J. E. (1968). Ion binding in solutions containing acid mucopolysaccharides. In: Quintarelli, G. (ed) The chemical physiology of mucopolysaccharides. Churchill, London: 171–187.

Scott, J. E. (1989). Ion binding: Patterns of 'affinity' depending on types of acid groups. In: Chantler, E. and Ratcliffe, N. A. (eds) Mucus and Related Topics. Company of Biologists Ltd, Cambridge: 111–115.

Schlenk, D., Handy, R., Steinert, S., Depledge, M. H. and Benson, W. (2008). Biomarkers. In: Di Giulio, R. T. and Hinton, D. E. (eds) The toxicology of fishes. CRC Press, Florida: 683–731.

Schlichter, L. C. (1981). Ion relations of hemolymph, pallial fluid, and mucus of *Lymnaea Stagnalis*. Can J Zool 59: 605–613.

Schlichter, L. C. (1982). Unstirred mucus layers: Ion exchange properties and effect on ion regulation in *Lymnaea stagnalis*. J Exp Biol 98: 363–372.

Sheffner, A. L. (1963) The reduction in vitro in viscosity of mucoprotein solutions by a new mucolytic agent, N-acetyl-L-cysteine. Ann NY Acad Sci 106: 298–310.

Shephard, K. L. (1981). The influence of mucus on the diffusion of water across fish epidermis. Physiol Zool 54: 224–229.

Shephard, K. L. (1982). The influence of mucus on the diffusion of ions across the esophagus of fish. Physiol Zool 55: 23–34.

Shephard, K. L. (1984a). Diffusion of chloride ions in the mucus on the esophagus of *Enophrys bison*, a marine teleost fish. Pflug Arch Eur Phy 402: 207–210.

Shephard, K. L. (1984b). The influence of mucus on the diffusion of chloride ions across the esophagus of the minnow (*Phoxinus phoxinus* (L)). J Physiol-London 346: 449–460.

Shephard, K. L. (1987). Ion-exchange phenomena regulate the environment of embryos in the eggs of freshwater fish. Comp Biochem Physiol A 88: 659–662.

Shephard, K. L. (1994). Functions for fish mucus. Rev Fish Biol Fisher 4: 401–429.

Slomiany, B. L., Murty, V. L. N., Piotrowski, J. and Slomiany, A. (1989). Effect of antiulcer agents on the physiochemical properties of gastric mucus. In: Chantler, E. and Ratcliffe, N. A. (eds) Mucus and Related Topics. The Company of Biologists Limited, Cambridge: 179–192.

Simonneaux, V., Humbert, W. and Kirsch, R. (1987). Mucus and intestinal ion exchanges in the sea water adapted eel, *Anguilla anguilla* L. Comp Biochem Physiol B 157: 295–306.

Simontacchi, C., Poltronieri, C., Carraro, C., Bertotto, D., Xiccato, G., Trocino, A. and Radaelli, G. (2008). Alternative stress indicators in sea bass *Dicentrarchus labrax*, L. J Fish Biol 72: 747–752.

Smith, A. C. and Ramos, F. (1976). Occult hemoglobin in fish skin mucus as an indicator of early stress. J Fish Biol 9: 537–541.

Smith, N. F., Eddy, F. B. and Talbot, C. (1995). Effect of dietary salt load on transepithelial Na^+ exchange in freshwater rainbow trout (*Oncorhynchus mykiss*). J Exp Biol 198: 2359–2364.

Singh, B. and Thakur, R. (1975). A histochemical study on the respiratory epithelia of an eel fish, *Amphipnous cuchia*. Acta Histochem 54: 161–167.

Stith, B. J. (1984a). Biochemical examination of *rana pipiens* epithelial mucus. J Comp Physiol B 155: 89–96.

Stith, B. J. (1984b). Effects of an external charged layer on transepithelial ion movement in frog skin. J Comp Physiol B 155: 97–101.

Subramanian, S., MacKinnon, S. L. and Ross, N. W. (2007). A comparative study on innate immune parameters in the epidermal mucus of various fish species. Comp Biochem Physiol B 148: 256–263.

Swidsinski, A., Loening-Baucke, V., Theissig, F., Engelhardt, H., Bengmark, S., Koch, S., Lochs, H. and Dörffel, Y. (2007). Comparative study of the intestinal mucus barrier in normal and inflamed colon. Gut 56: 343–350.

Tam, P. Y. and Verdugo, P. (1981). Control of mucus hydration as a Donnan equilibrium process. Nature, 292: 340–342.

Tworowski, D., Feldman, A. V. and Safro, M. G. (2005). Electrostatic potential of aminoacyl-tRNA synthetase navigates tRNA on its pathway to the binding site. J Mol Biol 350: 866–882.

Ultsch, G. R. and Gros, G. (1979). Mucus as a diffusion barrier to oxygen: Possible role in O_2 uptake at low pH in carp (*Cyprinus carpio*) gills. Comp Biochem Physiol A 62: 685–689.

Varanasi, U. and Markey, D. (1978). Uptake and release of lead and cadmium in skin and mucus of coho salmon (*Oncorhynchus kisutch*). Comp Biochem Physiol C 60: 187–191.

Vosloo, A. and Vosloo, D. (2006). Routes of water loss in South African abalone

(*Haliotis midae*) during aerial exposure. Aquaculture 261: 670–677.

Warren, L., Blacklow, R. S. and Spearing, C. W. (1963). Biosynthesis and metabolism of sialic acids. Ann N Y Acad Sci 106: 191–201.

Wendelaar-Bonga, S. E. (1978). Effects of changes in external sodium, calcium, and magnesium concentrations on prolactin cells, skin, and plasma electrolytes of *Gasterosteus aculeatus*. Gen Comp Endocr 34: 265–275.

Whitear, M. (1977). A functional comparison between the epidermis of fish and of amphibians. Symp Zool Soc Lond 39: 291–313.

Williams, S. E. and Turnberg, L. A. (1980). Retardation of acid diffusion by pig gastric mucus: A potential role in mucosal protection. Gastroenterology 79: 299–304.

Winne, D. and Verheyen, W. (1990). Diffusion coefficient in native mucus gel of rat small intestine. J Pharm Pharmacol 42: 517–519.

Wittemann, A. and Ballauff, M. (2006). Interaction of proteins with linear polyelectrolytes and spherical polyelectrolyte brushes in aqueous solution. Phys Chem Chem Phys 8: 5269–5275.

Wright, P., Heming, T. and Randall, D. (1986). Downstream pH changes in water flowing over the gills of rainbow trout. J Exp Biol 126: 499–512.

Wright, P. A., Randall, D. J. and Perry, S. F. (1989). Fish gill water boundary layer: A site of linkage between carbon dioxide and ammonia excretion. J Comp Physiol B 158: 627–635.

Index

Species are generally referred to by their common names from Latin binomials.
Page numbers in *italic* refer to tables or figures in the text.